The
SEATTLE
$UPER
$HOPPER

The Savvy Shopper's Guide to the Greater Puget Sound Area

8th Edition
Revised and Expanded

Vicki Koeplin

JOHNSTON
ASSOCIATES
INTERNATIONAL

P.O. BOX 313
MEDINA, WASHINGTON 98039
(206) 454-7333

The Seattle Super Shopper has been published since 1976. The listings and information appearing in this edition were current at the time of final editing but are subject to change at any time. Reports are based on store visitations, telephone interviews by the author and recommendations received from other shoppers. Neither the author nor anyone connected with the publishing company has a personal or financial interest in any of the companies appearing in this book, and no gratuities of any kind have been solicited or accepted from listed firms.

Cover and book design by Mike Jaynes
Typesetting by Kate Rose

JASI
P.O. Box 313
Medina, WA 98039
206-454-3490
FAX: 206-462-1335

Library of Congress Cataloging-in-Publication Data
Koeplin, Vicki, 1944-
    The Seattle super shopper: the savvy shopper's guide to the
Greater Puget Sound area / Vicki Koeplin. — 8th ed., rev. and exp.
        p. c.m
    Includes index.
    ISBN 1-881409-06-6
    1. Shopping—Washington (State)—Seattle Region—Guidebooks.
2. Discount houses (Retail trade)—Washington (State)—Seattle
Region—Guidebooks. 3. Outlet stores—Washington (State)—Seattle
Region—Guidebooks. 4. Seattle Region (Wash.)—Guidebooks.
I. Title.
TX336.5.W22S44 1994   94-7882
381'.45'00025797772—dc20   CIP

Printed in the United States of America

Table of Contents

Home Building and Remodeling 115

Home Furnishings 145

Plants, Flowers and Greenery 179

Office Needs 187

Recreation and Hobbies 211

Acknowledgements

As an avid user of the *Seattle Super Shopper* for many years, I never dreamed that one day I would actually be writing the seventh, and now the eighth, edition. It all started when I requested copies of the book to sell in my Cheap Chic classes. The rest is history. There are dozens of people who deserve credit for helping me out, especially the many sales clerks, store managers, and owners who took the time to tell me about their businesses, whether they were a small factory outlet or part of a big national chain.

Thanks to Priscilla Johnston and Dinah Stotler, the original authors and publishers of the Super Shopper, for hiring me sight unseen to write my first edition. Thanks also to my husband and daughter for putting up with late dinners and a house strewn with papers.

Introduction

If you adhere to the following guidelines, garnered during years of bargain hunting, I guarantee you'll save on everything from automobiles to zippers!

✔ Be open-minded when it comes to visiting low-overhead outlets that may not live up to your standards of service or housekeeping. Remember, that's how they keep their prices so low.

✔ Don't be afraid to negotiate a lower price, especially if the item is damaged or you're buying in quantity.

✔ Ask if you can get a discount by paying in cash.

✔ Comparison shop to get the best value for your money. Use the Best and J.C. Penney catalogs as starting points, as well as the Sunday supplements put out by mass merchandisers.

✔ Refer to Consumer Reports Magazine and their buying guide to find out which brand names offer the best value for your money.

✔ Whenever possible, use the telephone to comparison shop and to verify that the item you want is in stock.

✔ Read newspaper advertisements, get on mailing lists, and talk to sales clerks to find out about weekly, monthly and seasonal sales.

✔ To save time, shop in an area that has a lot of discounters or several stores that sell the same product. In the north end, Alderwood Mall is surrounded by over a dozen stores listed in the *Seattle Super Shopper*. In the south end, Andover Park and the Southcenter Parkway strip are home to a multitude of manufacturers, warehouse distributors and off-price retailers.

✔ Pick up a free copy of "Little Nickel Want Ads" or pay $1.00 for "Buy & Sell" at convenience stores and grocery stores for access to over a thousand classified ads that list every product and service imaginable.

✔ Check out seconds and irregulars for barely noticeable defects or problems that can easily be repaired or that you can live with.

✔ Whenever possible, buy from wholesalers, distributors or factory direct for the lowest price.

✔ Help recycle by buying second-hand goods from consignment shops, thrift stores, rummage sales and garage sales.

✔ Shop in outlying areas where prices will be lower because rent and the cost of doing business is cheaper.

✔ Set a budget before you go shopping. Decide how much you want to spend based on what you can afford and how often the item is going to be used.

✔ Take advantage of store policies that say they will meet or beat competitors prices.

And one final note: ***Read your Super Shopper for even more ideas!***

Definitions of Terms

Close-outs, overruns and **discontinued styles** are first-quality products that factories sell at big discounts to whomever offers them the best deal. Sometimes these goods were returned by retail stores simply because they weren't shipped on time or didn't sell.

Private-label merchandise is manufactured especially for a store and sold under the store's name or a label exclusive to the store, which makes it difficult to comparison shop. Products may be copies of more expensive labels or best selling items, but they sell for less than brand names because there is no middleman to deal with or high advertising costs, which can add 20% to 40% to the retail price. On private label clothing, stores cut their costs by using a less expensive material or by altering the style of the garment slightly so that it won't take so long to make, thus lowering the cost.

Loss Leader refers to an item that is advertised at cost or below in the hopes of attracting customers to the store who will then pay full price for other products.

Factory serviced or **factory reconditioned** products are returns from customers or stores that have been fixed or repackaged. Some had minor cosmetic flaws, while others needed major repairs. Some have simply been removed from the box for display purposes or used as salesmen samples.

Samples are prototypes used by sales reps when showing a line to prospective retail buyers. Sometimes, especially in the apparel industry, samples never sell well enough to be mass produced so they are "one-of-a-kind" items.

Irregulars or Seconds are flawed merchandise that should be marked as such. Sometimes the term "as is" appears on an item, which means you've been given fair warning that there is some defect or else the item can't be returned. Drastically reduced prices often indicate something is seriously wrong with the item. Sometimes the defects are barely noticeable or can be easily repaired.

And Finally...

Use the Additional Outlets sections at the end of each chapter, as well as the Table of Contents, to find specific items you're interested in buying. Many businesses sell products other than those related to the heading under which they appear.

Call to verify information before you head out on a cross-town shopping spree. Although the Super Shopper is current when it goes to press, listings may have moved, closed, changed their names or hours by the time you read this book.

Prices quoted in various write-ups are to serve as guidelines only since they reflect the going rate when I was doing research.

If you shop in one of the stores listed and find it disappointing, please let me know. If, on the other hand, you think a certain store is a bargain-hunter's heaven, tell your friends so it will still be in business when the next edition of the Super Shopper rolls around.

If I've failed to list your favorite spot and you are willing to share it with others, drop me a line. I'm continually updating my files to make the next edition of the Super Shopper bigger and better than ever.

Have fun bargain hunting!

Vicki Koeplin

Consumer Protection

There is no state law that says stores must take merchandise back unless goods sold as first-quality do not perform as advertised or a flaw is discovered after purchasing the item. Every business sets its own return policy, which should be clearly visible somewhere in the store or printed on the sales receipt. If you don't see a sign, ask.

Any item marked "as is" has something wrong with it or cannot be returned once it has been purchased.

Ask about warranties, guarantees and delivery charges before making your purchase.

The following resources will help to resolve a problem with a business if you file a written complaint with them. The Better Business Bureau will tell you if a business has had any complaints filed against it in the past three years. The Better Business Bureau and the State Attorney General's Office give out buying tips and consumer protection information via recordings and brochures that cover over a hundred different products and services. Call for a comprehensive listing.

The Times Trouble Shooter also distributes free advice from government agencies and copies of price surveys they have done on such subjects as dry cleaning, credit card rates, funerals and prescription drugs.

State Attorney General's Office Fair Practice Division
Seattle: 900 4th Ave., Second floor 464-6684
Tacoma: 1019 Pacific Ave. S., Third floor 593-2904
Hours: Mon-Fri 9-4
Consumer line: 464-6811, 1-800-551-4636 24 hours

Better Business Bureau
Seattle: 2200 6th Ave. #828 448-8888
Hours: Mon-Fri 9-3
Voice File: 4481-6222 24 hours
Tel-Tips: 448-8477 24 hours

Seattle Times Trouble Shooter
Seattle: Fairview N. & John St. 464-2262
Hours: Mon-Fri 9-5

Mail-Order Shopping

The Super Shopper contains several discount mail-order catalogs, all of which are free upon request. Once you get your name on their mailing list, chances are you'll receive unsolicited catalogs since many companies sell or trade mailing lists. If you don't purchase something within a year, you are usually taken off the lists.

Here are a few tips to keep in mind when shopping by mail:

✔ The best catalogs offer detailed descriptions, toll-free ordering service, satisfaction or your money back guarantees, and refunds on postage for returns.

✔ Laws enacted by the Federal Trade Commission and the U.S. Postal Service protect consumers from mail-order fraud. If you have a problem, write a letter to the Seattle Times Troubleshooter, the Post-Intelligencer Action column, or file a complaint with the Attorney General's Office and the Better Business Bureau.

✔ If you pay for your mail-order purchase with a credit card, orders will arrive much sooner than if you send a check. If you're in a big hurry, many companies will ship Federal Express, but you pay for the service.

Clothing

Never pay full price for clothing again! As the cost of apparel continues to rise, it's increasingly difficult to limit spending to the 7% or 8% usually suggested for clothing in family budgets. By shopping the many resources listed in this section, you can buy more for less and still get current-style, high-quality merchandise.

Factory Outlets and Sample Sales

Nationally known manufacturers of outerwear and casual sportswear such as Union Bay, Shah Safari, Brittania, Generra and Pacific Trail have put Seattle on the fashion map. If you don't see your favorite lines listed in this section, it's because the company either ships its overstock, samples and seconds to an out-of-state outlet or sells piecemeal to discounters.

Factory outlets will be bare-bones operations, frequently located at big distribution centers because the actual production is done offshore. Some manufacturers maintain outlets separate from the factory that operate more like retail stores, selling other brand names, offering better service and having more lenient return policies. Others, including wholesale distributors, open their doors to the public only during annual or periodic sales to clear out inventory. To find out more about these sales you have to call to get on their mailing lists. Shop carefully because sales are final at most factory outlets.

Many of the manufacturers listed in this section also turn up at Wholesale Heaven's periodic sales.

Bellarmine Sample Clothing Sale

Tacoma: 2300 S. Washington 752-7701
Periodic sales

In August, November and April, the Bellarmine Preparatory High School Mothers' Club sponsors terrific sales of sample clothes, which include a lot of Junior sizes and young mens' wear. Prices are wholesale plus 10%. Giftware, jewelry and holiday-related items are sometimes available. Call to get on the mailing list. No returns.

Checks, Credit cards

BRB Manufacturing Inc.

NEW LOCATION
Tacoma: 401 Alexander Ave. #9323 622-2881, 383-9727
Periodic sales

Since BRB makes private-label outerwear and sportswear for retail stores, merchandise varies from sale to sale. They specialize in polar fleece vests and jackets, sweats, windbreakers, and tights for children and adults. Styles may be basic but prices are super low. Sewing remnants, yardage and notions are also available at the sales. Put your name on a list and they will call you with a date. No returns.

Checks

Eighth Avenue Woolens

Seattle: 711 Virginia 248-8415 *Downtown*
Periodic sales

Better department stores all over the country, including Nordstroms, sell these beautiful classic tailored dresses and separates under private labels for $100 to $200, but you pay half that when the factory opens its doors to get rid of overstock. Sizes range from XS to L or 2 to 16 and fabrications focus on natural fibers, especially fine wool gaberdines, crepes and jersies. Enter at the foot of the loading dock. No returns.

Checks, Credit cards

Casual T's

NEW LISTING
Kent: 304 Washington Ave. S. 854-3887
Hours: Mon-Fri 10-8, Sat & Sun 10-6

Misprints and overstock from a local silk-screen company end up here at unbelievably low prices. There's even a $1 bin! Merchandise is mainly unisex T-shirts and sweatshirts printed with cartoons and artistic outdoorsy designs. Separates by leading brand names include classic polo and rugby shirts the same quality you would find in Land's End catalog but for only $8.95. Mailing list. Exchanges only within 30 days.

Checks, Credit cards

Christine Alexander

NEW LISTING
Federal Way: 34310 9th Ave. S. #101 874-5570
Periodic sales

If you like to wear fancy novelty T-shirts or sweatshirts decorated with studs, gemstones or embroidered designs, check out this design studio when they sell off samples and seconds. Prices vary from $10 to $50 on tops that sell for twice the price in resort and specialty shops. Dressier styles are embellished with Austrian crystals. Sizes go to up XXL. Mailing list.

Checks, Credit cards

Fraje'

Renton: 820 Thomas Ave. S.W. 255-6677
Hours: Wed-Sat 10-6

Fraje' manufactures moderately priced clothing for K-Mart and other mass merchandisers. Overstock ends up here, as well as clearance merchandise from well known local manufacturers like B.U.M. Equipment and L.A. Gear. Prices on apparel for the whole family range from $2 to $15, often dipping below wholesale. Accessories are also available, along with silk brocade jewelry boxes and travel accessories made in Thailand. Call to get on the mailing list for coupons and sale notices. No returns.

Checks, Credit cards

Herman & Blumenthal Co.

NEW LISTING
Tukwila: 405 Baker Blvd. 244-2600
Annual Sale

Around Christmas, this wholesale distributor opens his warehouse for 30 days to get rid of excess goods from local manufacturers and companies he represents, which in the past have included Mont-bell, Sorell, Pogo, Vanderbilt and Helly Hansen. Most of the merchandise is casual or recreational sportswear. Call to get on the mailing list. Exchanges accepted.

Checks

Item House

Tacoma: 2920 S. Steele St. 627-7168
Periodic sales

Get on the mailing list for this manufacturers famous "dock sales" and you can pick up some fantastic buys on classic wool coats, rainwear and suits sold under the Kristen Blake label or private labels made exclusively for department stores, including Nordstrom's Towne Square. These high-quality garments come in Petite, Misses and half-sizes. Item House also imports an active wear line called Aero. All sales final

Checks, Credit cards

Jump Sportswear

NEW LOCATION
Seattle: 159 Western Ave. W. 282-3713 *South of Seattle Ctr.*
Periodic sales

Jump Sportswear makes moderately priced but sophisticated, basic lycra knit coordinated separates that end up in specialty stores all over the U.S. The focus is on stirrup pants, leggings and matching pullover tops or sweaters that retail for $25 to $50. Call to get on the mailing list for periodic sales and pay half of that. No returns.

Cash

Karolyn's Sample Sales

NEW LISTING
Bellevue: 102 Bellevue Way N.E. 637-0363
Periodic Sales

The biggest and best sample sale you will ever find! Racks are jammed with over 100 lines featuring the latest styles by top names in the fashion industry such as Liz Clairborne, Jones of New York, Bonnie & Bill and Marisa Christina. The selection ranges from sportswear to career to dressy attire for the whole family. Call to get on the mailing list and you'll be notified about monthly sales that sometimes feature ski apparel, activewear, back-to-school or holiday apparel as well. Prices are wholesale plus 10%. No returns.

Checks

Morning Sun Outlet

Fife: 3500-A 20th St. E. 926-0801
Hours: Mon-Fri 9:30-8, Sat 9:30-5:30, Sun 10:30-5:30

Tables overflow with sweatshirts and T-shirts for the whole family at this huge outlet store located next to one of the largest and best-known imprint companies on the West coast. Motifs vary from sports logos to original artwork, with some of the designs using puff paints or embroideries. Sweatshirts that retail for $28 to $45 in apparel stores, sell for only $16.99. Prices are even lower on misprints and plain cotton knits. Morning Sun also sells first-quality clothing from other manufacturers at discount prices. Returns accepted.

Checks, Credit cards

Motto and Red Eraser

Kent: 1222 N. 6th 622-9888, 854-4650
Periodic sales

Two of the hottest names in the young men's and Junior contemporary sportswear market. Their warehouse sales offer some great buys on cotton knit sportswear in the latest styles. Call to get on the mailing list.

Checks

Over the Rainbow, Rainbow Babies

NEW LISTING
Mercer Island: 7855 S.E. 62nd 232-5471
Hours: Mon 11-1, Tues 5pm-9pm, first Sat of the month 9-1

The owner designs and manufactures her own line of apparel for women and children and sells it to selected stores, through private home parties and out of a small showroom in the back of her home. Styles are easy-fit, colorful basic separates in cotton knits, and washable rayons that can be purchased off-the-rack or made-to-order, with hundreds of fabric swatches to choose from. Prices range from $12 to $37 for the women's line, which is flattering on all ages, and $6 to $28 for children. Mailing list for big clearance sales in August and February. Exchanges or credit only.

Checks, Credit cards

Outrageous Sports

NEW LISTING
Seattle: 5508 1st Ave. S. 768-0701 *Georgetown*
Periodic sales

A popular local manufacturer who specializes in inexpensive, casual unisex outerwear for kids and adults, with an emphasis on the latest hip styles. Knock-offs of team sport jackets and grunge-inspired flannel vests were top selling items in the line the day I called. Look for big discounts off the $20 to $100 retail prices during periodic sales. Mailing list. No returns.

Checks, Credit cards

Pacific Trail Outlet

Seattle: 608 Yale Ave. N. 682-8196 *East of Seattle Center*
Hours: Mon-Fri 9-5, Sat 10-5

Outerwear by Pacific Trail, which has been in business for
over 40 years, is sold all over the country and at many local
stores. Weather Watch and Inside Edge are two private labels
they use. At the small outlet store you can save 30% to 50% on
nylon wind breakers, twill jackets, down parkas and ski apparel for the whole family. Sizes go from toddlers to XXL for
men. Mailing list for sales. 30-day exchange.

Checks, Credit cards

Parsinen Design

NEW LISTING
Seattle: 908 12th Ave. 329-4761 *Capitol Hill*
Periodic sales

Large sizes take note! If mix 'n' match cotton knits in solid
colors and basic styles similar to the "multiples" concept ap-
peal to you, shop the private sales sponsored by this manufacturer, whose garments can be found locally at Nordstrom and
Queen-size specialty shops. No returns.

Checks

Ragzdale

NEW LISTING
Burien: 2118 152nd Ave. S.W. 246-1800
Hours: Wed 11-5

A small, fun shop opened by two clothing reps so they would
have some place to sell their samples, which are mainly easy-
fit, feminine styles from import lines such as Star of India,
Caravan and New Options. All of the garments are made out
of natural fibers in muted prints and jewel tones. No returns.

Checks

Seabell Sportswear

Location to be announced 883-9128
Periodic sales

Prices range from $1.99 to $10 when this local silk-screen
printer unloads overstock, discontinued styles and irregulars.
The whole family will find a terrific selection of T-shirts,
sweats and sportswear, as well as sleepwear and maternity
clothes. All sales final.

Checks

Seattle Gear

NEW LISTING
Seattle: 3125 Western 282-7677 *Southwest of Seattle Center*
Bi-Annual Sales

If you want to save money on this wonderful line of contemporary women's co-ordinated sportswear named after our fair city, then buy overstock and seconds direct from the factory during closeout sales. Garments retail for $50 to $200 at specialty stores and better department stores all over the U.S. All sales final.

Checks

Sundrop Sportswear

NEW LISTING
Location to be announced 643-5270
Periodic sales

This big imprint company disposes of misprints and overstock during periodic sales. T-shirts, sweatshirts and night shirts for women and children, including toddlers, are adorned with original silk-screen designs that vary from pretty florals to cute teddy bears to exclusive motifs by famous greeting card artist Lucy. There is a limited selection of team sport logos for the guys. Call to get on the mailing list. No returns.

Checks, Credit cards

Union Bay Outlet

Kent: 21216 72nd Ave. S. 872-2946
Hours: Mon-Fri 10-5, 2nd & 4th Sat of every month, 10-5

The Pacific Northwest's largest clothing manufacturer is one of the hottest resources nationwide for boys, young men and Junior contemporary fashions. Styles cover a broad spectrum from casual separates to dressy sportswear in knits, silk, wovens and denim which are also sold under the Re-Union and Supplies label. Goods are manufactured offshore and shipped to this huge distribution center where the small factory outlet sells current styles at 30% or more below retail. Past-season goods end up in the Bargain Backroom where prices plummet. Get on the mailing list to find out about big clearance sale in August, December and April. No returns.

Checks, Credit cards

Off-price Stores

Off-price stores are the fastest growing segment of the apparel market nationwide. They sell the same merchandise found in department stores and specialty shops at 20% to 70% below retail. The big chains manufacture their own lines or use volume buying power to guarantee low prices. Many supplement their inventory with close-outs, overruns and discontinued styles from lines that may not be sold in local retail stores.

Big chains rely on a fast turnover, which means an ever-changing array of sale merchandise and a gold mine for hard-core bargain hunters interested in buying clothing and accessories at 70% or more below retail.

Return policies at off-price stores can be stricter than at full-price retailers, so be sure to inquire before you buy.

Consumer Tip

✔ Off-price stores locate in low-rent areas like strip shopping malls. Often several discounters cluster in one place, which is a real time-saver for the consumer. Alderwood Towne Center, Aurora Square, Northgate Village and the Pavilion Mall, the largest, are good examples.

Alki Beach Hut

NEW LISTING
West Seattle: 2514 Alki Ave. S.W. 937-8909
Hours: open weather permitting, sun up to sun down

A cute little shop overflowing onto the sidewalk with super buys on the latest casual sportswear favored by the many young adults who frequent the area on warm sunny days. Most of the inventory is closeouts, irregulars or salesmen samples priced from $7.95 to $14.95. Everything from B.U.M. Equipment T-shirts to Mumblesocks and Gotcha watches has turned up here. Exchanges only.

Checks, Credit cards

Burlington Coat Factory

NEW LOCATION
Edmonds: 24111 Hwy. 99 776-2221
Tacoma: 10401-S Gravelly Lake Dr. S.W. 588-3595 *Lakewood Mall*
Tukwila: 17900 Southcenter Pkwy. 575-3995 *Pavilion Mall*
Hours: Mon-Sat 10:30-9:30, Sun 11-6

With the largest inventory of outerwear in the Pacific Northwest (over 12,000 coats per store), this big national chain has coats for every occasion, for every member of the family by famous brand names and designer lables, including suede and leather outerwear. Career-oriented suits, dresses and coordinates can be found in Misses, Petite and Large sizes, along with contemporary separates by Liz Claiborne, Carole Little and Chaus. The men's department offers an outstanding selection of suits, sport jackets, dress shirts and slacks by top names like Colours, Henry Grethel, Pierre Cardin and Jordache in sizes 38 to 54. Casual wear includes Big and Tall sizes up to 4XX. And, you'll find well-stocked departments for Juniors, young men and children. Try to hold out for special promotions, seasonal sales and the gigantic coat sale in January. Credit or exchanges within 7 days.

Checks, Credit cards

Clothestime

NEW LOCATIONS

Des Moines: 32041 Pacific Hwy. S. 946-0511 *Ross Plaza*
Everett: 305 S.E. Everett Mall Way 348-9566 *Target Center*
Factoria: 4074 128th Ave. S.E. 643-1235 *Factoria Square*
Federal Way: Pacific Hwy. S. at 320th S. 946-0511
Lynnwood: 3105 Alderwood Mall Blvd. 774-7961 *Alderwood Towne Ctr.*
Redmond: 2172 148th N.E. 644-8312 *Overlake Fashion Plaza*
   17252 Redmond Way 883-0929 *Bear Creek Shopping Center*
Seattle: 325 Broadway E. 325-7803 *Capitol Hill*
   4501 Roosevelt Way N.E. 632-0820 *U-District*
   160th & Aurora Ave. N. 362-3571 *Aurora Square*
   832 N.E. Northgate Way 362-9480 *Northgate Village*
Silverdale: Silverdale Way & Bucklin Hill Road 698-1223 *Ross Plaza*
Tacoma: S. Steele at 38th 473-4279
   3304 S. 23rd St. 305-0042 *Target Center*
Tukwila: 17900 Southcenter Parkway 575-8110 *Pavilion Mall*
Woodinville: 14031 N.E. Woodinville-Duvall Rd. 489-0899
Hours: Generally, Mon-Fri 10-9, Sat 10-8, Sun 11-6

With over 500 stores nationwide, Clothestime is one of the leading off-price chains for Junior sportswear and trendy fashions. Although the majority of the inventory is manufactured especially for the stores, they also sell close-outs and overruns from such popular name-brands as Judy Knapp, Kitty Hawk, Limited Express and Bongo. To keep the goods

moving, clearance racks are always jammed with terrific buys.
30-day return policy

Checks, Credit cards

Dress Barn

Tukwila: 17900 Southcenter Pkwy. 575-1916 *Pavilion Mall*
Hours: Tukwila Mon-Fri 9:30-9:30, Sat 9:30-8, Sun 11-6;
Redmond Mon-Fri 10-8, Sat 10-6, Sun 12-5

Career women who want to maintain a professional ap-
pearance shop at the Dress Barn, a big national chain, where
fashionable but classic dresses, suits and coordinates fill the
racks. Leading brands such as Jonathan Martin, Sasson,
Casper, and Seville are priced 20% to 50% lower than department stores.You can always find a good-looking suit for
around $100. Sign up to get postcards announcing fabulous
suit sales in February and August.

The Pavilion Mall store has an excellent selection of sale merchandise year-round because it is the clearance center for all
the stores in the Pacific Northwest. Two week return policy.

Checks, Credit cards

Discount Leather & Stuff

NEW LISTING
Seattle: 10219 Aurora Ave. N. 522-1824 *Greenwood*
Hours: Mon-Fri 10-8, Sat 10-6, Sun 11-5

Since this place is owned by Bent Bike, inventory focuses on
leather garments and accessories for bikers but you will also
find some great buys on basic as well as fashion-oriented
styles. Many of the coats and jackets are priced at $100 or less
because they are samples, irregulars or discontinued styles.
The store also stocks dresses, skirts, jackets, vests and bustiers
for the ladies, plus handbags, belts, hats, and boots, which I'm
told are a super buy. Exchanges accepted.

Checks, Credit cards

Etruscan Designs

NEW LISTING
Seattle: 1530 Post Alley 623-1077 *Downtown, Pike Pl. Market*
Hours: Mon-Sat 10-6, Sun 10:30-5

A retail store that sells top grade leather garments for men
and women at factory direct prices. The designing is done locally, the manufacturing in Europe and the Orient. Styles
range from basic bomber jackets to shearling coats, as well as
fashionable skirts, vests and dresses. Seven-day return policy.

Checks, Credit cards

Fashion Directions

Factoria: 4065 128th S.E. 641-6708 *Factoria Square*
Seattle: 1530 5th Ave. 622-5400 Ext. 242 *Downtown*
Hours: Factoria Mon-Fri 10-9, Sat 10-6, Sun 12-5; Seattle
Mon-Sat 9:30-8, Sun 11-6

Fashion Directions is Jay Jacobs's budget store. Thrifty moms
encourage teenagers to shop here for trendy clothes and accessories at half the price. Some of the inventory is clearance
merchandise from the retail stores, but the majority is special-
purchase items and factory overruns. In-store promotions
bring prices down even more. The downtown store is located
in Jay Jacobs's basement. Returns accepted.

Checks, Credit cards

Fem de Fem

NEW LISTING
Everett: 1001 N. Broadway *259-4598*
Seattle: 4200 S. Othello St. 725-3617 *King Center, Rainier*
  717 Virginia 467-9050 *Downtown*
Tukwila: 14802 Pacific Hwy. S. 439-8731
Hours: Mon-Sat 10-8, Sun 10-6

Geared to Junior sizes, 3 through 11, Fem de Fem keeps prices
low on the latest fashion by selling closeouts and clearance merchandise purchased direct from manufacturers in California.
Prices for basic sportswear range from $4 to $9, dresses and
novelty separates $15 to $40. Credit or exchanges only.

Checks, Credit cards

The Hub

NEW LISTING
Auburn: 402 Auburn Way S. 833-7879
Puyallup: 733 River Rd. 770-1080 *Kmart Plaza*
Tacoma: 9714 Pacific Ave. 531-0661
  8012 S. Tacoma Way 588-6054 *B&I Store*
Hours: Generally Mon-Fri 9-9, Sat 10-6, Sun 11-5

The Hub offers everyday low prices on first-quality current
style brand names for the whole family from toddlers to Plus
sizes. Clothing is mainly casual wear, with lots of jeans,
sweatshirts and T-shirts in stock by familiar name like Levi's,
Hanes and London Fog. Prices average 20% to 60% off retail
because the 25-store chain buys in volume and operates on a
low overhead. Returns accepted.

Checks, Credit cards

J. Thompson

NEW LOCATIONS

Seattle: 205 Pine St. 623-5780 *Downtown*

   701 5th 382-6661 *Columbia Seafirst Tower, Downtown*

Hours: Pine: Mon-Fri 9:30-6, Sat 10-5:30, Sun 12-5;

5th: Mon-Fri 9:30-5

The owner of these small downtown Seattle stores spent 13 years as a buyer for Nordstrom's Rack. Focusing on career women sizes 6 to 16, he offers the same service and selection as better specialty stores, but at discounted prices. Fashionable separates and coordinates in classic styles by Georgio St. Angelo, Oscar de la Renta, Evan Picone and Rafael show up frequently. I spotted wool gabardine jackets for only $69. Raincoats and dressier garments are available in season. 30-day return policy.

Checks, Credit cards

Jeans Direct Discount Jean & Tops

NEW LOCATIONS

Auburn: 416 E. Main 833-3100

Bellevue: 11822 N.E. 8th Ave. 453-9517

Burien: 15823 1st S. 431-1466

Kenmore: 6522 Bothell Way 820-2207

Kent: 326 W. Meeker St. 854-4774

Puyullup: 106 S. Meridian 840-1018

Hours: Mon-Fri Kent, Auburn 10-6; Burien, Puyullup 11-7;

Kenmore, Bellevue 10-8, All stores Sat 10-6, Sun 12-5, Auburn closed on Sun

Bargains galore on jeans galore by such well-known manufacturers as Lee, Levi and Lawman fill these low overhead stores. Women's sizes go up to 18, men's range from 24 to 42, and there's a limited selection for children. Prices are low because most of the inventory is overruns and close-outs. Average cost for a pair of jeans is $19.95. Casual tops, sweaters, lightweight jackets and denim separates are also discounted. 15-day return policy.

Checks, Credit cards

Kameko Sales

NEW LISTING

Federal Way: 2408 S. 288th 946-4155

Puyallup: 12305 Meridian E. 840-0963 *South Hill*

Hours: Mon-Fri 10-5:30, Thurs 10-7, Sat 10-5

Save up to 75% on unisex sportswear by leading brand names as well as local manufacturers Union Bay, Enuf, Punch, Brittania and B.U.M. Equipment. Most everything is priced under $20 because of the low overhead and the fact that the owner buys mainly samples, irregulars and close-outs factory direct. Sweatshirts and jeans are best sellers. Exchanges only.

Checks, Credit cards

L.A. Connection

Kent: 25824 104th Ave S.E. 859-4973 *Kent Hill Plaza*
Renton: 318 Meeker 226-6641 *Renton Shopping Center*
Tacoma: 8720 S. Tacoma 581-4933
Hours: Generally, Mon-Fri 10-9, Sat 10-6, Sun 12-5

Although these local, privately owned stores look a lot like Clothestime, staff says customers include all ages because inventory is mainly basic sportswear that includes one-size-fits-all and Plus size garments. Dresses, suits and blazers are also available from California labels sold exclusively here. Look for savings of 20% to 30% on clothing normally priced from $5 to $50. Exchange or credit within 7 days.

Checks, Credit cards

Loehmann's

Factoria: I-90 at I-405 641-7596 *Loehmann's Plaza*
Hours: Mon-Fri 10-9, Sat 10-7, Sun 12-6

A pioneer in the concept of off-price marketing, Loehmann's was the first big chain to sell top designer labels at discount prices. Some women make weekly treks to snap up the best stuff. Sizes range from 4 to 16 with a few Junior and Women's sizes mixed in. Petite dresses are displayed separately.

The legendary Back Room features expensive coordinates, dresses and evening wear by such top American designers as Donna Karan, Anne Klein and Ralph Lauren.

In the Fall the store brings in gorgeous leather and suede garments. In the Summer they sell swimsuits by Gottex, the most expensive line in the marketplace. but you pay 70% off since they are last year's styles. Shoes, lingerie and accessories boast top labels.

Join the Insider Club and you'll get periodic discounts along with 15% off on your birthday. Returns within 7 days for credit or exchange.

Checks, Credit cards

Marshall's

Redmond: 2150 148th Ave. 644-2429 *Overlake Fashion Plaza*
Lynnwood: 3205 Alderwood Mall Blvd. 771-6045 *Alderwood Towne Center*
Seattle: 160th & Aurora Ave. N. 367-8520 *Aurora Square*
Tukwila: 17900 Southcenter Parkway 575-0141 *Pavilion Mall*
Hours: Mon-Fri 9:30-9:30, Sat 9:30-8, Sun 11-6

Marshall's, one of the oldest off-price chains in the country, carries a full range of clothing for every member of the family, along with linens, housewares and decorative gift items. Less expensive brands share space with better quality goods. Women's apparel features the usual array of Junior and Misses fashions, plus petite and large-size departments.

Working women will find stylish suits, dresses and coordinates by contemporary designers like Chaus, Evan Picone, Jones of New York and Nina Piccolino, along with an excellent selection of costume jewelry, and accessories to complete their wardrobe. Men's apparel tends to be casual but updated although dress shirts and pants are stocked. The Redmond store, which is the largest, frequently carries suits and sport coats by Perry Ellis, Calvin Klein, and Burberry. Children's departments outfit toddlers though pre-teens.

Please note that I have seen Waterford Crystal and beautiful hand painted Italian pottery in the Housewares department. Liberal return policy.

Checks, Credit cards

Modern Woman

Factoria: I-90 & I-405 643-2274 *Factoria Square*
Everett: 1402 S.E. Everett Mall Way 355-7808 *Everett Mall*
Lynnwood: 3105 Alderwood Mall Blvd. 774-3550 *Alderwood Towne Center*
Seattle: 160th & Aurora Ave. N. 361-1812 *Shoreline, Aurora Square*
Silverdale: 10406 Silverdale Way N.W. 698-1805 *Ross Plaza*
Tacoma: 3304 S. 23rd St. 572-4309 *Tacoma Center*
Hours: Generally, Mon-Fri 10-9, Sat 10-6, Sun 12-5

This big national off-price chain caters to the full-figured woman with a taste for fashionable apparel and accessories. Sizes range from 16W to 24W on career and active wear from well-known lables as well as clothing manufactured exclusively for the chain. Inventory is a mixture of basics to the latest styles, which varies from store to store. Modern Woman has frequent sales, so visit often, get on the mailing list, or watch for newspaper ads. Liberal return policy.

Checks, Credit cards

The New Look

Tacoma: 1108 S. K St. 272-1701
Hours: Mon-Sat 10-6

Prices average 50% or more off retail on sophisticated, contemporary fashions for Misses, Junior, and large sizes, with an emphasis on glamorous evening wear. Inventory includes overruns, close-outs and samples from such well known-labels as Wild Rose, Climax, and D.B. Designs that the owner, a former clothing rep, buys factory direct in Los Angeles. Women 25 to 60 can purchase a gorgeous outfit for under $100 and look like a million! Costume jewelry and accessories are also available. No returns.

Checks, Credit cards

Ross Dress for Less

Bellevue: 14327 N.E. 20th 644-2433
Federal Way: 32075 Pacific Hwy. S. 941-2122
Lynnwood: 18930 29th Ave. W. 778-9706
Seattle: 13201 Aurora N. 367-6030 Haller Lake
Silverdale: 10406 Silverdale Way N.W. 698-3180 *Ross Plaza*
Tacoma: 2931 S. 38th 474-3888 Cascade Plaza
Tukwila: 17672 Southcenter Parkway 575-0110 *Parkway Plaza*
Hours: Mon-Fri 9:30-9, Sat 9:30-6, Sun 11-7

Apparel at this popular off-price chain focuses on basics as well as fashion-oriented merchandise. Women's clothing includes Junior, petite and large sizes, mainly separates for career and casual wear, plus updated co-ordinates by well-known labels such as Karen Kane, Evan Picone and Jones of New York, as well as lingerie, sleepwear, outerwear, accessories and handbags. Ross has the largest selection of women's hosiery around and their big shoe department features moderately priced dress, casual and athletic footwear for the whole family.

The outstanding men's department stocks the latest styles for young men plus a terrific selection of dress shirts and accessories. Don't forget to check out the children's apparel.

The Bellevue store, which is the largest, carries better labels. The new "Home Accent" department features domestics, housewares and decorative items. On Tuesdays anyone over 55 years of age qualifies for a 10% discount. 30-day return policy.

Checks, Credit cards

Smart Sizes

Everett: 1402 S.E. Everett Mall Way 347-2629 *Everett Mall*
Renton: 36 S. Grady Way 228-7827
Seattle: 10005 Holman Road N.W. 784-0537 *Greenwood*
Tacoma: 10401 Gravelly Lake Drive S.W. 582-5929 *Villa Plaza*
Hours: Generally, Mon-Fri 10-9, Sat 10-7, Sun 12-5

Good news for the full-figured woman! An off-price chain that specializes in sizes 14W to 32W in basic casual clothing for work and play starting at $19.99. All of the merchandise bears the store's private label, which means you can't buy these styles anywhere else. Lingerie and accessories are also available. The Renton store stocks more fashion-oriented career and dressy apparel than the other stores plus it has a much larger clearance section. 30-day return policy.

Checks, Credit cards

Source Outlet

NEW LISTING
Kirkland: 13131 N.E. 124th 823-8192
Hours: Mon-Sat 10-6, Sun 11-6

Eastsiders visit this barebones warehouse operation if they want to buy better quality sportswear for the whole family at wholesale prices or less. Inventory includes overruns, samples and irregulars from well-known manufacturers such as Challe Line, Fila, New Balance, Asics, Sperry and Ralph Lauren's Polo. Prices start as low as $1.99. The outlet also carries athletic shoes for children and adults, and dressy shoes for women. A pair of Converse close-outs go for the unbelievable price of $12.99. No returns.

Checks, Credit cards

Super Star Outlet

NEW LISTING
Lynnwood: 19800 44th Ave. W. 774-6870 *Lynnwood Square*
Hours: Mon-Fri 10-8:30, Sat 10-6, Sun 11-5:30

This store is owned by the same people who run the Six Star Factory Outlet across the parking lot. Clothing is mainly inexpensive basic sportswear for men and women, plus outfits for infants 9 to 24 months old. You will find lots of imprint T-shirts and sweats for bargain basement prices plus socks and lingerie. The store also specializes in big framed posters, celebrity prints and mirrors with pictures. Returns accepted within 30 days.

Checks, Credit cards

Swanee's
NEW LISTING
Everett: 6309 Evergreen Way #D 353-5821
Lynnwood: 19820 Hwy. 99 S. 670-1233
Hours: Mon-Fri Everett 11-7, Lynnwood 10-8, Sat 10-6, Sun 12-5

Super low prices on jeans and casual wear make this a popular spot for men and women to shop. The owner buys close-outs and irregulars direct from Lee, Levi, Wrangler and Lawman. 501's sell for $19.99 every day! Boys levis cost only $9.99 and T-shirts, two for $10. Get on the mailing list for discount coupons. 15-day return policy.

Checks, Credit cards

TC's 12 Dollar Store
NEW LISTING
Kent: 17051 S.E. 272nd St. 630-1357 *Covington Square*
Hours: Mon-Wed 10-6, Thurs & Fri 10-8, Sat 10-5, Sun 12-5

Basic sportswear as well as the latest Junior fashions from popular lines such as L.A. Gear, Jocko, Punch and Palmetto sell for $12 and under here, with leggings one of their best selling items. More expensive dresses are displayed in the boutique section. Two-week exchange policy.

Checks, Credit cards

T.J. Maxx
NEW LOCATIONS
Federal Way: 1910 S. 320th 946-2887 *Seatac Village*
Seattle: 11029 Roosevelt Way N.E. 363-9511 *Northgate Village*
Silverdale: 10300 Silverdale Way N.E. 692-8821 *Kitsap Place*
Tacoma: 3216 S. Center 272-4422 *Tacoma Central Plaza*
Hours: Mon-Sat 9:30-9:30, Sun 11-6

T.J. Maxx delivers the max for the minimum! The stores offer apparel for the whole family, with a special section set aside for petites and large sizes. Racks are a mixed bag of dresses, separates, and outerwear for career and casual wear, with updated co-ordinates by Liz Claiborne, Diane Gilman, Karen Kane and Chaus showing up frequently. Outerwear, sleepwear, activewear, lingerie and accessories are also carried, and during the holidays, party dresses.

The children's departments feature top name-brand clothing. Menswear is mostly casual. Dress shirts and slacks are available year-round, but sport coats and overcoats only show up occasionally.

All stores except Seattle include a limited, but fashionable, selection of shoes. Sterling silver and 14K gold jewelry is sold in the Tacoma, Seattle, and Federal Way stores. T.J. Maxx also sells linens, housewares, and decorative items. 30-day return policy.

Checks, Credit cards

Valerie's

NEW LOCATION

Seattle: 4508 University Way N.E. 547-0918 *U-District*
Hours: Mon-Sat 10-6, Thurs 10-8

Students and young women shop here for sportswear and separates in the latest styles from Judy Knapp, Limited Express, the Gap, Esprit and Paris Blues. Dresses that retail for $100 cost $39.99 because the owner buys overruns and closeouts factory-direct in Los Angeles. Be sure to sign up for notice of sales. Seven-days exchange or credit.

Checks, Credit cards

Zakk's

NEW LISTING

Lynnwood: 19509 Highway 99 670-2719
Hours: Mon-Fri 10-7, Sat 10-6, Sun 11-5

Zakk's caters to women who like to wear sophisticated but easy-fit separates in soft, drapey rayon fabrics, with three-piece ensembles and embellished tops a specialty. Glamorous angora sweaters show up in the fall. Prices range from $20 to $150 on lines exclusive to this store, some of which are overruns from a resort wear factory the owners operate in Indonesia. Mailing list for seasonal sales. Exchanges within 3 weeks.

Checks, Credit cards

Clearance Centers

When stores have to make room for new merchandise, clothing that's been on the sale racks for a long time is usually donated to a charity, sold to a discounter, or shipped to a clearance center. The advantages of shopping clearance centers, if you are a faithful retail customer, are that you know the merchandise and prices start at 50% off. The drawbacks are one-of-a-kind styles and sizes, broken groupings, shop-worn or damaged goods, and out-of-season or year-old merchandise.

The Bon Marche Final Countdown

NEW LISTING
Seattle: N.E. Northgate Way & 5th Ave. N.E. 361-2121
Northgate Mall
Hours: Mon-Sat 9:30-9:30, Sun 11-6

I'm going to let you in on a well-kept secret. Located on the lower level of the Northgate Mall, behind Woman's World, is a small clearance room for better women's apparel from several of the Bon's stores where you can get some fabulous buys on expensive designer labels like Ellen Tracy or Diane Gilman. Everything is already 50% off when it comes into the room, but then it is placed on racks that say 30% to 50% off the last marked price, which means you can get a $300 dress for $75! The selection varies tremendously and often you'll find out-of-season garments, but it pays to visit frequently since the best stuff goes quickly. Returns accepted.

Checks, Credit cards

Nordstrom Rack

Lynnwood: 3115 Alderwood Mall Blvd. 774-6559 *Alderwood Towne Center*
Seattle: 1601 2nd Ave. 448-8522 *Downtown*
Tukwila: 17900 Southcenter Pkwy. 575-1058 *Pavilion Mall*
Hours: Tukwila and Lynnwood; Mon-Fri 9:30-9:30, Sat 9:30-7, Sun 11-6; Seattle; Mon-Sat 9:30-7, Sun 12-6

I know Nordie fans who shop the retail stores, decide what they want to buy, wait the 3 to 4 months it takes for their favorite items to reach The Rack, then snatch them up for a fraction of the original cost. Prices start at 50% off, but progressive markdowns and tag sales create unbelievable savings. Fashion addicts zero-in on top designer labels. Co-ordinated sportswear and separates purchased especially for The Rack are priced at 30% below retail. Once a month the stores have a sensational sale, during which specific items get marked down 30% to 50%. Get on the mailing list for advance notice, and come early to cherry pick the racks. Nordstrom's service extends to their clearance operation — all Racks have a personal shopper. 30-day return policy.

Checks, Credit cards

Women's Consignment Shops

Consignment shops are the crème de la crème of used clothing stores. They offer a fun, easy way to upgrade the whole family's wardrobe or to make money recycling your "gently worn" clothing and accessories. People who would never set foot in a thrift shop feel right at home in consignment shops because most of them look and operate just like retail stores.

The variety and quality can be astounding, so you don't have to spend hours sifting through marginal cast-offs to find the good stuff. Many items have hardly been worn, some never. Sometimes the tags are still on them. Who among us hasn't purchased something that ends up hanging in the closet unloved? Samples, close-outs, and merchandise from retail shops going out of business or left-over after clearance sales also turn up at consignment shops.

Prices, which average one third of the original retail value, will vary from store to store depending upon the clientele, location and inventory. Some stores keep prices low to ensure a fast turnover. Others just don't realize the value of an item. In Bellevue you'll find higher prices, but better quality and more designer labels. You can visit three or four of these shops in an afternoon since they're all concentrated in a fairly small area. The U-District to Northgate is another locale dotted with consignment shops. Sales are usually final so inspect each item carefully. Some shops will let you take things out on 24-hour approval.

Consignment shops, just like retail stores, have seasonal clearances, special promotions and sales racks that deliver incredible bargains. Remember, the best values get snatched up fast, so visit your favorite haunts frequently. Happy hunting!

Consumer Tips

Here's how to make money selling your clothes in consignment shops:

✔ The best months to bring your clothes in are April and September. Clothing must be in season, clean, pressed and on hangers.

✔ Most consignment policies require that merchandise be brought in on specific days or by appointment. Garments can be no more than 3 years old unless they're designer labels or timeless styles, and no more than 20 items can be consigned at a time.

✔ Visit several consignment shops in your area to determine which one will yield the greatest return. What doesn't sell at one shop may be a hot number at another.

✔ You sign a contract agreeing to leave the clothes in the store for 6 to 8 weeks. The owner sets the price, and the usual commission is 50% of the selling price, which may be reduced 20% or more after 30 days at the discretion of the store. Some shops give you 60% if the item sells for $50 or more. Any clothing not picked up on the specified date is donated to charity or becomes the property of the store.

✔ Payment is by check on a monthly or bi-monthly basis. You can pick your check up or arrange to have it mailed in a self-addressed stamped envelope.

A Class Act

Seattle: 2205 N.E. 65th 523-6750 *Ravenna*
Hours: Mon-Sat 10-5, Sun 11-4

The shop may be small but there's a lot to choose from and the owner only takes in current style consignments. The focus is on better contemporary sportswear and professional attire from top names like Liz, Jones of New York and Vittadini, along with clothing made from soft drapery fabrics or that has an ethnic look. No returns.

Checks, Credit cards

Act II Consignment Boutique

Federal Way: 1610 S. 341st 927-7190 *Spectrum Business Park*
Hours: Mon-Fri 9-7, Sat 9-6

Act II offers a great selection and low prices for women age 25 and up in sizes 2 to 24. Clothing for work or play fills the racks, including classic business suits, maternity wear, party dresses and wedding gowns, all in good condition by well-known manufacturers. Samples show up frequently as well as new items sold at off-prices. Get on the mailing list for seasonal sales. Credit on returns.

Checks, Credit cards

Act II Ladies Apparel

Edmonds: 512 5th Ave. S., Suite C 774-1787
Hours: Mon-Wed 10-6, Thurs & Fri 10-7, Sat 10-5

A small boutique-like shop filled with lots of samples and up-dated sportswear purchased off-price by the owner, who used to be a wholesale clothing rep and knows where to get good deals. Half of the store is consignment, mainly better apparel including tailored suits and special occasion dresses. Exchange or credit within 3 days on new apparel only.

Checks, Credit cards

Alexandra's

NEW LISTING
Seattle: 415 Stewart 623-1214 *Downtown*
Hours: Mon-Sat 10-6, Thurs 10-8

If you want to look like you just stepped out of Vogue magazine, shop at Alexandra's where exclusive labels by top American and European designers sell for a fraction of their original cost. Although the majority of the garments are priced at $50 to $200, for $800 you can buy a stunning $3,000 suit by Escada, a name that turns up frequently. The store always has a good selection of beautiful evening wear and even the accessories, shoes and hand bags sport names like Gucci and Ferregamo. Alexandra's will pick clothing up at your home. The mailing list is a must for fashion addicts. No returns.

Checks, Credit cards

Alice's Consignment & Gifts

NEW LISTING
Seattle: 1226 S. Bailey 762-6320 *Georgetown*
Hours: Wed-Sat 10:30-5:30

Clothing for every member of the family is sold here, as well as small appliances, housewares, toys, antiques, and collectibles. Children's sizes range from infant to age 6. Ladies apparel goes up to size 48. Men will find suits and sport jackets at super low prices. No returns.

Checks

Between Friends

Seattle: 818 3rd Ave. 624-2220 *Downtown*
Hours: Mon-Fri 10-6, Sat 11-4

Since the store is located in downtown Seattle, inventory is geared toward the working woman who will find lots of classy suits, dresses, and separates to give her that "dress for success" look. Sportswear and accessories round out the selection.

Some of the garments are samples and off-price goods. Between Friends pays cash instead of consigning, except on expensive items. Mailing list for seasonal sales. Credit for returns.

Checks, Credit cards

Budget Boutique

Everett: 1830 Broadway 259-1285
Hours: Mon-Sat 10-5

Ever since 1980, Budget Boutique has been supplying women with affordable clothing from lingerie to coats, suits, dresses, sportswear, wedding dresses and formal wear, as well as accessories. Sizes range from 3 to 52 with a good selection in the large size category. The store is bigger than most consignment shops so you are sure to find something. No returns.

Checks

Buying Used Levis/Left Turn Sportswear

NEW LISTING
Tacoma: 325 Garfield S. 531-7658
Hours: Mon-Fri 11-6, Sat 11-3

Not only do they buy used levis here, they sell them as well, in any size or style imaginable for men, women and Junior sizes. Condition varies so prices range from $4.99 to $16.99, with over 500 pairs to choose from. All jeans are washed and processed before they are put in the store. Exchanges only.

Checks, Credit cards

Cecil's

NEW LISTING
Seattle: 2224 Queen Anne Ave. N. 283-3676 *Queen Anne*
Hours: Mon-Fri 10-7, Sat 10-5, Sun 12:30-5

Formerly located in the University district, Cecil's is now the only consignment shop on Queen Anne. Inventory is geared to customers who like better quality fashionable clothing for work and play. No returns.

Checks, Credit cards

The Change House

NEW LISTING
Normandy Park: 19925 First Ave. S. 878-1271
Hours: Tues-Sat 10-6

One of the biggest consignment shops around with a huge assortment of apparel and accessories for all occasions for women size 1 through 40. Only leading brand names like Karen Kane, Liz Claiborne and Jones of New York are carried and I'm told that prices are quite low on many items. New inventory includes samples and selected ready-to-wear lines such as Peter Popovich, which sell at discounted prices. Mailing list. 24 hour return on consignment clothing.

Checks, Credit cards

Clothesline Consignment

NEW LISTING

Seattle: 6307 24th Ave. N.W. 784-9974 *Ballard*
Hours: Tues-Fri 11-6, Sat 11-5:30, Sun 11-5

There's something for every member of the family at this small shop, including a lot of gently-worn children's clothing for infants to size 7. Women will find career and casual wear, men a limited selection. No returns.

Checks

Champagne Taste

NEW LOCATION

Kirkland: 147 Park Lane 828-4502
Hours: Mon-Sat 10-5:30, Sun 12-5

Only one of the Eastside's many fashion-oriented boutique-like consignment shops. Not only do they carry the usual array of designer labels, but an extensive selection of evening wear and wedding gowns, including veils. It seems that the store is selling off clearance merchandise from bridal shops, so there are over 300 dresses in stock at close-out prices. Some of the clothing and jewelry is purchased from off-price wholesalers. The store also consigns unusual antiques and furniture. All sales final.

Checks, Credit cards

Closet Transfer

Bainbridge Island: 562 Bejune Drive 842-1515
Hours: Mon-Sat 10:30-4

Clothing for men, women and children must be in mint condition and natural fibers are preferred. Shop for everything from casual to formal wear, accessories and jewelry. New merchandise from India includes basic as well as ethnic-looking dresses, hats, socks and mittens. Located below and behind the Streamliner Diner. No returns.

Checks

The Clothes Connection

Bellevue: 11026 N.E. 11th Street 453-2055
Hours: Mon-Fri 10-5, Sat 10-4

The quiet neighborhood and cozy white house will make you feel like you're visiting a friend instead of shopping! Every room contains fashionable clothing and accessories, all in tip-top condition. Inventory is career-oriented, with a lot of suits, dresses and separates to choose from, many of which sport better labels like Anne Klein and Ellen Tracy. All sales final.

Checks, Credit cards

Crystal Threads

NEW LOCATION
Issaquah: 35 B West Sunset B   392-9456
Hours: Mon-Fri 10-6, Sat 10-65

Life is more laid back in Issaquah so the clothes will be more casual-oriented, but in a classic, contemporary vein. There's a special rack set aside for evening wear and Queen sizes. The store always carries samples and name-brand sportswear, such as Peter Popovich, marked below retail prices. Accessories and estate jewelry complement the inventory. Mailings announce seasonal sales.

Checks, Credit cards

The Dark Horse

Bellevue: 11810 N.E. 8th   454-0990 *Bellevue Lake Mall*
Hours: Mon-Fri 10:30-6, Thurs 10:30-8, Sat 10:30-5, Sun 12-5

The Dark Horse is the oldest and one of the largest consignment shops in the Pacific Northwest. Glamorous cocktail dresses are in stock year-round, ski and tennis wear in season. Look for expensive designer labels in the center of the store. Sizes range from 2 to 24, with lots of accessories, shoes, handbags and jewelry at tempting prices. An outstanding selection of men's apparel in sizes 36 to 50 hangs on one wall. The store is located behind the Hunan Garden Restaurant. No returns.

Checks, Credit cards

Designer Consignor

NEW LISTING
Edmonds: 9605 Firdale Ave.   546-0866 *Firdale Village*
Hours: Tues-Fri 11-7, Sat 10-7

With over 2,000 sq. ft., Designer Consignor has one of the biggest and best selections around, from lingerie to coats, sportswear to career wear in all sizes and price ranges. The day I stopped by there were a lot of glitzy evening dresses priced way below wholesale because they came from a shop that had recently gone out of business. Accessories for every occasion abound. The store takes in over a hundred new items a day so there's a constant turnover. No returns.

Checks, Credit cards

Emily's Trunk

NEW LISTING
Everett: 607 S.E. Everett Mall Way 348-9722
Hours: Tues-Fri 11-6, Sat 11-5

A small boutique-like shop that carries everything from lingerie to formal attire for Junior thorugh Plus sizes. The owner only accepts high-end merchandise in perfect condition. Mailing list. No returns.

Checks

Encore Consignments

Lynnwood: 17602 Hwy. 99 745-0768
Hours: Mon-Fri 10-6, Sat 11-5

The whole family can shop economically at this store, which has been in business for over 20 years. Ladies apparel ranges from Junior sizes to a "Big and Beautiful" rack, as well as wedding gowns, which are super cheap. Men can buy jackets, suits, slacks, shirts and sweaters. Encore stocks children's clothing from newborn through pre-teen. Merchandise not picked up by consignors goes on the $1.00 rack. What a deal! No returns.

Checks

Fashion Quest

Renton: 123 Wells Ave. S. 271-2886
Hours: Tues-Fri 11-6:30, Sat 10-5:30

The owner is committed to top brand names like Jones of New York, Evan Picone and Liz Claiborne. Separate rooms in this converted house display an excellent selection of clothing for work or leisure, which looks like it's never been worn. One room is devoted to fashionable apparel for Queen sizes. The store carries a lot of accessories so you can put together a total look. No returns.

Checks, Credit cards

Felipa's

NEW LISTING
Seattle: 3234 N.E. 45th 524-7649 *U-District*
Hours: Mon-Fri 10-5:30, Thurs 10-7, Sat 10-5

Serving the Laurelhurst area, Felipa's caters to a clientele who likes top quality fashionable clothing for career or casual wear. The store may be small but the selection is outstanding, from designer label sportswear to cocktail dresses. No returns.

Checks, Credit cards

Finer Consigner

NEW LISTING
Seattle: 6407 Roosevelt Way N.E. 522-7441 *Roosevelt*
Hours: Mon-Sat 10-6, Sun 12-5

Inventory includes quality clothing for women, from sweatshirts to tailored suits to party dresses as well as apparel for children, newborn through teens. I'm told that Finer Consigner is a good place to buy Osh Kosh for the kids. The store may be small but it has a good variety and prices that may be lower than those found at other consignment shops. 24-hour return policy.

Checks

Furie, Ltd.

Seattle: 2810 E. Madison 329-6829 *Madison Park*
Hours: Tues-Sat 10-5

Fashionable labels appear on everything from jeans to silk dresses in this upscale shop, which also sells clearance merchandise from small local specialty retailers. The selection of accessories is limited, but stylish. Get on the mailing list for big sales in early August and February. No returns.

Checks, Credit cards

Gena's Resale Fashions

Tacoma: 10227 Bridgeport Way S.W. *581-0236*
Hours: Mon-Sat 10-4

Although Gena's is a small consignment shop, it's been around nearly 20 years, so business must be good! They focus on better sportswear and clothing for the working woman in a full range of sizes, with an emphasis on name-brands in good condition. The mailing list will notify you of seasonal sales. No returns.

Checks, Credit cards

Glad Rags Boutique

NEW LOCATION
Bellevue: 140 105th Ave. N.E. 454-9377 *Bellevue Plaza*
Hours: Tues-Fri 11-6, Sat 10-5

The latest designer labels and classic styles ensure a fast turnover on clothes for business, leisure or formal wear at Glad Rags. However, sizes are limited to 2 through 16. Watch for frequent markdowns and get on the mailing list to find out about sales. No returns.

Checks, Credit cards

Image Awareness

NEW LISTING
Everett: 745-8755, 334-2224
Hours: By appointment

The owner, an image consultant and former Mrs. Washington, only sells consignment clothing from a select group of clients, which includes some very wealthy women. Inventory may be limited to a couple of racks but everything is high-end designer labels in excellent condition, from Anne Taylor suits to Ungaro dresses, to fabulous evening gowns at prices to die for.

Checks

Island Treasures

NEW LISTING
Mercer Island: 3024 78th Ave. S.E. 236-1977
Hours: Mon-Sat 10-5

An art gallery, coffee house, antique shop, consignment furniture and clothing store all rolled into one. The owner prefers clothing in soft romantic styles or that looks like something from the 1960's or 70's which is, of course, making a comeback. A lot of the garments are purchased new off-price from manufacturers like Star of India. Children's apparel is sold on consignment as well. No returns.

Kathy's Kloset

Seattle: 4751 12th Ave. N.E. 523-3019 *U-District*
West Seattle: 4738 42nd S.W. 937-2637 *Jefferson Square*
Hours: U-District, Mon-Sat 10-6, Thurs 10-8, Sun 12-5; West Seattle, Mon-Fri 10-8, Sat 10-6, Sun 11-5

The 12th Avenue location has long been a favorite of University of Washington students and career women because the two-story gray house overflows with clothing of all kinds, from trendy to traditional in Junior and Misses sizes. The West Seattle store, which will have a new name (Funky Jane's) in 1994 since it is no longer owned by Kathy, handles more casual-oriented clothing and children's sizes infant to 6X. No returns.

Checks, Credit cards

Kopps Furniture

NEW LISTING
Everett: 2723 Colby 258-9435
Hours: Mon-Sat 9:30-5

A furniture store may seem like an unlikely place to buy clothes but the owner's wife decided to add consignment clothing. The selection may be limited but prices are reasonable and she plans on expanding. Apparel is career-oriented in sizes 6 to 18. No returns.

Checks, Credit cards

Labels

NEW LISTING

Seattle: 7212 Greenwood Ave. N. 781-1194 *Greenwood*
Hours: Tues-Sat 10-6, Thurs 10-9, Sun 12-5

This store may be small, but it's jam packed with sportswear and career wear along with clothing for infants and children to size 14. The owner prefers natural fibers, and familiar names like Liz Claiborne and Karen Kane turn up frequently. 24-hour return policy.

Checks, Credit cards

L'Armoire Consignments

NEW LISTING

Renton: 410 Burnett Ave. S. 255-6415
Hours: Mon-Sat 10-6:30

Wander from room to room in this homey converted house and you'll notice lots of better labels like Cassini, Blass and Claiborne on the sportswear and career wear, which includes large sizes. I'm told that some of the clothes are cast-offs from stewardess's closets. The selection of fine lingerie is exceptional and the owner plans on adding Queen size lingerie made especially for the store. You'll also find classy accessories and unusual jewelry, some of which is antique. L'Armoire also rents wedding gowns, furs and elegant formal wear. No returns.

Checks

Le Frock

NEW LISTING

Seattle: 317 E. Pine 623-5339 *Capitol Hill*
Hours: Mon-Fri 12-7, Sun 12-5

The eclectic selection reflects the neighborhood: from cutting-edge fashions by Betsey Johnson and local designers to traditional suits and sportswear by Anne Taylor and the Bannana Republic. Men's apparel includes the latest in casual attire as well as suits made in Italy. You can even buy Doc Martin's here. Clothing and accessories are purchased outright. No returns.

Checks, Credit cards

The Model's Closet

NEW LISTING
Seattle: 2909-B E. Madison 322-8460 *Madison Park*
Hours: Tues-Sat 10-5, Thurs 10-6:30

Because the owner is a model, clothing always represents the latest styles from upscale lines like Ellen Tracy, as well as local designers who sell their fashion forward samples and overstock here. Although the main focus is career, you'll also find a wonderful selection for casual or formal wear. No returns.
Checks, Credit cards

The Other Place

NEW LOCATION
Seattle: 8320 5th N.E. 527-0766 *Northgate*
Hours: Mon-Sat 10:30-5:30, Thurs 10-8

This is a very popular store because of the low prices and big variety of apparel which ranges from outerwear to lingerie, dresses, suits, sportswear and maternity wear, all in current styles. Dressy clothes are displayed in an antique armoire. Keep your eyes open for better labels and contemporary merchandise brought in by a well-known downtown specialty store. No returns.
Checks, Credit cards

Pandora's Box

Bellevue: 10867 N.E. 2nd Pl. 455-3883
Hours: Mon-Sat 10-5

Nestled in a small yellow house on a residential side street, the most chic of Bellevue's consignment shops contains a potpourri of designer labels for career and casual wear in perfect condition. Karen Kane, Metropole, Escada, Bis and Harve Bernard are only a few of the many contemporary lines. Lingerie and outerwear is carefully selected, as are the handbags, shoes, belts and jewelry. Look for beautiful evening clothes during the holidays. No returns.
Checks, Credit cards

Proctor's Consignment

NEW LISTING
Tacoma: 2726 N. Proctor 752-6434
Hours: Mon-Sat 10-5

A very classy shop filled with updated apparel for work and play. The impressive selection of suits and dresses includes fashion-oriented labels like Liz Claiborne, Anne Klein, and Trahari. The good news is that sizes range from petite to Queen size. Return within 24 hours for credit or exchange.

Checks, Credit cards

Queen's Closet

Tacoma: 2117 Tacoma Ave. S. 627-1221
Hours: Mon-Fri 12-6, Sat 10-4

Tall and large sizes will find everything they need for work or play, including coats, furs, lingerie, cocktail and wedding gowns. Large sizes start at 18 and can go as high as 70, tall sizes go from 10 to 16. New samples and off-price goods are purchased directly from manufacturers. What doesn't sell ends up on the $2 rack out front. Fill out a card and get 20% off anything in the store on your birthday. No returns.

Checks, Credit cards

Ragamoffyn's

NEW LOCATION
Kirkland: 127 Park Lane 827-4693
132 Park Lane 828-0396
Hours: Mon-Fri 10-5:30, Sat 10-5

The most exclusive consignment shop north of San Francisco reflects the owner's European background and taste for quality. Labels read like a Who's Who of the fashion industry, from Ralph Lauren and Ellen Tracy to St. Laurent or Galanos in sizes 2 through 14. There's always a fantastic selection of evening wear, leather and suede garments, along with elegant accessories, jewelry, handbags and shoes. The store on 127th is known as "The Rack" because this is where clearance merchandise sells for 50% to 75% off the last marked price, which makes couture fashion accessible to even those on a tight budget. Sign up for the newsletter. No returns.

Checks, Credit cards

Razz m' Tazz

Seattle: 623 Queen Anne Ave. N. 281-7900 *North of Seattle Center*
Hours: Tues-Fri 10-6, Sat 10-5

Apparel in this small exclusive shop is beautifully displayed and carefully selected. Contemporary sportswear and career wear comes from better labels like Anne Klein, Kennar and Trahari in sizes 2 through 14. Sophisticated cocktail dresses and fashionable leather garments are always available along

with one of the best selections of stylish jewelry and accessories you'll ever find in a consignment shop. Don't forget to
put your name on the mailing list.

Checks

ReDress

Bellevue: 513 156th S.E.   746-7984 *Lake Hills Shopping Center*
Hours: Mon-Fri 10:30-6, Sat 10:30-5, Sun 11-4

Redress stocks a big inventory of current style merchandise
for sizes 4 to 16, from outerwear and jeans to suits and evening wear as well as wedding dresses and their specialty,
mother-of-the-bride dresses. Names like The Gap and Liz pop
up frequently along with better designer labels. No returns.

Checks, Credit cards

Satin Hanger

NEW LOCATION
Midway: 24618 Military Rd. S.   941-8648
Hours: Mon-Sat 10-5

Management claims prices are so low that enterprising shoppers ferret out the best buys and make money selling them to
other consignment shops. Racks are jammed with apparel for
petite to large sizes for all occasions. Home furnishings, small
appliances and decorator items are also sold on consignment.
No returns.

Checks, Credit cards

Savvy

Redmond: 8072 160th N.E.   883-6441
Hours: Tues-Fri 10:30-5:30, Sat 10:00-5

Savvy delivers bargains on women's apparel in the latest
styles, including outerwear and lingerie, for sizes 4 through
18. Smart shoppers drop by to purchase jeans as well as business attire. No returns.

Checks, Credit cards

Sebastian's Closet

Tacoma: 1205 Regents Blvd.   565-3503 *Fircrest*
Hours: Mon-Fri 11-5:30, Sat 11-5

The most upscale consignment shop in Tacoma caters to
professional women who like to wear top quality labels like
Jones of New York and Evan Picone, which sell for $40 to $60.
Inventory includes contemporary sportswear, plus a terrific
selection of formal wear and bridal gowns. Some of the garments are on consignment from specialty shops or come from
local manufacturers, which means they have never been worn.

First time shoppers and senior citizens qualify for a 10% discount. No returns.

Checks, Credit cards

Second Avenue Consignments

Edmonds: 527 Main Street 771-5667
Hours: Tues-Sat 10-5

The main focus at Second Avenue is business apparel from better labels so you'll always find a good selection of suits, dresses and jackets. However, they also stock casual wear to round out your wardrobe. No returns.

Checks, Credit cards

The Second Act

NEW LISTING
Friday Harbor: 450 Spring St. 378-3828
  80 Nichols St. 378-5554
Hours: Mon-Sat 11-6, Sun 12-5

If you're visiting Friday Harbor, be sure to check out these two small shops. They're crammed with top quality contemporary clothes for men and women from resort wear to dressy attire, including wedding gowns and sport jackets. The Spring Street store carries children's apparel. The owner says that even people who don't live on the island mail stuff to her to sell. No returns.

Checks

Sivel America/Ragbone Clothing Company

NEW LISTING
Kent: 310 Washington Ave. 850-7315
Hours: Mon-Sat 10-6, Sun 12-5

Sivel started out buying used denim and exporting it overseas, which is why the store name is Levis spelled backwards. Now they've opened a retail store and expanded the inventory to include second hand, casual but cutting edge fashions for men and women ages 14 to 40. Overalls, carpenter pants and motorcycle jackets are only a few of the unusual things that turn up here. Cash or credit for merchandise brought in.

Checks

Take Two

Seattle: 430 15th Ave. E. 324-2569 *Capitol Hill*
Hours: Mon-Fri 10-7:30, Sun 12-6

Take Two caters to a younger clientele, so there are a lot of separates and dresses in trendy as well as contemporary styles for work and play. They also carry more samples, closeouts and off-price lines than most consignment shops and display them separately. These can vary from basic cotton knits by CP Shades to romantic ethnic styles from Star of India or We Be Bop. There's always a good selection of unusual jewelry and fun accessories. No returns.

Checks, Credit cards

Twice is Nice Boutique

Bothell: 19215 Bothell Way N.E. 483-1991
Hours: Mon-Fri 10-5, Sat 10-3

For over a decade this shop has been selling today's clothing at yesterday's prices. Although office wear is the main focus, teenagers to Queen sizes will find something to suit their needs, from jeans to formal wear, outerwear to lingerie. There's even a special rack for tennis, golf and ski apparel. Every Monday customers over 55 qualify for a 25% discount. No returns.

Checks, Credit cards

Wild West Trading Co.

NEW LISTING
Bremerton: 3035 Wheaton Way 373-7188
Everett: 1915 B Broadway 258-8193
Lynnwood: 19714 Hwy. 99 778-4620
Seattle: 7525 Aurora N. 781-9781 *Greenwood*
Hours: Mon-Fri 9-9, Sat 9-6

Used Levi's, jeans, denim jackets, cutoffs, and overalls for men and women are brought and sold here. Condition varies tremendously — remember some people like their jeans well worn — but everything is washed before it's put on the racks. The stores also sell basic T-shirts, sweats, shorts, and woven shirts at off-prices. Call first to find out what brand names and styles they are buying. Exchanges.

Checks

Wonder-Full Size

NEW LISTING
Seattle: 8331 15th Ave. N.W. 783-8341 *Crown Hill*
Kenmore: 6524 N.E. 181st 481-1914 *Kenmore Plaza*
Hours: Tues-Sat 10-5

Two shops devoted to Queen sizes, where you will be surprised by the variety and quality offered. The emphasis is on career apparel with a lot of nice suits and dresses in stock by the likes of Pendleton, Liz Sport and Jones of New York.

Sportswear is also available and during the holidays dressier garments show up. No returns.

Checks

Yesterday's

Lynnwood: 7300 196th St. S.W. 771-4225
Hours: Mon-Sat 10-5:30

An impressive collection of better and designer labels makes Yesterday's the most upscale consignment shop in the North end, and prices will be lower here than what you would pay on the Eastside. Names like Anne Klein, Ellen Tracy and DKNY pop up frequently, as well as samples in the latest styles. Sizes range from petite to XL for leisure or office attire. No returns.

Checks, Credit cards

Your Hidden Closet

NEW LOCATION
Bellevue: 1075 Bellevue Way N.E. 453-5999 *Bellgate Plaza*
Hours: Mon-Thurs 10-6, Fri & Sat 10-5

Big is beautiful at this shop, which began in 1987 when two sisters searched in vain for transitional wardrobes during a weight loss program. They tell me customers drive for miles to save 50% or more on clothing that originally came from "Pennys to Paris," including outerwear, lingerie, formal attire and wedding dresses. Sometimes the store gets in new stuff from Queen size shops going out of business. The mailing list is a must. No returns.

Checks, Credit cards

Discount Clothing Catalogs

Call the numbers listed below to receive free copies of some of the better known clothing catalogs available. All have operators on duty 24 hours daily, except Anthony Richards, which takes calls from 9am until 10pm Mon-Fri, Sat 9-5 (Eastern time).

Anthony Richards

Cleveland, OH: 1-800-359-5933

Because everything is designed and made by Anthony Richards, dresses and ensembles in easy-care washable polyesters or synthetic blends sell for $14.99 to $49.99 in petite, misses, women's and half sizes. Special occasion attire, jewelry and lingerie show up as well.

Chadwick's of Boston

Boston, MA: 508-583-6600

The leading off-price fashion catalog in the country offers contemporary separates and dresses for work and play by such well-known names as Jonathan Martin, Nina Piccalino, Tess and Adolpho, which are discounted 25% to 50%. Basic items from wool blazers to silk blouses to cotton turtle necks come in a multitude of colors at super low prices, especially when you order more than one. Some styles are available in petite and large sizes. Call to find out about weekly specials.

Fashion Galaxy

Hanover, PN: 1-800-752-5552

This catalog serves as a clearance house for half a dozen women's apparel catalogs put out by a major catalog retailer whose publications include Simply Tops, Premier Edition, Silhouettes (for large sizes), and Essence (for black women). You can easily save 50% or more on a wide range of quality, fashionable garments made exclusively for the company or purchased from leading brand names.

Newport News

NEW LISTING

Hampton, VA: 1-800-688-2830

Styles are a lot like those you'd see in Victoria's Secret but prices are a lot less. The main focus is on colorful, basic but updated sportswear and career wear that starts at $5 for a tank top and goes up to $50 for a sand-washed silk dress in Junior and Missy sizes. Look for "key items" where you buy two or more garments in the same style and get $5 off on each one. Catalogs include lingerie, shoes, swimsuits and holiday attire in season.

The Ultimate Outlet

Chicago, IL: 1-800-332-6000

If you like the merchandise you see in the Spiegel Catalog, you'll love their clearance catalogs. Clothing and home furnishings include top designer labels. Apparel, accessories and shoes vary from casual to high fashion. Sizes are limited to stock on hand, but the catalogs include misses, petite and large sizes for ladies, tall, short and XL for the men. Markdowns start at 20% and can go as high as 60% off.

Menswear

Although there are only a few places that sell men's apparel exclusively, see the Additional Clothing Outlets section at the end of this chapter for other stores that carry menswear.

Cutter and Buck

NEW LISTING
Seattle: 1809 7th Ave. 3rd Floor 622-4191 *Downtown*
Bi-Annual Sale

Clothing by this local manufacturer of quality, classic men's sportswear can be found in Nordstrom and the Yankee Peddler. Call to get on the mailing list for sample sales that include pants, sweaters and shirts in wovens, knits and denim. The company specializes in fancy polo and golf shirts. No returns.

Checks, Credit cards

Gentlemen's Consignment

Seattle: 2809 E. Madison 328-8137 *Madison Park*
Hours: Tues-Sat 10-5

One of the few consignment shops in the Pacific Northwest devoted exclusively to men's apparel, accessories and "amusements" (games, binoculars, fishing poles, books, etc.). Only first-quality goods are accepted, with natural fibers preferred. You'll find a great selection of stylish suits, sport jackets, dress separates and outerwear in sizes 36 to 54. Suits sell for

$70 to $350, including such labels as Armani. Tuxedos are always available, as well as casual wear to round out weekend wardrobes. Alterations for a minimal fee. No returns.

Checks, Credit cards

His

Seattle: 2226 Queen Anne Ave. N. 281-0265 *Queen Anne*
Hours: Tues-Fri 10-6, Sat 10-5

Good news, guys! Another men's consignment shop with an outstanding selection. Business attire makes up half the inventory, so young professionals entering the job market can save on suits, sport coats, dress shirts, slacks and accessories that look brand new. Some of the labels feature top designer names like Hugo Boss and Versace. The store even carries tuxedos for that special night out. Sizes range from 36 to 48 for career wear, small to large and Tall for sportswear. The owner says women shop here for themselves as well. No returns.

Checks, Credit cards

International News Outlet Store

NEW LOCATION
Kent: 19226 70th Ave. S. 872-3542
Hours: weekday hours vary, Sat 10-4

You can't walk into a major department store locally without spotting this popular manufacturer's fun, distinctive apparel for young men, which is also worn by young women. Although the company is best known for their trademark T-shirts and sweats, they also make shirts, pants and jackets in denim, wovens, and thermal fabrications under the Razzy Jeans label. Periodically the outlet store hosts terrific sales, so be sure to get on their mailing list. No returns

Checks, Credit cards

Large and Tall Fashions for Less

Federal Way: 31313 Pacific Hwy. S. 941-0611 *Federal Way Shopping Center*
Seattle: 160th & Aurora 365-5701 *Aurora Square, Shoreline*
Tacoma: 2528 S. 38th St. 472-6049
Hours: Mon-Fri 10-8, Sat 10-6, Sun 12-5

Everything from underwear to outerwear for the big guys, be they "portly" or "athletic." Inventory includes private labels as well as leading brand names such as Wrangler, Greenline, Palm Beach, Dockers and Members Only. Prices vary from 20% to 50% below retail and I'm told that suits and dress shirts are especially good buys. Liberal return policy.

Checks, Credit cards

M. Genauer & Co.

NEW LISTING

Seattle: 2005 8th Ave. 2nd Floor   624-5351 *Downtown*

Periodic Sales

If you want that "dress for success" look at wholesale prices, call to get on the mailing list for spectacular suit and sport jacket sales when this manufacturer's rep sells off samples and overstock. Lines represent some of the top names in the marketplace, including Bagir, Jones of New York and Courrege. No returns.

Checks, Credit cards

The Men's Wearhouse

NEW LOCATION

Bellevue: 610 Bellevue Way N.E.   635-1025

Federal Way: 1918 S. 320th   839-6996 *Sea-Tac Mall*

Lynnwood: 2701 184th S.W.   776-7618 *Pacific Linen Plaza*

Redmond: 2110 148th N.E.   643-0987 *Overlake Fashion Plaza*

Silverdale: 3236 N.W. Plaza Rd.   692-7770

Seattle: 4th & Union   622-0570 *Downtown*

Tacoma: 2505 S. 38th St.   474-2795 *Lincoln Center*

Tukwila: 16971 Southcenter Pkwy.   575-4393

Hours: Mon-Sat 10-9, Sun 12-6

You've seen their ads on TV, and we're happy to report that The Men's Warehouse does indeed sell the same suits found in better department and specialty men's stores for 20% to 30% less. Styles range from European cut to banker's classics to sporty tweeds, including designer labels by Ives St. Laurent, Oscar de la Renta and Nino Cerruti. Tuxedos start at $229. Dress shirts, slacks, sportswear, accessories, and shoes are also available. Clothing comes in a full range of sizes including Big, Tall and Short. With 80 locations on the West Coast, they keep prices low year-round through volume buying and private-label manufacturing. Big sale after Christmas. Liberal return policy.

Checks, Credit cards

Nu Yu Fashions

NEW LOCATION

Lynnwood: 3105 Alderwood Mall Blvd.   771-3374 *Alderwood Town Center*

Hours: Mon-Fri 10:30-9, Sat 10:30-7, Sun 11-6

This shop is a showcase for trendy unisex and young men's apparel but prices are 30% to 50% off retail since the owner buys close-outs, irregulars and overruns. Some of the labels that turn up frequently include Red Eraser, Enuf, Cross Colors and B.U.M. Equipment, as well as jeans by Levi and Lawman. Visit the backroom where everything is $2 to $8. Lenient return policy.

Checks, Credit cards

Pacific Big and Tall

NEW LISTING

Seattle: 2313 3rd Ave. 448-2936 *Downtown*
Hours: Mon-Sat 9:30-5:30

Pacific Big and Tall charges 20% to 30% less for men's apparel in their downtown store than they do in their Bellevue Square store. Overhead is lower plus they cater to a different clientele. Merchandise includes outerwear, career wear and casual clothes that go up to size 6X. 7 day exchange.

Checks, Credit cards

Maternity and Children's Apparel

Kids! What's the matter with kids today? For one thing, their clothes cost too much and they grow too fast. And what about all that baby gear they need during the first few years, not to mention the demand for toys fueled by peer pressure and TV commercials as children get older? Hopefully this chapter and the following suggestions will help you cope with these problems. Don't forget to check out off-price chains and factory outlets where there are lots of stores that sell children's clothing.

Consumer Tips

✔ When you are purchasing children's clothing, always opt for the next size up to accommodate shrinkage and growth spurts. Cotton/polyester blends hold up better than 100% cotton and textured knits won't pill as quickly. Velour is expensive, but it washes beautifully.

✔ I suggest picking up a copy of Northwest Baby, Seattle's Child, Eastside Parent or Pierce County Parent. These monthly newspapers are filled with informative articles, a calendar of events, and ads for products and services. Complimentary issues are distributed through children's retail and consignment clothing stores, as well as day care centers.

Burlington's Baby Room

NEW LOCATION
Edmonds: 2411 Hwy. 99 776-2221
Tacoma: 10401-5 Gravelly Lake Dr. S.W. 588-3598 *Lakewood Mall*
Hours: Mon-Sat 10:30-9:30, Sun 11-6

Tucked away in a corner of this huge off-price chain's massive clothing inventory is a special section where there's everything you'd need for a baby or toddler. The impressive selection of baby gear and furniture includes over 35 styles of cribs, as well as lamps, bedding and fun mobiles. The store also carries nursing supplies, maternity wear and lots of clothing for newborns and up. Credit or exchange within two weeks.

Checks, Credit cards

Carter's Factory Outlet

Tacoma: 1415 E. 72nd 472-9340
Hours: Mon-Sat 10-6, Sun 12-5

Save on clothing for infants to size 6X at the regional outlet for one of the most popular brand names in the country. Underwear, sleepwear and socks go up to size 14. First-quality close-outs average 20% to 30% off retail. Irregulars start at 50% off. (What toddler is going to complain about slight imperfections?) Discounted merchandise from other leading manufacturers includes bedding, mattress covers and layette supplies. Something goes on sale every month and there's a mailing list for out-of-town customers. Returns accepted.

Checks, Credit cards

Cotton Caboodle Outlet

NEW LISTING
Seattle: 203 West Thomas St. 282-2701 *Lower Queen Anne*
Hours: Tues-Sat 10-3

If you are a fan of this very popular local manufacturer's comfy colorful unisex cotton knits, which can be worn by ages 6 months to adult, visit their small factory outlet where overstock and seconds sell for 30% to 70% off retail. Styles range from basic tops and bottoms to leggings, dresses and cardigans. No returns.

Checks, Credit cards

Health-Tex Sample Sales

Bellevue: 743-2436, 828-9883
Periodic sales

Call to get on the mailing list for big sample sales held three or four times a year by a sales rep for one of country's best-known manufacturers of children's clothing. You can stock up on the latest styles at prices that average 50% below retail. Sizes are limited to 3-month, 12-month, 3 and 4 for toddlers, and 4 and 5 for children. No returns.

Checks

Kid's Mart

NEW LOCATION
Everett: 505 S.E. Everett Mall Way 353-7259 *Greentree Sqr.*
Factoria: 4086 128th Ave. S.E. 562-1495 *Factoria Square*
Federal Way: 320th Pacific Hwy. S. 839-6306 *Century Sqr.*
Hours: Generally, Mon-Fri 10-9, Sat 10-6, Sun 11-5

Parents rejoiced when this national off-price chain moved into the Puget Sound area. Volume buying keeps prices low on well-known name-brand clothing and lines manufactured exclusively for the stores. A big selection of fashionable cotton knits and denim in the 7-14 category brings in the pre-teen set. Head for the clearance rack where savings can be astounding. The mailing list is a must for back-to-school, pre-holiday and anniversary sales. Lenient return policy.

Checks, Credit cards

Lil' People Warehouse Sale

NEW LISTING
Seattle: 109 West Denny Way #305, Seattle WA 98119
Bi-Annual Sale

Moms who like to shop at Lil' People's stores in Westlake Mall and Bellevue Square flock to these big blow-out sales, usually held at Greenlake Community Center, for fantastic buys on overstock, discontinued styles and clearance merchandise. The stores specialize in fun, contemporary all-cotton clothing and matching accessories for newborns through age 6 made exclusively for them. Sometimes local children's apparel manufacturers join in. Drop Lil' People a postcard at the above address to get on the mailing list. No returns.

Checks, Credit cards

Little Naturals Warehouse Outlet
NEW LISTING
Seattle: 80 S. Washington 682-2886 *Pioneer Square*
Hours: Fri 11-1:30

Here's another place to save on clothing from a very popular local manufacturer whose bright cotton knits and wovens are sold all over the country. Sizes range from newborn to 6X and you'll be paying $6 tó $14 for overstock, samples and seconds. Mailing list for big sales in May and November. No returns.

Checks

M & L International
Auburn: 1302 29th St. N.W. 939-7713
Annual sale

M&L is a big distributor of outerwear and sportswear for infants and children. In the fall they have a warehouse clearance sale where you can get some great buys on overstock, discontinued styles and samples from well-known lines like Osh Kosh and Eclipse. Call to get on the mailing list. No returns.

Cash

Sample Sales
Redmond: P.O. Box 2121, Redmond, WA 98073
Periodic sales

Send in your name and address for details about these terrific sample sales. The inventory, which comes from reps in four major West Coast cities, includes such well-known names as Healthtex, Carters, Polly Flinders, Calabash, Spumoni and London Fog. Prices start at wholesale plus 10%. The bargain rack offers incredible buys. Hair ornaments, small toys and books are also available. Locations vary from Everett to Fife to Issaquah, and they always book three rooms at Wholesale Heaven (See Index). All sales final.

Checks, Credit cards

Village Maternity
NEW LISTING
Seattle: 25th Ave. N.E. & N.E. 50th 523-5167 *University Village, U-District*
Hours: Mon-Fri 10-8, Sat 10-6, Sun 11-5

Although Village Maternity is not a discount store, they do rent very elegant dresses and ensembles for a one-time fee of $50. Styles may be limited but where else could the mother-to-be find a glamorous beaded dress or a black velvet cocktail suit that fits over that beautiful belly?

Checks, Credit cards

Maternity and Children's Consignment

Not only do consignment shops sell maternity wear and children's clothing at one-third of it's original value, but everything you'd need for newborns and toddlers shows up as well — from nursery furniture to car seats, strollers, toys, bedding, backpacks and miscellaneous items.

Although clothing for children goes up to size 14 in many stores, there's always a better selection for infants through size 6X because their apparel just doesn't get worn that much, especially when it comes to expensive items like coats, snow suits, party clothes and dress shoes. Accessories, socks, underwear, layette and gift items are often purchased brand new and sold at discount prices. Some stores carry beautiful hand-made clothing and crafts you won't be able to find anywhere else.

Consumer Tip

✔ The art of buying and selling in children's consignment shops follows the same guidelines as those outlined in women's clothing, but merchandise usually remains longer and gets marked down faster. Some stores buy outright or trade for in-store credit, which is advantageous if you're moving or need cash.

A to Z

Seattle: 2812 #3 E. Madison 325-9903 *Madison Park*
Hours: Tues-Sat 10-5:30, Thurs 10-7

A boutique atmosphere and stylish merchandise make this shop special. Clothing ranges from infants through size 10 for boys and girls, as well as maternity wear. Better labels for children such as Polly Flinders and Mouse Feathers turns up regularly. You'll also find shoes, nursery furniture, baby gear and handcrafted items. One small room is filled with books, games and toys. Look for the picket fence painted like pencils. Mailing list. All sales final.

Checks, Credit cards

About Face

Lynnwood: 7300 196th S.W. 771-4190
Hours: Tues-Thur 10-5, Fri & Sat 10:30-4:30

Over half the inventory is devoted to up-dated maternity wear ranging from jeans to party dresses, which means this is the largest resale shop for moms-to-be in the Puget Sound area.

The store even carries new Discreet Wear™ nursing tops at below retail prices. Clothing, furniture and baby gear for infants through size 6 takes up the rest of the space. Returns within 24 hours.

Checks, Credit cards

A Child's Place

NEW LISTING
Edmonds: 201 5th Ave. S. #13 771-8341 *Old Mill Town*
Hours: Mon-Sat 10-6, Sun 12-5

Shop here for quality children's apparel, accessories, toys and gifts at affordable prices. Half of the merchandise is new, the other half "nearly new," which includes an impressive selection of dress-up clothes. Two week return policy. Exchanges only on consigned items.

Checks, Credit cards

AJ's

Kent: 16408 S.E. 256th 630-9048
Hours: Mon-Sat 10-5:30, Sun 12-4

New and consigned clothing for infants to size 10 as well as nursery furniture and baby equipment fills this small store which has a reputation for low prices. Some items, such as quilts, bibs and hats, are handmade especially for the store, while others are brand new. Returns within one week.

Checks, Credit cards

Almost New Kid's Clothes

NEW LOCATION
Everett: 1512 N. Broadway 252-6907
Hours: Tues-Sat 11-5

When you visit, you'll find an old house that has been turned into a darling children's shop for newborns through pre-teens. Only clothing, furniture, baby equipment and toys in excellent condition are accepted. The store always has a big rack of Osh Kosh as well as the complete line of socks and underwear from Buster Brown. Mailing list a must for seasonal sales. Exchange or credit.

Checks

Born Again

NEW LISTING
Kent: 26220 Pacific Hwy. S. 529-1787 *Woodmont Place*
Hours: Mon-Fri 10-7, Sat 10-6, Sun 12-5

Although Born Again is crowded with clothing for infants to size 14, the best selection is in the baby through toddler age bracket, especially blankets and sleepers. Maternity wear is available, as well as baby equipment, furniture, toys, and accessories. The owner buys outright and trades. Credit or exchange on returns.

Checks, Credit cards

Fifth Ave. Kids

NEW LISTING
Seattle: 8312 5th Ave. N.E. 526-5683 *Roosevelt*
Hours: Wed-Sat 11-6

A small consignment shop with lots of clothes and toys. I hear the selection of Osh Kosh is outstanding and you'll always find brand new items by Cotton Caboodle, a very popular local manufacturer. Sizes range from infant to size 6. Returns within 24 hours.

Checks

Good As New

NEW LISTING
Des Moines: 21927 Marine View Dr. S. 878-5036
Hours: Tues-Sat 9-5

The owner calls her shop a "Grandmother's Haven" and says that moms like it because one room has been set aside as a playroom. Maternity wear and clothing for infants to size 14 is mended, washed, and pressed before it's put out, so it looks brand new. One room holds baby furniture, strollers, car seats, back packs, and toys. Clothing is purchased outright. No returns.

Checks

Grandmother's House

Lynnwood: 7331 196th S.W. 771-4640
Hours: Mon-Sat 9:30-5:30, Sun 12-5

For almost 20 years Grandmother's House has been helping families save money on toys, baby furniture and clothing for infants through size 6X. Everything is in mint condition because the store only purchases outright or trades for in-store credit. Nothing goes on the floor until it has been cleaned and repaired. The line-up of strollers, high chairs, playpens, walkers, trikes, bikes and car seats is astounding. Over 400 cribs go out the door each year at an average price of $100. Look for low prices on baby joggers purchased factory direct and furniture made especially for the store. Every Sunday all clothing is 50% off. No returns.

Checks, Credit cards

Hand Me Down Kids

NEW LISTING
Everett: 607 S.E. Everett Mall Way 347-9096 *Plaza Shopping Center*
Hours: Tues-Fri 10-5, Sat 10-4

Clothing varies from newborn to girls sizes 14, all of which is in very good condidion. Accessories and toys are also available.

Checks

Heaven Sent

NEW LOCATION
Federal Way: 1200 S. 324th 946-2229
Tacoma: 9514 Gravelly Lake Dr. S.W. 581-2526 *Lakewood*
Hours: Mon-Sat 10-6

These are big stores, so there is a big inventory of furniture and baby equipment, especially cribs, changing tables and outdoor toys, all of which are clean and in working order since the owners buy outright. Consignment clothing includes maternity wear and children's apparel for girls up to size 14, boys up to size 10 and the owners are very selective about what they take in. Toys and assorted kiddie items round out the inventory. Credit or exchange.

Cash only

Just For You

Seattle: 1114 N. 183rd 542-3993 *Shoreline*
Hours: Mon-Fri 9:30-5, Sat 10-4

You'll find a terrific assortment of gently used apparel for infants to age 10, plus maternity wear, toys, books and accessories. Samples and affordable lines show up occasionally. The store specializes in inexpensive party favors, balloons and hand crafted gift items such as Cabbage Patch doll clothes, Barbie furniture and darling knitted booties. Mailing list for seasonal sales. 24-hour exchange or credit.

Checks, Credit cards

Just For Kids

NEW LISTING
Everett: 7510 Beverly Blvd. 347-5002
Hours: Tues-Fri 11:30-5:30, Sat 12-5

A tiny little shop with toys, baby gear and clothing for infants to size 10, some of which is new. There's lots of baby stuff. Merchandise is taken in on consignment or store credit. Exchanges only on returns.

Checks

Kid's Exchange

NEW LISTING

Tacoma: 2608 Bridgeport Way W. 565-4824
Hours: Mon-Sat 10-5

Moms make a beeline for the 50% off rack and the $1 rack. Inventory includes maternity wear, furniture, toys, and clothing for infants to size 14, some of which is new. Returns within three days.

Checks, Credit cards

Kids on 45th

Seattle: 1720 N. 45th St. 633-5437 *Wallingford*
Hours: Mon-Sat 10-6, Sun 11-4

Kids on 45th is a popular spot for moms who like bargains on new as well as gently-used clothing for infants through preteens. The line of affordable basic cotton knit separates made especially for the store sells like hotcakes. In 1993, Kids on 45th was voted the Golden Bootie Award by the readers of Seattle Child. Inventory includes lots of shoes, accessories, and handcrafted items, plus furniture, strollers, car seats, etc. Consignors get store credit and a 20% discount on new merchandise. 30-day return policy.

Checks, Credit cards

Kym's Kiddy Corner

Seattle: 11721 15th Ave. N.E. 361-5974 *Northgate*
Hours: Mon-Sat 10-5, Sun 12-5

You can't miss the colorful line-up of trikes, strollers, walkers and riding toys displayed outside. Step inside the largest resale shop in the area and you'll discover lots of clothing for infants to 6X, along with toys, furniture and baby equipment. About one-fourth of the inventory is new, including beautiful hand-made garments, but prices are a lot less than what you'd pay in a retail store. In 1993 the store won the Golden Bootie Award for its outstanding selection of toys and furniture. All used items are purchased outright or traded for credit. 30 day exchange or credit.

Checks, Credit cards

Little Troopers

NEW LISTING

Bothell: 6522 "C" N.E. Bothell Way 486-2081
Hours: Mon-Fri 10-5, Sat 10-4

Little Troppers is jam packed with clothing for newborns to size 14, along with shoes and accessories. Parents can pick up bargains on strollers, walkers, cribs, toys and books as well. The owners have high standards so everything is in good condition. No returns.

Checks, Credit cards

Lollipops

NEW NAME

Burien: 2038 S.W. 152nd 243-1795
Hours: Mon-Sat 9:30-5:30

Although the main focus is on children from birth and on up, the whole family can shop for clothing at Lollipops, which looks like a mini-department store. There's a big display of baby equipment and related items. Apparel for men, women and teenagers tends to be more casual-oriented. The store buys outright or consigns. No returns.

Checks, Credit cards

Maxine's Baby World

Tacoma: 510 1/2 112th S. 535-2742
Hours: Mon-Sat 10-5

Maxine's has been open for over a decade, so she has built up a following who know they can find premium consignment clothing for newborns through size 7 as well as new garments and accessories at discount prices. As a matter of fact, the store was voted best consignment shop by readers of the Pierce County Child. Toys, books and furniture can be purchased here as well. 30-day exchange.

Checks, Credit cards

Me 'n' Mom's Inc.

NEW LISTING

Seattle: 1021 N.E. 65th 524-9344 *Roosevelt Square, Roosevelt*
Hours: Mon-Fri 9:30-8, Sat 10-5, Sun 11-5

Although this popular retail store holds mainly full-price clothing, one corner has been set aside for consignment apparel for infants to size 10, most of which is better brand names. No returns.

Checks, Credit cards

Mommy and Me

NEW LISTING

Kent: 23215 Pacific Hwy. S. 878-2250
Hours: Mon-Sat 10-7, Sun 12-5

A big store where mothers-to-be shop before and after the baby is born. Maternity wear and apparel for newborns to size 6 is half new, half gently-used. Cribs, strollers, high chairs, car seats and walkers show up as well. Everything is purchased outright except for furniture. 30 day return.

Checks, Credit cards

Mother Goose Children's Resale and Women's Designer Consignments

NEW LISTING

Tacoma: 8415 Steilacoom Blvd. S.W. 582-4401

3715 Bridgeport Way West 565-9125

Hours: Mon-Sat 10-6

An upscale store that caters to women as well as children. Better labels like Liz Wear show up on the girls as well as the women's racks. The baby section includes new and consignment clothing, toys, books, shoes and nursery needs. Apparel for women runs the gamut from maternity wear to business attire, special occasion dresses and bridal gowns, all in current styles and perfect condition. Most merchandise is purchased outright. Returns within three days on children's items. No returns on women's apparel.

Checks, Credit cards

Mom's 'n' Tot's

NEW LOCATION

Bellevue: 137 106th St. N.E.   451-4439 *Bellevue Plaza*

Hours: Mon-Sat 10-5

Mom's can shop for children's clothing as well as maternity wear, career and casual wear, including business suits. Only current styles, and better labels in good condition are accepted. Baby furniture of all kinds comes and goes, but strollers and car seats are always in stock. All sales final.

Checks, Credit cards

Mouse Closet

Bellevue: 521 156th S.E.   641-0531 *Lake Hills Shopping Ctr.*

Hours: Mon-Sat 9:30-5:30

Fun, trendy samples purchased from local sales reps make up half the inventory. Popular lines include Patty Cakes, Sweet Potatoes, Monkey Wear and Mouse Feathers for girls and boys 12 months through age 8. Prices start at 30% below retail and drop 20% more when they hit the clearance rack. Top-quality consignment clothing for mothers-to-be, infants and children makes up the other half of the inventory. One-of-a-kind, handmade baby sweaters, quilts and toys are an added attraction. Two day return policy.

Checks, Credit cards

Outgrown Treasures

NEW LISTING
Seattle: 3311-A West McGraw 285-1809 *Magnolia Village*
Hours: Tues-Sat 10-5

The shop may be small but top quality names like Baby Dior, Ralph Lauren and Liz Wear pop up frequently, and there's always a big rack of Osh Kosh. Toys, handcrafted items and miscellaneous baby stuff rounds out the inventory. Staff says the low rent keeps their prices down. Credit or exchange only.

Checks

Rainbow Boutique

Seattle: 9518 Roosevelt Way N.E. 522-1213 *Northgate*
Hours: Mon-Fri 10-5:30, Sat 10-4

Rainbow Boutique has expanded, making it one of the largest resale shops in Seattle. Racks are jam packed with an incredible variety of clothing and accessories for infants to preteens, as well as maternity wear and apparel for work and play after the baby is born. You'll also find anything you'd need for the nursery from changing tables to lamps, blankets and decorative wall hangings, along with a lot of toys and baby gear. Mailing list. No returns.

Checks, Credit cards

Ritzy Rags Budget Boutique

Tacoma: 4102 S. "M" Street 475-7602
Hours: Mon-Fri 11-6, Sat 11-5

Ritzy Rags carries quality used apparel for infants through 6X, plus toys and nursery furniture. The owner, who is very selective about what she accepts, says baby clothes outsell everything else. Furniture is sold on consignment, clothing taken in on credit. Exchange or credit on returns.

Checks, Credit cards

Saturday's Child

NEW LISTING
Bothell: 18012 Bothell-Everett Hwy. 486-6716
Hours: Mon-Sat 10-5

A good-size store with everything you'd need for infants and toddlers. Toys, baby gear, furniture and clothing up to size 14 flows in and out. The selection of handmade items and clothing for infants, especially girls, is consistently outstanding. Exchange within 7 days.

Checks, Credit cards

Stars

NEW LISTING
Issaquah: 55 N.E. Gilman 392-2900
Hours: Mon-Wed 9-6, Thurs & Fri 9-9, Sat 10-5, Sun 12-5

Finally, a superstore for kids! Over 25,000 square feet of top brand name fashions for infants to size 14 for girls, size 20 for boys, all at 25% to 40% off the regular retail price. Clothing varies from moderately-priced to better lables. representing over 350 different manufacturers, and all of it is current styles, first quality goods. The low rent and volume buying allow the owners to offer some fabulous buys. Returns accepted.

Checks, Credit cards

Sweetpea Boutique

NEW LISTING
Kent: 10612 Kent-Kangley Rd. #101 859-0202
Hours: Mon-Sat 10-5:30

Sweetpea advertises that they sell "pre-adored" merchandise which is a charming way to let people know that everything is in tip-top condition. Inventory includes maternity wear, clothing for infants to size 10, furniture, toys and lots of baby gear — strollers, car seats, swings — all by well-known brand names. The store is selective because they buy outright instead of consigning. Seven-day exchange policy.

Checks, Credit cards

The Tree House

Redmond: 15742 Redmond Way 885-1145 *Redmond Center*
Hours: Mon-Fri 9-6, Thurs 9-8, Sat 10-5, Sun 1-5

With 3,000 sq. ft., the Tree House is undoubtedly the largest children's apparel shop around. They've been in business for over 15 years and the incredible selection earned them the Eastside Child Golden Bootie Award in 1993. Inventory is divided evenly between new and used clothing for infants to size 14. Three times a year the Tree House sends out a mailing with 20%-off coupons, good on all merchandise in the store. No returns on consignment.

Checks, Credit cards

The Unicorn Boutique

Kirkland: 12537 116th N.E. 823-4868 *Totem Lake West*
Hours: Mon-Sat 10-5, Sun 12-5

There is a lot to chose from in this large, well-stocked shop. Half the inventory is children's clothing, plus toys and nursery furniture. The rest of the store holds maternity wear and apparel that can be worn after the blessed event, in a full range of sizes. All sales final.

Checks, Credit cards

A Womb with a View

NEW LISTING
Bothell: 23732 Bothell-Everett Hwy. 486-2734 *Country Village*
Hours: Mon-Sat 10-6, Thurs 10-8, Sun 11-5

Focusing on childbirth and children, this unique shop serves as a resource for parents looking for new and used maternity and children's clothing as well as toys, furniture, and nursing items. You'll even find cloth diapers, books on parenting and free advise to help you through the blessed event. The store is large and carries any and every thing you'll need.

Checks, Credit cards

Shoes and Accessories

It would be impossible to cross-reference all the stores that carry shoes and accessories, but be sure to look in off-price chains like Ross, Marshall's and T.J. Maxx for moderately priced footwear for the whole family as well handbags, hosiery and costume jewelry.

Accessories are also inexpensive and plentiful in consignment shops where I've purchased shoes and handbags in perfect condition.

Picway and Volume Shoe Source, with over two dozen stores each in the Puget Sound area, are the lowest priced discount footwear chains around, but selection is limited to basic styles and man-made materials. However, they do carry a lot of close-out name-brand athletic shoes for the whole family at super low prices. Other stores that discount athletic shoes include Athletic Express, Big 5, Chubby & Tubby, Source Outlet and Ross Dress for Less.

Consumer Tips

✔ When it comes to buying shoes, it's best to invest in good-quality, comfortable footwear whenever possible, which means leather uppers and a well-cushioned sole.

✔ If you find a pair of shoes that fit and the price is right, but the color isn't, consider having them dyed. This is also a great way to reclaim shoes ruined by stains or scratches.

✔ To prevent spotting, treat all new shoes with a water repellant and stain resistant spray before wearing. Rain protection is a must in Seattle!

✔ Re-heel shoes before they wear down too far, and put rubber non-skid protectors on the soles.

Factory Outlet L'Eggs Brands, Inc.

P.O. Box 9984 Rural Hill, N.C. 27099-9984 919-744-1170

Here's a mail order outlet for slightly imperfect pantyhose by Hanes, L'Eggs and Just My Size which sell for as little as 84¢ a pair. Hanes Alive heavy support costs only $10 for a package of three. Knee highs are $2.22 for a 6-pack. Tiny flaws, like a slight change in the knit or a color variation, won't affect the wearability. Call or mail in your order. No minimums.

Checks, Credit cards

Nordstrom Shoe Rack

Lynnwood: 3115 Alderwood Mall Blvd. 774-6569 *Alderwood Towne Ctr.*
Seattle: 1601 2nd Ave. 448-8522 *Downtown*
Tukwila: 17900 Southcenter Parkway 575-1058 *Pavilion Mall*
Hours: Tukwila & Lynnwood Mon-Fri 9:30-9:30, Sat 9:30-7, Sun 11-6; Seattle Mon-Sat 9:30-7, Sun 12-6

Nordies is simply the best place to get fantastic bargains on top quality fashionable footwear for men, women and children. The selection of styles and range of sizes reflects their inventory at the retail level. Although some shoes are purchased just for the Rack. You can save big on expensive dress shoes, and boots are super-cheap after Christmas. Be prepared to wait on yourself as this is a clearance operation. 30-day return policy.

Checks, Credit cards

Pacirim

Seattle: 1501 Western Ave. 625-1826 *Downtown*
Hours: Daily 10-6

Pacirim specializes in clothing and accessories made from ellskin, fishskin and snakeskin. You can even buy a salmon skin swimsuit here! Handbags, wallets, shoes and jackets sell for 30% less because the owner imports factory direct for distribution all over the U.S. Prices are lower in the summer during the tourist season. Lenient return policy.

Checks, Credit cards

Shoe Pavillion

NEW LOCATIONS
Bellevue: 14339 N.E. 20th 747-3620 *Ross Plaza*
Factoria: I-90 at I-405 643-3828 *Loehmann's Plaza*
Lynnwood: 3225 Alderwood Mall Blvd. 672-0322 *Alderwood Towne Center*
Seattle: 830 N.E. Northgate Way 368-0719 *Northgate Village*
    N. 160th & Aurora 367-8716 *Aurora Square, Shoreline*
    1501 4th Ave. 382-0258 *Downtown*
Tacoma: 2919 S. 38th 473-1473 *Cascade Plaza*
    10959 Gravelly Lake Dr. 584-9564 *Lakewood Mall*
Tukwila: 17900 Southcenter Pkway 575-0196 *Pavilion Mall*
Hours: Generally, Mon-Fri 10-9, Sat 10-6, Sun 11-5

One of my favorite resources for quality name-brand footwear for men and women, this locally-owned off-price chain has grown rapidly since it opened in 1980, a testimonial to its popularity. Inventory includes dressy as well as casual shoes, in a wide range of sizes by such well known names as Amalfi, Anne Klein, Caressa, 9 West, Van Eli, Bandolino and Bally. Prices vary from 30% to 70% off retail and drop even more during seasonal sales. Loehmann's Plaza has the largest selection. 30-day return policy.

Checks, Credit cards

Waisted Belt Co., Inc.

Lynnwood: 18609 76th Ave. W. 778-4885
Annual sale

From December 1st to the 20th, the public can purchase over-stock at wholesale prices or below from this manufacturer of women's moderately priced leather and stretch belts sold mainly in department stores. Prices range from $5 to $8, so they make good gift items. You can also stock up on men's, women's and children's fashion and basic socks during this sale. No returns.

Checks

Formal Wear, Bridal Attire and Furs

Everyone has to get dressed up now and then, whether it's for New Year's Eve, a charity ball or dinner out with the boss, which can get expensive unless you have a fairy godmother to wave her magic wand and turn your "rags" into fancy attire. And what about cruises, class reunions, anniversaries plus the most important event of all, your wedding day?

Although a lot of off-price stores carry dressier clothes, Loehman's and the New Look specialize in elegant evening wear year round. Consignment shops are another good resource, but like most apparel stores, the selection is much better during the holiday season. If you are looking for designer label cocktail dresses or an elaborate beaded evening gown, check out Alexandra's, Designer Consignor, The Model's Closet, Razz M' Tazz or the more exclusive line-up of consignment shops on the Eastside.

Sometimes you can find a fantastic deal on a wedding gown through the classified ads in the newspapers. Maybe the wedding was canceled at the last minute and the gown was never worn!

Retailers overprice furs knowing full-well that the majority will sell for 40% to 70% below their marked price when they go on sale in January and February. Some consignment shops carry furs, usually less expensive pelts and vintage styles. In the fall, visit the more high-fashion-oriented stores for the best selection. Even Goodwill has a fur sale.

Black Tie Men's Formal Wear

Lynnwood: 18027 Hwy. 99 #F 778-5376
Annual sale

> Call to get on the mailing list for the fabulous December warehouse sale of special promotion goods and discontinued rental garments from six retail stores in the Puget Sound area. New tuxedos start at $159. Used designer-label tuxes go as low as $50. Accessories, including shoes, jewelry, top hats, even canes, are sold at ridiculously low prices. Request a V.I.P. card for a 10% discount on regular merchandise at any Black Tie store. No returns.
>
> *Checks, Credit cards*

Discount Bridal Service, Inc.

NEW LOCATION
Bellevue: 746-1601
Kent: 630-9075
Tacoma: 952-7833
By appointment only

Save 20% to 40% on the same wedding gowns found in bridal shops and national publications by calling local reps with this nationwide franchise for a price quote. Have the manufacturer's name, the style number, and, if you saw it in a magazine, the page number. They'll help you determine size, based on charts from the various companies, and recommend someone for alterations if needed. Payment is in-full, in advance, and merchandise is shipped UPS directly to your home. You can also order dresses and accessories for bridesmaids, mothers-of-the-bride and flower girls, as well as candles and wedding invitations. No returns.

Checks

Corinna's

NEW LISTING
Puyallup: 1105 River Road 840-5440
Hours: Mon-Fri 11-6, Sat 11-5

Save 50% to 75% on bridal and formal wear at Corrina's where they rent as well as sell both new and used attire for special occassions. Some of the garments are on consignment. No returns.

Checks, Credit cards

Eilers Furs Ltd.

NEW LISTING
Seattle: 8213 Greenwood Ave. N. 782-8563 *Greenwood*
Hours: Tues-Fri 10-5 or by appointment

For over a decade this furrier has operated out of a small showroom in a low rent part of town. Clientele appreciate the fact that he can custom-make or special order any style or type of pelt they want for 50% less than what most retailers charge, be it a $450 mink jacket or a $10,000 sable coat. Mailing list for new arrivals. Exchanges on special orders only.

Credit card

Emperor's New Clothes

Seattle: 1503 2nd W. 282-8878 *Queen Anne*
Hours: Mon-Fri 11-6, Sat 11-3

Fantasies come to life at the Emperor's New Clothes where you can rent both outrageous original costumes and elegant formal wear, from elaborate beaded dresses suitable for beauty pageants to fun costumes for the kids. Bridal gowns for theme weddings from the medieval to the Great Gatsby eras are a specialty. A newsletter announces the sale of new and used costumes and formal wear in September.

Checks

Forrester Furs

Seattle: 1424 4th Ave. 622-8785 *Downtown*
By appointment only

Based in Seattle since 1928, Forrester Furs is considered one of the leading furriers in the United States. This second-generation business opens its doors to the public, so now you can save big bucks on fashionable, luxurious fur coats purchased direct from the manufacturer. No returns.

Checks, Credit cards

Mr. Formal Warehouse Sale

NEW LISTING
Location to be announced
Annual sale: 1-800-284-4889

If the name isn't familiar it's because this men's formal wear chain is based in Oregon. Every year in the early Fall they host a great warehouse sale (usually in a major hotel) to get rid of tuxedos, which are only rented 10 times before they are sold off at bargain basement prices. The sale includes shirts, shoes, accessories and jewelry to complete the look. No returns.

Checks, Credit cards

Nothing to Wear Annex

NEW LISTING
Tacoma: 2805 Bridgeport Way West 565-6737
Hours: Mon-Fri 12-6, Sat 11-5

Although the main business here is rentals, the Annex is a separate room for consignment bridal and formal wear where everything is $50 or less, a price that can't be beat! Sizes range from 3 to 26 which makes this a popular spot for teens shopping for a prom dress or brides on a budget. Children's party clothes show up occasionally. No returns.

Checks, Credit cards

The Tux Shop

Seattle: 1509 N.W. Market 789-6047 *Ballard*
Hours: Mon-Fri 10-9, Sat 10-6, Sun 12-5

Rentals from the Tux Shop's 15 stores are shipped to their warehouse store in Ballard and sold at discounted prices, which makes this a popular stop for singers, musicians, and performing groups. Wool tuxes in good condition go for $125, white diner jackets for $49.99. Best time to shop is January and September. No returns.

Checks, Credit cards

Rental Shops

Rent instead of buying formal attire and not only will you save money but you can wear something new and different every time you go out! Rental fees run 20% to 30% of the retail price of the dress plus the cost of cleaning. Considering the average wedding gown sells for $500, brides-to-be can save a bundle!

The following stores lease bridal gowns and formal wear. Inventory, prices and sizes will vary from store to store, so call first. Rental shops sometimes have big sales, usually in January or February to make room for new styles. Call to inquire about specific dates if you are more interested in buying than in renting.

A Grand Affair

NEW LISTING
Bellevue: 10218 N.E. 8th 453-7300
Lynnwood: 18411 Alderwood Mall Blvd. 778-7300
Seattle: 6th & Olive 467-7300 *Downtown*
Hours: Tues-Fri 11-6:30, Sat 11-6

Bridal Visions

NEW LISTING
Federal Way: 32034 23rd Ave. S. 946-3406
Tukwila: 321 Tukwila Parkway S. 246-4919
Hours: Mon-Fri 10-6, Sat 10-5, Sun 12-4

Chapel of the Lakes

NEW LISTING
Tacoma: 9119 Gravelly Lake Dr. S.W. 581-5683
Hours: Tues-Fri 12-6, Sat 11-5

Fashion Tux Rentals
NEW LISTING
> **Tacoma:** 3820 S. Yakima Ave. 472-3372
> **Hours:** Mon-Fri 7:30-6, Sat 9-5

Lakewood Bridal Shop
NEW LISTING
> **Tacoma:** 9603 Bridgeport Way S.W. 581-3708
> **Hours:** Mon-Fri 8:30-6, Sat 9:30-4:30

L'Armoire Consignment
NEW LISTING
> **Renton:** 410 Burnett S. 255-6415
> **Hours:** Mon-Sat 10-6:30

Nothing to Wear
> **Tacoma:** 2805 Bridgeport Way West 565-6737
> Mon-Fri 12-6, Sat 11-5

Page One Designs
> **Lynnwood:** 4001 198th S.W. 778-9020
> **Hours:** Wed, Fri, Sat 11-5, Tues & Thurs 11-7

Silken Lady
NEW LISTING
> **Tukwila:** 16850 Southcenter Parkway 575-8473 *Toys R Us Shopping Center*
> **Hours:** Mon-Sat 11-7, Sunday 12-6

Uniquely Yours Rent-A-Gown
NEW LISTING
> **Tacoma:** 474-1527
> By appointment only

Weddings, Etc.
> **Seattle:** 9731 Greenwood N. 783-7881 *Greenwood*
> **Hours:** Mon 12-7, Tues-Sat 11-5, Fri 11-7

Fine Jewelry

The markup on jewelry sometimes goes as high as 200%, so beware of stores advertising 50% off sales on already inflated prices. Retail jewelry stores with low prices are usually located in out-of-the-way places. They buy direct, manufacture on the premises, and take a low mark-up. Service at these establishments is as good or better than that at exclusive outlets.

Wholesalers and brokers open to the public offer the best buys on quality gemstones and jewelry. Their showrooms vary from fancy to bare-bones and entry is usually by appointment only. Don't be surprised to find bars on the windows and locked doors. Here, gold, silver and gemstones are sold by weight according to market value, unlike retail stores where the cost also includes craftsmanship, design and a high profit margin. It's hard to compare prices unless you have a trained eye, so insist on an independent appraisal before you purchase expensive jewelry. Returns at wholesalers are normally limited to exchange or credit.

If you are an educated buyer, auctions, pawnshops and the classified ads can sometimes yield incredible deals.

Ally Chandon & Co.

NEW LISTING
Seattle: 520 Pike St. #1212 622-9674 *Downtown*
Hours: Mon-Fri 10-5

A well-stocked jewelry store that keeps prices low on diamonds, pearls, gemstones and fine gold jewelry, especially wedding sets and gold chain. Custom design available.

Checks

Dahnken of Tacoma

Tacoma: 1127 Broadway Plaza 627-7181
Hours: Mon-Fri 9:30-6, Sat 10-5

Once a large discount store with merchandise similar to Best's, Dahnken's has scaled down to fine jewelry, crystal and giftware priced at 20% or more off retail. Shop here for diamond earrings, wedding rings, pearls, 14K gold chains or birth stones the next time a special occasion comes up. The glassware and porcelain figurines make nice gift items as well. Senior citizens get a 10% discount. Returns accepted.

Checks, Credit cards

The Gemologist, Inc.

Bellevue: 12000 N.E. 8th #206 455-4653
By appointment only

> This wholesaler purchases quality diamonds and precious stones from importers in Antwerp and Tel Aviv for resale to local jewelers. He also sells fine jewelry, consigns rare or unusual collector's items and custom-makes signature art jewelry in his small retail shop where prices average 10% to 20% above wholesale.

Checks, Credit cards

Fifth Ave. Jewelry Plaza

NEW LISTING
Seattle: 1512 5th Ave. 233-9235 *Downtown*
Hours: Mon-Sat 10-6

> You will find over a dozen jewelry dealers clustered together in independent showrooms which makes this a good place to start if you want to educate yourself and compare prices. Payment varies from vendor to vendor.

Keefer Design Gallery

Seattle: 10570 15th Ave. N.W. 364-6273 *Ballard*
By appointment only

> Because the showroom is located in her home, the owner, who used to be a wholesale jewelry rep, guarantees the lowest prices possible on loose gemstones, pearls, jade and lapis, as well as fine quality gold jewelry of all kinds, including watches and bezels. Couples shopping for wedding sets are frequent customers. Seven-day return policy.

Checks, Credit cards

Marci Jewelry

Bellevue: 40 Lake Bellevue #310 455-4561
Hours: Wed 10-6 or by appointment
Open Mon-Sat the three weeks before Christmas

> If diamonds are a girl's best friend, then so is Marci, who stocks one of the largest collections of loose diamonds in the Northwest, plus gemstones and fine jewelry custom-designed and manufactured on the premises. Prices range from $50 to

$50,000 and that's half off retail! Earrings, tennis bracelets, wedding and anniversary rings are best-sellers. Mailings announce big sales in May and before Christmas, when the store extends their hours. Exchanges only.

Checks, Credit cards

Orogemma/Emiko Pearls International
NEW LISTING
Seattle: 1424 4th Ave., 4th floor 382-1472 *4th & Pike Bldg., Downtown*
Hours: Mon-Fri 9:30-5

If you like pearls, then buy them direct from the importer loose or made up into jewelry. Gemstones and finished gold jewelry are also sold here.

Checks, Credit cards

Rhyne & Associates
Seattle: 425 Pike St. #403 623-6900 *Downtown*
Hours: Mon-Fri 9-5:30, Saturdays from Thanksgiving to Christmas

This family-owned jewelry store operates on a low overhead and doesn't take as big a mark-up as other stores. Inventory includes everything from loose diamonds and gemstones to fine 18K gold jewelry, gold and silver chain, pearl necklaces and earrings, consignment and estate jewelry. For those who like to invest in precious metals, there's lots of coin jewelry. Sales announced via mailings. 7 day returns.

Checks, Credit cards

Swissa
NEW LISTING
Seattle: 1518 5th Ave. 625-9202 *Downtown*
By appointment only

The public is welcome to shop at this wholesaler of diamonds and fine 14K or 18K jewelry. He advertises that his prices are lower than the New York Index.

Checks, Credit cards

Scott Michael's Fine Jewelry
Tacoma: 7504 27th W. 565-7684
Hours: Mon-Fri 9-7

The owner advertises he'll meet or beat any price in the Northwest. His store stocks everything from loose precious stones to fine settings, custom-made and estate jewelry, coins and watches. Seven-day return policy.

Checks, Credit cards

The Shane Co.

Seattle: 1902 4th Ave. 587-6200 *Downtown*
Hours: Mon-Fri 10-8, Sat 10-5, Sun 12-5

The largest selection of wedding sets in the state can be found at this discount jewelry store. The owner sits on the Diamond Exchange, so he buys direct in volume for his seven stores and passes the savings on to customers, which is why prices may be 20% to 40% lower than competitors. Diamonds, rubies, emeralds and sapphires purchased loose can be set in one of the many mountings on display, or choose from jewelry in stock. The 30-day return policy is an added plus.

Checks, Credit cards

The Vault

Bellevue: 500 108th Ave. N.E. #800 646-7337 *Koll Center*
By appointment only

Inventory at this wholesale showroom includes loose diamonds, precious stones and gold jewelry comparable to what you would find in better retail stores, but for a lot less money. Credit only

Checks, Credit cards

West Coast Diamonds and Gems

Seattle: 1424 4th #325 624-8828 *Downtown*
By appointment only

Although the main business here is custom work, you can buy costly gemstones and fine gold jewelry for as much as 50% off retail. If you want to design your own setting, there are hundreds of mountings and wax models in classic or contemporary designs to choose from.

Checks

Williams & Son, Inc.

NEW LOCATION
Seatac: 2800 S. 192nd. #110 878-7966 or 1-800-24-CARAT
By appointment only

Open since 1974, this small, low-overhead diamond broker, importer and custom-goldsmith guarantees substantial savings on quality jewelry and precious stones, including pearls. All gemstones are independently certified. Using state-of-the-art equipment, staff will gladly explain what to look for in buying fine diamonds. For a small deposit, you can take home a video on the subject. Returns accepted.

Checks, Credit cards

Additional Clothing Outlets

(See index for page numbers)

Factory Outlets and Sample Sales

Bur-Bank Domestics
Eddie Bauer Outlet Store

Off-Price Stores

Chubby & Tubby
Doc's Marine Warehouse
Liquidators Outlet
Six Star Factory Outlet
Two Bucks or Less

Menswear

The following factory outlets, off-price stores and consignment shops carry menswear:

Alki Beach Hut
Alice's Consignment & Gifts
BRB Manufacturing
Burlington Coat Factory
Buying Used Levi's
Casual T's
Clothesline Consignment
Closet Transfer
The Dark Horse
Discount Leather and Stuff
Eddie Bauer Outlet
Encore Consignment
Etruscan Designs
Fraje'
The Hub
Jeans Direct
Kameko Sales
Karolynn's Sample Sales

Le Frock
Lollipops
Marshalls
Morning Sun
Motto and Red Eraser
Nordstrom Rack
Outrageous Sports
Pacific Trail
Ross Dress for Less
Seabell Sportswear
The Second Act
Sival America
Source Outlet
Swanee's
TJ Maxx
Union Bay
Wild West Trading

Women's Consignment Shops

Lollipops
Mommy 'n' Me
Mother Goose
Mom's 'n' Tots
Rainbow Boutique
The Unicorn Boutique

Maternity and Children's Apparel

Bellarmine Sample Clothing Sale
Bur-Bank Domestics
Burlington Coat Factory
BRB Manufacturing
Eddie Bauer Outlet
The Hub

Fraje'
Karolynn's Sample Sale
Marshall's
Morning Sun Outlet
Nordstrom Rack
Over the Rainbow
Outrageous Sports
Pacifc Trail
Ross Dress for Less
Seabell Sportswear
Source Outlet
Sundrop Sportswear
Super Star Outlet
TJ Maxx
Union Bay

Maternity and Children's Consignment

Act II Consignments
Alice's Consignment & Gifts
Closet Transfer
Clothesline Consignment
Encore Consignments
Finer Consigner
Island Treasures
Kathy's Closet
Labels
The Other Place
The Second Act

Formal Wear, Bridal Attire and Furs

Act II Consignment
Budget Boutique
Champagne Taste
Crystal Threads
The Dark Horse
Designor Consignor
Encore Consignments
Gentleman's Consignment
His
Image Awareness
L'Armoire
Pandora's Box
Queen's Closet
Ragamoffyn's
Razz m Tazz
Redress
Sebastain's Closet
Your Hidden Closet

Fine Jewelry

Best
TJ Maxx

Food

According to statistics put out by the U.S. Department of Labor, the average urban family of four, with a median income of $36,000 a year, spends 11.5% of its income on food. The lower the income, the higher this percentage. Current figures indicate that food costs can vary from $90 to $158 per week, so careful shopping habits and a few changes in diet can significantly reduce your annual food budget. Below are a few tips that will help you achieve that goal:

✔ Check out what's on sale in the food section of the newspapers and weekly grocery store supplements. Shop at the store that is offering the best buys or plan your menus around your favorite store's specials, also known as "loss leaders." Watch for weekly specials on items that you use regularly and purchase them only when they're on sale.

✔ Buy in quantity or the largest size available, using unit pricing to guarantee you are getting the lowest price available. Share bulk purchases with friends or relatives.

✔ Buy store or generic brands whenever possible and you'll cut your cost by 10% or more.

✔ Collect coupons and cents-off labels to maximize your savings. Safeway, Bartell's and Payless regularly put out coupon books that offer discounts on packaged and canned food items. By using coupons, you can save an average of 30% on cereal, cat food, snack items, cleaning products and bake mixes.

✔ Avoid expensive snacks and convenience foods. Cook from scratch, buy frozen juice in cans instead of cartons, and make popcorn to snack on.

✔ Limit your food shopping to once or twice a week and always go with a list. This saves both time and money since most people succumb to impulse buying at the supermarket.

✔ Try to consume everything you buy. Learn to be creative with leftovers. Store odds and ends in the freezer for later use in soups and casseroles.

A Word of Caution:

When you shop at big warehouses and distributors that usually sell by the case or carton, please respect their minimum orders and buy in volume. Most welcome the public as long as they follow wholesale procedures. Some warehouses operate on a "will call" basis, which means you must call first to place your order and pick it up at a specified time. Many will send price lists on request, and I suggest you use these whenever possible since browsing is not always acceptable. Insisting on special services or interfering with wholesale business practices disrupts warehouse operations, and I wouldn't like to see their doors closed to Super Shopper readers.

Food Service Warehouses and Grocery Stores

I suggest you visit a food service warehouse in your area to get an idea of how they operate and to familiarize yourself with their unusual inventory. Some cater to the cooking and equipment needs of restaurants, hotels and institutions, while others stock your local supermarket or convenience store.

Food runs the gamut from fresh produce to bakery goods, canned, refrigerated, or frozen items, plus specialty foods not available at grocery stores. Prepared and canned mixes are the best sellers and you will be buying them in bulk. Some warehouses will break up case lots or sell smaller quantities. Be sure to compare prices when you buy; volume does not always guarantee savings. Look for weekly or monthly sales on specific items, plus low prices on surplus or salvaged goods.

Bar supplies, paper products, cleaning compounds, commercial grade cookware and appliances are usually available as well.

A & B Food Market

Tacoma: 608 N. Oakes 627-2011
Hours: Mon-Fri 10-6, Sat 10-5

A & B caters to the restaurant business, but anyone can shop here for packaged, frozen and canned food. Surplus goods damaged in shipping are the best buys. Inventory also includes table settings, janitorial supplies and paper products.

Checks

Canned Foods Grocery Outlet

NEW LOCATION
Bremerton: 2521 6th St. 377-1142
Everett: 710 S.E. Everett Mall Way 353-6224
Tacoma: 11011 Pacific Hwy. S.W. 581-5333
Hours: Mon-Sat 10-7; Sun 11-7

This California-based chain keeps prices 20% to 40% lower than supermarkets by buying direct from the manufacturer and stocking only packaged, frozen and canned groceries. They also boast an excellent deli section. Discounts extend to most housewares, health and beauty aids. Food products can be purchased by the can, box, or case. Because they buy closeouts and test products from manufacturers all over the U.S., some labels won't be familiar. Shop the small section that displays 10-lb. cans and 5-lb. jars for the greatest savings. The last time I called they quoted me excellent prices on cereal, diapers and name-brand frozen foods.

Checks

Castle Cash and Carry

NEW LISTING
Renton: 601 Rainier Ave. S. 227-8316
Hours: Mon-Sat 9-7, Sun 12-6

Castle bills itself as a discount mini-warehouse similar to Costco but without the membership fee. Prices are low every day on name-brand groceries, candy, pet food and beverages, with milk and cigarettes the best selling items. Imported jams, jellies, and cookies can also be purchased here, as well as a limited selection of health and beauty aids, cleaning products, household goods and small electronic appliances like you would find in drugstores. I even spotted transmission fluid and computer paper.

Checks, Bank cards

Food Services Tacoma

NEW LOCATION
Mt. Vernon: 1101 West Division 424-2239, 1-800-377-7147
Hours: Mon-Fri 8-5, Sat, 10-4

The over 5,000 product inventory that Food Services Tacoma stocks includes food, paper products and janitorial supplies. There's an extensive selection of frozen food, with breaded fish and prime rib the best-selling items.

Checks

Fred Meyer

Auburn: 801 Auburn Way N.
Bellevue: 2041 148th N.E.
Everett: 8530 Evergreen Way
Federal Way: 33702 21st Ave. S.W.
Kent: 24250 Pacific Hwy. S.
Kirkland: 12221 120th Ave. N.E.
Lynnwood: 4615-A 196th
Puyallup: 1100 N. Meridian St.
Renton: 17801 108th Ave. S.E.
Seattle: 183rd and Aurora
Tacoma: 5115 100th St. S.W.
　　7250 Pacific Ave.
　　4505 S. 19th

Prices can vary as much as 11% from one grocery store to another. Some even charge 30% more for produce than their competitors. Three different surveys of Puget Sound grocery chains, all done within the last five years by impartial research groups, revealed that Fred Meyer had the lowest prices overall — testimonial to their policy of "true minimum pricing." While most people think of Fred Meyer as a mass merchadiser, the Superstores listed above all house full-service grocery departments.

Meat Distributors Inc.

Kirkland: 715 8th 827-0506
Hours: Mon-Fri 6-3:30

Although this wholesale distributor started out selling mainly meat to hotels, restaurants, and institutions, they now stock anything you'd find in a grocery store plus specialty items like kosher food, frozen soups and hors d'oeuvres. Steak must be purchased by the box, lean ground beef in 5-lb. packages. Call for a product list and place your order over the phone for will call.

Checks

Monte Vista Distributors Bulk Warehouse Sales

Snoqualmie: 140 North Falls Ave. 888-1811, 747-6701
Hours: Mon-Fri 8-4

Monte Vista supplies many of the local Dairy Queens, so here's a great place to check out when your church, school, social or business organization is looking for fast food items for a fundraiser or picnic. Hamburger patties, fish, french fries, prepared salads, hot dogs, onion rings and dairy products are sold by the case or carton. Cheese comes in 5-lb. blocks but eggs can be purchased by the dozen. Prices quoted and orders taken over the phone. Will call only.

Checks

Peterson Co.

NEW LISTING
Auburn: 1102 D Northwest 735-0313
Hours: Mon-Fri 7:30-4:30

A terrific selection of domestic and imported food products can be purchased direct from this wholesaler whose customers include delis, grocery stores, and fine restaurants. The product list covers over 30,000 items, from canned, frozen and packaged goods to pizza toppings, deli meats, prepared salads, and fancy deserts. Stouffers, one of the well-known brand names they stock, supplies restaurants with delicious entrees. Peterson's will gladly send you a product list upon request. Put your order in over the phone for will call or have it shipped UPS.

Checks

Primo's Sales

NEW LISTING
Tacoma: 3815 S. Cedar 474-6191
Hours: Mon-Fri 8-5

The public is welcome to shop at Primo's, even though they are a wholesale distributor frequented mainly by restaurants, mini-marts, and delis. Inventory includes packaged, frozen, and canned staples plus frozen entrees, bakery products and prepared foods you wouldn't normally find in a grocery store. There's a big selection of candy and snacks, like those used in vending machines. The store also carries bar supplies, cleaning and paper products. Call for a product list.

Checks

Price Chopper

NEW LISTING

Seattle: 15505 Westminster Way N. 363-9226 *Shoreline*
   8500 3rd Ave. N.W. 782-1610 *Greenwood*
Hours: Daily 8-10

Self-service, warehouse shelving and a low overhead keep prices down at these large, no-frills neighborhood grocery stores. The owners strive to consistently offer customers the lowest prices possible on bread, tuna fish, mayonnaise, and toilet paper. Although they stock nationally known brand names, the lowest prices are on products by Western Farms and Market Choice, especially when you buy by the case or in large containers. Grains, seeds, snacks, pasta and cookies are sold out of bulk bins. Be sure to check out the "Aisle of Values" for fantastic money-saving specials. Both stores have fresh meat and produce departments, but only the Shoreline store includes a deli. In-store flyers announce weekly sales and discount coupons. You'll be bagging your own groceries, but remembers, that's just one of the many ways Price Choppers keeps their costs down.

Checks, Credit Cards

Sysco Cash & Carry/Continental Food Service

Seattle: 1242 6th S. 447-9113 *Southeast of Kingdome*
Hours: Mon-Fri 7:30-4:30, Sat 10-4

Order fresh fruits, vegetables and meats a day in advance. Steaks are sold by the dozen and lettuce, six heads at a time. For parties you can buy liquor mixes by the quart and frozen bakery items that appear on the menus of fine restaurants, as well as the makings for espresso, including the machines. Janitorial supplies and paper products are also available. Watch for monthly specials and terrific deals on distressed and closeout merchandise from Sysco's huge Kent warehouse, which only sells to businesses.

Checks

Bakery Goods

One of the easiest ways to keep your food bill down is to buy day-old bakery products, which are really three days old and no longer considered fresh by industry standards. If you shop at a local bakery or a supermarket with an in-store bakery, find out when they put their breads, rolls, and pastries on sale. Savings start at 20% but remember, the early shopper gets the best selection.

Consumer Tips

✔ Commercial bakeries, like Wonderbread, pick their day-old products up twice a week at supermarkets and sell them in their many thrift stores at incredibly low prices. Monday and Thursday are the best days to shop if you want "fresh" day-old bakery goods. Since most bakery products have about a one week shelf life, thrift shops mark overstock down to super low prices on Wednesday and Saturday.

✔ To offer customers a full range of products, thrift stores buy bakery snacks, cookies, crackers, and other items from local manufacturers, such as Keebler, Archway, and Mother's Cookies, and sell them at discounted prices.

✔ Put day-old bakery products in the freezer as soon as you get home if you aren't going to consume them within the next few days. Thaw them out a couple of hours before serving or pop them in the microwave, and they'll taste almost as good as fresh-baked.

Bader's Dutch Biscuit Company

NEW LOCATION
Seattle: 7224 1st Ave. S. 764-1001 *Sodo*
Hours: Mon-Fri 8-4:30

If you need cookies in large quantities for a school or church function, Bader's is your place! Although they bake and sell in bulk for grocery store chains, you or your organizations can shop here if you purchase by the case. Cookies run the gamut from traditional favorites like peanut butter, chocolate chip and oatmeal, to fancy assortments and seasonal cut-out styles. Shortbread is the best-seller at around $8 for a case of 22 dozen. Call ahead to order or to check what's in stock.

Checks

Buns Master Bakery

NEW LISTING
Seattle: 13020 Aurora Ave. N. 365-7720 *Haller Lake*
Tacoma: 7304 Lakewood Dr. W. 473-0696 *Stanford Court*
Hours: Mon-Fri 7-6, Sat 8-5, Sun 10-4

Everyday low prices keep customers coming back to these retail outlets, where bakery products are also made for Sam's Club, Costco, pizza parlors, and delis. A loaf of fresh white bread sells for 89¢ with several other varieties to chose from, including rye, wheat, and multi-grain. Dinner rolls can be purchased for 11¢ each out of bulk bins or for $1.19 a dozen. Bagels, croissants, and sandwich buns are available, along with cakes, cookies, and pastries. Staff tells me customers really like their cheese sticks. Day-old products get marked down 40%. Ten percent discounts to seniors on Wednesdays.

Checks

Cascade Cookie Company

NEW LOCATION
Kent: 22435 68th Ave. S 872-7773
Hours: Mon-Fri 7-5

The Cascade Cookie Company supplies cookies to major supermarket chains but you can buy direct at the small thrift shop in their bakery, where cookies sell for 99¢ a dozen out of bulk bins or $8.00 for a case of 12 dozen. Fancy blends and seasonal cookies cost more. There's always a big rush around Christmas for their popular triple-assorted box. If your house is occupied by cookie monsters, buy the three pound bags of broken or mis-shapen cookies priced at only $2.95. Cascade's cookies have a 3-month shelf life despite the fact that they have no preservatives.

Checks

Gai's Bakery Thrift Stores

NEW LOCATION
Bellevue: 13823 N.E. 20th 641-0293
Bremerton: 2547 Perry Ave. 377-6377
Everett: 1515 E. Marine View Dr. 252-6260
Kent: 23009 Military Road S. 878-2242
Lynnwood: 430 164th S. 743-5799
Redmond: 7956 178th N.E. 869-6569
Seattle: 2006 S. Weller 726-7535 *International District*
    1431 N.E. 49th St. 782-4992 *Ballard*
    5980 1st Ave. S. 762-2186 *Georgetown*

Tacoma: 8203 Durango S.W. 584-4200
Hours: Generally, Mon-Sat 9:30-5:30, Sun 10-5

Although Gai's product list includes over 3,000 items, they are best known for their delicious Seattle sourdough and French bread, which is served in many Seattle restaurants. Their newest addition, a rustic Italian bread, promises to be just as popular. Breads of every type line the shelves of their thrift stores. A loaf of fresh sliced French bread sells for $1.49 while day-old drops to the astonishingly low price of three for $1.99. Look for savings on rolls, croissants, pastries, bread sticks, croutons, and muffins as well.

Checks

High-Quality House of Pies (Hi-Q)

Woodinville: 17611 128th Place N.E. 488-0200
Hours: Mon-Fri 9:00-5:30

Hi-Q bakes yummy cakes, cookies, pastries and muffins daily for delis, restaurants, and grocery stores. They specialize in every kind of pie you can imagine, including exotic flavors like kaluha creme. Fresh products are discounted but you save up to 50% off retail on day-old and damaged goodies, which may look a little strange but they still taste good! Pies sell for $5.25 fresh, $3.00 day-old, with apple and banana creme the long-standing favorites. The big selection of 9-inch round cakes makes this the perfect stop for birthday parties. Organizations get a discount, so inquire the next time your school has a bake sale. If you want to sample Hi-Q's products, you can find them at QFC and Red Apple grocery stores under the Flaherty label.

Checks

Langendorf Bakeries

NEW LOCATION
Bellevue: 13823 N.E. 20th St. 562-9208
Bremerton: 4800 Auto Center Way 373-8221
Everett: 3931 Smith St. 252-6613
Kent: 8621 212th St. 872-2244
Mountlake Terrace: 4804 212th S.W. 774-4170
Seattle: 2901 6th Ave. S. 682-2244 *Sodo*
  9112 E. Marginal Way S. 762-6850 *South Park*
Tacoma: 11216 Golden Givens Road 537-0749
Hours: Generally, Mon-Sat 9-5, Kent, Mountlake Terrace, and Tacoma open Sun 10-5

Almost every Langendorf product you see in grocery stores appears on the shelves of their thrift shops, but selection varies. Sales are based on inventory, and while you can always count on bargains on day-old products, fresh goods also get marked down when the bakery brings in overstock. Prices are particularly good on white bread, which sells for only $1.79 for five loaves. Country Hearth was marked down to $2.54 for three loaves the day I called. You'll also find great buys on pastries.

Checks

Orowheat Bakery Outlet

NEW LOCATION
Auburn: 3310 Auburn Way N. 939-3430
Bellevue: 1405 134th N.E. 641-3116
Everett: 125 S.W. Everett Mall Way 745-1669
Kent: 1510 S. Central 854-1303
Seattle: 1604 N. 34th 634-4401 *Fremont*
   7009 Greenwood Ave. N. 634-4426 *Greenwood*
Hours: Generally, Mon-Fri 9-6, Sat 9-5

Both fresh and day-old bakery products are sold at these outlets. Inventory varies from store-to-store as stock is geared to the different neighborhoods. Although Orowheat is best known for their whole grain breads, they also make pastries, cakes and cookies sold under the Entenmann's label in grocery stores. A fresh loaf of Oatnut sells for $1.35 while day-old is marked down 30%. Muffins, priced at three packages for $1.39, and Boboli pizza crust at $1.79, attract bargain hunters who don't mind day-old products. Orowheat does not supply paper bags, so take your own and a few extra to leave. Senior citizens receive a 10% discount.

Checks

Roos Market

Seattle: 1534 Pike Place Market 624-2945 *Downtown*
Hours: Mon-Sat 10-6

Prices average 50% or more below retail because Roos Market sells only day-old bakery products from Brenner Brothers and Jasmine Bakery, whose well-known goods show up on the shelves of most local grocery stores. Best selling items are bagels, pocket bread and rye bread, which comes in ten varieties. Those with a sweet tooth take advantage of the low prices on pastries.

Checks

Wonder Bread Hostess Cake Thrift Stores

NEW LOCATION
Bellevue: 14311 S.E. 16th St. 649-9628
Bremerton: 3411 11th 377-4881

Everett: 430 Casino Road 743-7775
Kent: 310 N. Washington 852-7050
Seattle: 1924 S. Jackson 322-4247 *International District*
   14701 15th Ave. N.E. 364-1991 *North City*
Tacoma: 1720 7th St. 627-0137
   10014 Pacific Ave. S. 536-1435
Hours: Generally, Mon-Sat 9:00-6, Sun 11-4

All bakery goods at these outlets are fresh except for day-old bread and cakes, which sell for incredibly low prices. You can buy Wonder Thin Sandwich bread for 49¢ a loaf or snack size cakes and pies for 35¢ a piece or six for $1.99. The Value Pack, a box of 90 cookies, sells for around $2. Don't forget to ask for a punch card. When it's full, you get a rebate in merchandise. Senior citizens qualify for a 10% discount on Tuesdays. Shop "Bargain Days" on Wednesday and Sunday.

Checks

The following community colleges have bakeries where products are made by students, so be prepared for some irregular sizes. Cookies, pastries, and breads are priced below retail, but it's hard for schools to compete with big super markets that have in-store bakeries. If you want to special order pies or cakes, give the staff three days notice. Allow a week for wedding cakes.

European pastries and breads sold in the bakery at South Seattle reflect the influence of the Swiss and Austrian chefs who teach there. Wedding cakes are rumored to be works of art. The culinary school also teaches candy making, so hand-dipped chocolates are sold as well. Fruit or liqueur truffles go for the low price of 40¢ a piece. Edible chocolate boxes filled with goodies cost only $8.50.

Lake Washington Technical College
NEW LISTING
   Kirkland: 11605 132nd Ave. N.E. 828-5600 ext. 415 *East Bldg.*
   Hours: Mon-Thurs 6:45-10:45

Renton Technical College
NEW LISTING
   Renton: 3000 N.E. 4th St. 235-5845
   Hours: Mon-Fri 7-1

Seattle Central Community College
   Seattle: 1701 Broadway 587-6917, *Capitol Hill*
   Hours: Bakery, Mon-Fri 7:45-2:00

South Seattle Community College

West Seattle: 6000 16th Ave. S.W. 764-5818 *Cascade Court*
Hours: Bakery, Mon-Fri 10-6

Eggs and Dairy Products

Amberson Egg Farm

Everett: 9131 42nd St. N.E. 334-7272
Hours: Mon-Fri 8-4

Chex eggs, which have a small crack or color defect in the outer shell, are sold here for 70¢ a dozen. Although the membrane on these eggs must be intact, it's best to use them for baking or hard-boiling. Prices on graded and brown eggs will be less than what you pay at grocery stores, and you know they're fresh. Amberson's also stocks butter and cheese from Washington Cheese Co-op.

Checks

Gaffney Suppliers, Inc.

Puyallup: 10514 8th St. E. 927-2800
Hours: Mon-Fri 6-4:30

Visit this egg processing plant and you can purchase B grade eggs fresh from local farms for only 75¢ a dozen. A grade eggs must be purchased in flats of 15 dozen. As a warehouse distributor to bakeries, Gaffney's also sells butter, shortening, salad oil and 30-lb. tins of frozen fruit or berries.

Cash

Green River Cheese & Dairy Products Co.

NEW LOCATION
Kent: 8260 S. 192nd 872-7600
Hours: Mon-Fri 7:30-3:30

This wholesaler stocks a terrific selection of cheeses, but the best buy is on Mozzarella, which they make themselves on the premises. You'll also find unsalted cheeses for those on a restricted diet and special blends for pizza and Mexican dishes. Check out the prices on American and Swiss cheese the next time you plan on making a lot of hamburgers or sandwiches. Most cheese is sold in 5-lb. loaves but sometimes smaller sizes are available. Deli meats are also available here. Call to request a product list.

Checks

Fruits and Vegetables

Fresh produce is the most unpredictable expense in your food budget because prices change weekly. If you buy in season when prices are the lowest, and splurge only occasionally during the rest of the year, your savings will add up fast. (Raspberries and asparagus are my downfall!) Since most fruits and vegetables have a shelf life of five to ten days, buying in volume is not a good idea unless you are planning on freezing or canning them. Apples, oranges, onions and potatoes can be purchased in bulk because they do stay fresh longer.

Consumer Tip

✔ During the summer, visit one of the many roadside stands and U-pick farms on the outskirts of Seattle for garden fresh fruits and vegetables. The trip will be fun for the whole family and you'll save money on produce you pick yourself. Copies of the Puget Sound Farm Markets Association's yearly guide are available at libraries or the Cooperative Extension Service office in downtown Seattle (3rd floor, Smith Tower). Send a self-addressed, stamped envelope to P.S.F.M.A., P.O. Box 1011, Puyallup, WA 98371 to receive the guide by mail. If you live in the Snohomish County area, a similar guide to U-picks is available through the Snohomish County Cooperative Extension Service. Call 338-2400 for more information.

Country Farms

NEW LISTING
Edmonds: 22800 Hwy. 99 774-3463
Everett: 1529 Broadway 252-1005
Hours: Daily 8-8, open later in summer months.
Closed January-March

The owner calls these old-fashioned, open-air markets the last of a dying breed. Because they only sell produce in season (April to October) and buy direct from area farms, prices beat the going rate at grocery stores, especially when you buy by the case or in bulk. For instance, oranges cost 39¢/lb or $10.95 for 40 lbs. In the spring time, Country Farms sells plants, shrubs, and flowers. In December they supply the neighborhood with Christmas trees.

Checks

Cerbone's

Federal Way: 31229 Pacific Hwy. S. 941-0937 *Old Federal Way Shopping Center*
Hours: Mon-Sat 8-7, Sun 8-6

For over 40 years prices at this huge family owned and operated indoor produce market have been lower than most grocery stores, plus you get personal service. Lettuce is always a good buy, and when I called, they quoted me outstanding values on tomatoes, mushrooms and Granny Smith apples. Red grapefruit was five for 99¢, sweet red peppers 69¢/lb. Produce is purchased six days a week to ensure quality. Located behind Highline Community College.

Checks

City Produce Co.

Seattle: 710 7th Ave. S. 682-0320 *International District*
Hours: Mon-Fri 8-4:30, Sat 8:30-3

Catering to the Asian community, this small wholesale/retail company stocks a large variety of fresh fruits and vegetables. Produce includes such exotic items as bitter melons, long beans and lily roots. You can purchase small quantities, but the savings increase when you buy by the case or carton. City Produce also carries packaged and canned food items like you would find at oriental markets. Since this is not a supermarket, try to shop without disturbing their more-profitable wholesale business. Call for a product list.

Checks

Garden Fresh Foods

Woodinville: 19600 144th Ave. N.E. 568-4388
Hours: Mon-Fri 7-5

Garden Fresh Foods prepares vegetables for restaurants and produce houses. Potatoes can be purchased whole or cut up for french fries, hash browns, potato salad, etc. Broccoli, cauliflower, carrots, celery, mushrooms, onions and peppers are also stocked. Minimum order is a 10-lb. bag, and you must call 24 hours in advance.

Cash only

Rising Sun Farms & Produce

Seattle: 6505 15th Ave. N.E. 524-9741 *Ravenna*
Hours: Mon-Sat 8-7, Sun 10-7, Summers open until 8

You can't miss this colorful outdoor market with its bright blue exterior and big signs proclaiming everyday low prices on

fruits and vegetables. Because they operate on a low overhead
and buy direct, prices on many items will beat the going rate
at grocery stores by 10-20%. The best buys sell out fast, so
visit often and take advantage of volume pricing. You'll also
find bulk pasta, cereal and legumes, a small dairy department
and bakery items, plus friendly service.

Checks

S.T. Produce

Seattle: 426 S. Massachusetts 622-5492 *Sodo*
Hours: Mon-Fri 6-3

Want to set up a salad bar at your next family picnic or office
function? S.T. Produce supplies restaurants and delis with the
fixings. You can order prepared salad mixes or the markings
separately already chopped, shredded, peeled, diced or sliced,
and put them together yourself. All products are packed fresh
in 5-lb. bags. Just add the dressing of your choice. The most
popular salad is the "ST" (80% iceberg, 15% Romaine and 5%
cabbage) at 84¢/lb. in season. Coleslaw is another favorite.
Five pounds of salad serves about 30 people!

Checks

Twenty-Fifth Street Market

Everett: 2431 Broadway 252-8773, 252-3111
Hours: Mon-Sat 5am-6pm

For 50 years this corner fruit and vegetable stand has been
supplying King and Snohomish County restaurants with fresh
produce trucked in daily from local farmers. While the displays may not be as fancy as those found in grocery stores, the
prices are hard to beat. Apples, oranges, bananas and
tomatoes are dirt cheap in season. You'll also find exotic items
like star fruit and blood oranges, as well as prepared salads,
coleslaw and garnishes. Dairy products are competitively
priced. Home delivery within a designated area costs only $2.

Checks

Valley Harvest

NEW LOCATION
Renton: 743 Rainer Ave. S. 277-0221 *Payless Shopping Center*
Hours: Mon-Fri 7-6:30, Sat 7-6, Sun 7-6

Since the last edition, Valley Harvest has moved into a new
25,000 sq. ft. warehouse, making them the largest indoor
produce market in the South end. The owners take a low
mark-up and don't spend any money on advertising. The day I

called they quoted me 49¢ for tomatoes, which were selling for
99¢/lb at my local supermarket. Apples sell for only 39¢/lb.
year round. You'll also find competitive prices on bulk beans,
grains, flours and rice, as well as health food products.

Checks

Meat, Poultry and Seafood

Meat is the most costly item in a food budget, and many people
consume 50% to 100% more protein than they need in a day. To
save money, choose your cuts based on cost-per-pound and the
number of servings you can get out of a package. For instance, a
1-lb. package of hamburger serves four people while the same
weight in blade cut pork chops serves only two.

Find out if the store near you marks the price of meat down
after the date on the package has expired. Reduced-price meats
may look discolored, but the stores would not sell them if they
weren't edible. For the best selection, shop early in the morning,
when dated meat is marked down, and freeze or cook it the same
day.

If you have a large family, consider investing in a freezer so
you can buy in quantity.

Jones Brothers Meats

Seattle: 5404 22nd Ave. N.W. 783-1258 *Ballard*
Hours: Mon-Fri 9-5:30, Sat 9-5

Although this is a retail meat market, low prices on choice
New York steak and fresh or frozen ground beef has earned
them a listing! Lean ground beef goes for $1.39/lb. while New
York steaks by the strip (10-14 lbs.) sell for $3.99/lb. which in-
cludes cutting and wrapping. If you have a freezer, check out
the prices on quantity meat packs, which are a big seller. Free
delivery with minimum orders of $60. Call for a price list.

Checks, Credit cards

Lampaert Meats

Duvall: 1.2 miles No. of Duvall on Snoqualmie River Rd.
467-9841
Hours: Mon-Fri 10-6

This local meat-packer offers a 100% guarantee on their
products, which are sold mainly to restaurants. Everything is
frozen and must be purchased by the case or in large cuts ex-

cept ground beef and boneless chicken breasts. However, the price goes down 10¢/lb. if you buy more than 25 lbs. Whole pigs, goats, and lambs can also be ordered for large barbecues. Call for a price list and place orders a couple of days in advance.

Checks

MJ Meats

NEW LOCATION

Lynnwood: 6325 212th St. S.W. Suite J 778-2712
Hours: Mon-Fri 8-4:30

As long as you're willing to buy by the case or larger cuts of meat and spend at least $100, you're welcome to shop at MJ Meats, which supplies restaurants with fresh or frozen beef, pork, poultry, veal, and seafood. If you're planning a picnic for a large group, check out their prices on lean ground beef or hamburger patties. A product list, which includes cheese, eggs, and butter, is available upon request. Call in your order a day in advance.

Checks

Oberto Factory Outlet Store

NEW LOCATION

Kent: 26135 104th Ave. S.E. 852-1219 *Kent Hill Plaza*
Seattle: 1715 Rainier Ave. S. 322-7524 *East of Kingdome*
   9891 Aurora Ave. N. 525-5701 *Greenwood*
Hours: Kent: Mon-Fri 10-8, Sat 10-6; Rainer: Mon-Fri 8-6, Sat 9-5; Aurora: Mon-Fri 7-6, Sat 9-6; All stores: Sun 11-5

Since 1918 Oh Boy! Oberto has been turning out tasty packaged Italian specialty meats, and today their popular products can be found in grocery stores and delis all over the country. Odd sizes, end pieces, overstock, test products and production overruns end up at these factory outlet stores. Everything is fresh, and you can save as much as 50% on some items. Purchase the "Sausage du Jour" or buy in quantity for the best deal. Gourmet items and gift boxes often show up at reduced prices, especially around the holidays. Get on the mailing list to find out about special sales and to receive discount coupons.

Checks, Credit cards

Torino Sausage Co.

Seattle: 700 S. Dearborn 623-1530 *International District*
Hours: Mon-Fri 9-4,

The bulk of Torino's old world gourmet specialty meats are made exclusively for local restaurants, although Larry's Market does stock their salami. Shop at this small retail outlet and deli for hot, mild, or salt-free sausage, salami or pepperoni. They recently added Coppa, which is similar to proscuitto. Whole pieces are cheaper than cuts but the best buy is on ends sold by the bag, which make great pizza toppings or snacks for the kids. Cheese, ham, olive oil and dried pasta is priced competitively.

Checks

Wild Salmon

NEW LISTING

Seattle: 1900 West Nickerson St. #105   283-3366 *Fisherman's Terminal, Magnolia*

Hours: Mon-Sat 10-6, Sun 11-6

Buy direct from this wholesale seafood distributor and get the freshest fish in town! Salmon is their number one selling item but any thing sold at a fish market can be purchased here. Needless to say, price and availability will vary with the season.

Checks, Credit Cards

Beverages

Soda Pop, Juice and Coffee

To save money on beverages, stock up when they go on sale at local supermarkets or drugstores. If you're buying in quantity for parties or fund-raising events, shop at food service warehouses or warehouse buying clubs.

Bargreen Coffee

Everett: 2821 Rucker 252-3161

Hours: Mon-Fri 7-4

The Bargreen family has been in the coffee-making business since 1898. Beans are roasted right on the premises, so you know they're fresh. Restaurants account for the majority of their business, but the public can take advantage of outstanding prices. Best sellers to the industry are Hotel Blend and Mt. Baker. For those with more sophisticated tastes, there's espresso and gourmet blends. Coffee can be purchased prepackaged or by the pound (whole or ground). Tea comes in a variety of flavors.

Checks

Cascade Coffee, Inc.

NEW LOCATION
Kent: 20640 84th Ave. S. 575-1243
Hours: Mon-Fri 8-4:30

Cascade services offices, specializing in ground or roasted gourmet blends. They also carry herbal and decaf teas. Coffee sold in portion packs costs $20 to $40 per case. Tea is sold by the box. Cocoa, soups and juices are also available. Call for a product list.

Cash only

The Cider Shed

Snohomish: 17902 Interurban 668-5888
Hours: Mon-Sun 8-6

Look for this popular label in grocery and health food stores. If you're in Snohomish, take time to visit their "backyard factory" and stock up on freshly made cider at below retail prices.

Checks

Cold Mountain Juice Co.

Seattle: 2311 N. 45th St. 632-0446 *Wallingford*
Hours: Mon-Fri 8:30-7, weekends during summer months

Cold Mountain fruit and vegetable juices show up on the shelves of Larry's Market and Puget Sound Consumer's Co-op. Buy factory-direct by the gallon and save 20% or more. Orange and carrot juice are their best sellers, but they also stock apple, papaya and grapefruit, plus tropical mixtures and lemonade. For health food practitioners, fresh wheat grass juice is available by the glass. Since fresh juice only lasts 3 to 5 days, buy no more than you can consume or share with friends.

Checks

Market Spice

Seattle: 85-A Pike Place Market 622-6340 *Downtown*
Hours: Mon-Sat 9-6, Sun 11-5

Buy in bulk and save on Market Spice teas and coffees, which are sold all over the country and locally at Safeway and QFC. With over 100 varieties to choose from, including gourmet blends, you're sure to find something you like. Prices average $8.50/lb. Large glass jars filled with spices and herbs vary from familiar cooking condiments to exotic spices. Over 25 salt-free seasonings to flavor soups, beef or fish are available.

Checks, Credit cards

Wax Orchards

NEW LOCATION
Vashon Island: 22744 Wax Orchard's Rd. S.W. 463-9735
Hours: Mon-Fri 9-4:30

Visit the farm where Wax Orchard's products are made and pay less than retail store prices. A half-gallon of thirst-quenching apple cider goes for $2.50. Blends like apple-raspberry cost a bit more. Other products you might like to sample include syrups, fancy preserves, butter and chutney. Products contain no sugar or additives, and they taste "just like Grandma used to make."

Checks, Credit cards

Beer and Spirits

Grocery stores and specialty beverage houses offer the best selections of beer and wine, but the Washington State Liquor Stores and membership buying clubs offer the best prices. Most merchants give a 10% to 15% discount on cases. Look for discount coupons at the Liquor Store and in the beer or wine departments of supermarkets.

Beverage House

Des Moines: 21411 Pacific Highway S. 824-6031
Hours: Mon-Thurs 10-10, Fri & Sat 10-11, Sun 10-9

Prices are lower on beer, wine and pop because the owner takes advantage of sales offered by distributors and passes the savings on to his customers. Although Budweiser is the #1 selling beer, the selection of imports is impressive. Discounted 6-packs can be mixed or matched. Buying by the half case saves you money, and full cases are even cheaper. Washington State wines are featured, but you'll also find a limited selection of California and premium labels. Watch for specials.

Checks

Cost Plus

NEW LISTING
Bellevue: 10300 N.E. 8th St. 453-1310
Lynnwood: 18205 Alderwood Mall Blvd. 774-8892 *Target Plaza*
Seattle: 2108 Western 443-1055 *Downtown*
Tukwila: 17680 Southcenter Parkway 575-0646
Hours: Mon-Fri 9-9, sun 10-7

Cost Plus, a chain of import stores located mainly on the West Coast, added wine departments in the Fall of 1992 and comparison shopping proves that in some instances, their prices are even lower than Costco's. The selection zeros in on Northwest and California wine priced at $3.99 to $12.99, plus imports from France, Spain, Italy, and Yugoslavia. The Cost Plus label offers customers a terrific value for their money while Columbia Crest sometimes sells for as low as $4.99. While you're in the store, check out their gourmet and specialty food items from around the world, which usually cost more at grocery stores.

Checks, Bank Cards

K's Beverage House & Deli

NEW LISTING
Bellevue: 1100 Bellevue Way N.E. 455-4301
Hours: Mon-Fri 7-9, Sat 8-10, Sun 10-5

Everyday low prices and a terrific selection of beer and wine keeps customers coming back to K's. Inventory includes over 1300 wines priced from $2.99 to $200, plus over 100 varieties of beer — domestic, imported and microbrews. You can even buy a keg here. Every month something different goes on sale. Call to compare prices.

Checks, Bank Cards

Lakeshore Mini-Mart, Pete's Wines & Pete's Supermarket

NEW LOCATION
Bellevue: Pete's Wines: 134 105th Ave. N.E. 454-1100
Seattle: Lakeshore Mini-Mart, 4036 E. Madison 325-2150 Madison Park

Pete's Supermarket, 58 E. Lynn 322-2660 *East Lake Union*
Hours: Bellevue, Mon-Sat 10-8, Sun 12-6; *Madison Park,*
Mon-Sat 7-10, Sun 9-10; Lake Union, Mon-Sat 7-9:30, Sun 9:30-9:30

These three stores are owned by George Kingen, who has carved out a niche in the beverage market by consistently beating supermarket prices. All beer, soft drinks and wines are discounted 15%. Sparkling wines and champagnes range from $5 to $60 a bottle, with over 1400 labels to choose from. Every two weeks the store runs a special promotion on at least 20 different wines.

Checks, Credit cards

McCarthy & Schiering Wine Merchants

NEW LOCATION

Seattle: 6500 Ravenna Ave. N.E. 524-9500 *Ravenna*

2209 Queen Anne Ave. N. 282-8500 *Queen Anne*

Hours: Ravenna, Mon-Sat 10-6

Queen Anne, Tues-Fri 11-7, Sat 10-6

Beer and wine are competitively priced, but the big savings come when you join their Vintage Select Club, which allows you to purchase any bottle or case of wine at 17% off retail. The $100 one-time membership fee includes a monthly newsletter, special dinners, wine tasting parties, and notification of highly allocated or sought after items. The shop will special-order rare wines, deliver for a minimum fee, and quote prices over the phone.

Checks, Credit cards

Mondo's World

Seattle: 4223 Rainier Ave. S. 725-5433 *Rainier Valley*

Hours: Tues-Sat 12-6

Wine connoisseurs will find some terrific bargains hidden on the shelves of this well-stocked store. The selection of cabernet's is outstanding. For $30/year you can join The Academy of Wines and receive a monthly hot-sheet listing sales and special wine tasting events. In addition, you can order any of the 10,000 wines sold in the state of Washington at 10-15% above wholesale. Close-outs run below wholesale.

Credit cards

QFC

Seattle: N.E. 45th St. & 25th Ave. N.E. 523-5160 *University Village, U-District*

Hours: Daily, 24 hours

Although most QFC's have a wine and beer department, the staff at this store does a fantastic job of offering customers quality wines at affordable prices. A wine expert is on hand daily from 8-5, and you can find something for every budget and taste. Best buys are in the $5 to $7 price range for dry wines and Northwest labels.

Checks, Bank Cards

Sav-On Beverages

NEW LISTING

Kirkland: 14310 124th Ave. N.E. 823-6246

You'll want to stop by frequently at this specialty store because every week something different goes on sale. Budweiser is the best selling beer at $4.29 a 6-pack, and you save even more if you purchase by the case. Customers with more sophisticated taste can choose from 200 different specialty beers, including imports and microbrews. Wine and champagne, priced form $2.99 to $90, focuses mainly on Washington and California labels, with a few imports tossed in.

Checks, Bank Cards

Warehouse of Wines Inc.

NEW LISTING

Seattle: 4530 Union Bay Place N.E.   525-6113 *Behind University Village*

Hours: Mon-Sat 10-6

This low-overhead operation offers everyday low prices on a very good selection of wines in the $5 to $25 price range, from-local as well as international vineyards. Keep your eyes open for big discounts on special purchases. The owner used to be affiliated with St. Michelle Winery, so he knows what he is doing.

Checks, Credit cards

Washington State Liquor Stores

Wine prices are lower at the Washington State liquor stores than at most retail outlets because the state buys in volume and has a lower overhead. Something different goes on sale each month and stays on sale until the end of the month or the inventory sells out. Sometimes you can find exceptional buys on award-winning labels. In August and September the Washington State Liquor Board sponsors "Washington Wine Month", a rare opportunity to stock up on your favorite wines or to sample new labels at bargain prices. Because it's illegal for the liquor stores to advertise, you have to shop regularly to catch the lowest prices. If you're buying hard liquor, be sure to check for coupons that offer mail-in rebates.

Checks

The Wine Warehouse

Kirkland: 128 Park Lane   827-0859

Hours: Tues-Sat, 12-8

A large, well-stocked store where prices range from $2 to $25, with an emphasis on California and Washington labels from well-known vineyards. The owner buys a lot of close-outs and special purchases which keeps prices 20% to 50% below what grocery stores charge. Periodic mailings announce specials.

Checks

Sweets and Treats

I can guarantee you'll save money at the outlets listed in this category, but I can't guarantee you'll keep your waistline! Watch for candy sales in supermarkets and drugstores before and after Easter, Halloween, Valentines Day and Christmas. You know the candy is fresh, so why not treat yourself?

Consumer Tip

✔ If you're contemplating a large purchase of your favorite candy, inquire about its shelf-life. Chocolate requires a cool, constant temperature, and the flavor will deteriorate after about two months. Wrapped hard candies are good for months, maybe even years. Soft caramels and taffy should be eaten sooner, but their shelf-life is longer than chocolate.

Boem's

NEW LOCATION
Burien: 140 S.W. 148th 243-2027
Issaquah: 255 N.E. Gilman Blvd. 392-6652
Lynnwood: 18411-C Alderwood Mall Blvd. 774-5455
Seattle: 559 N.E. Ravenna Blvd. 523-9380 *Ravenna*
Hours: Burien, Mon-Sat 7:30-7, Sun 10-7; Issaquah, Daily 9-6; Lynnwood, Mon-Thurs 10-9, Fri-Sat 10-10, Sun 12-6; Seattle, Mon-Fri 8-6, Sat 8-5, Sun 9-4

Boehm's opened its first candy kitchen in 1942 and has since become nationally known for their quality hand-dipped European chocolates. All stores sell imperfect and broken chocolates, but the best selection and lowest prices can be found at the factory in Issaquah. You can't miss the picturesque building as you drive past on I-90, where visitors can peek through the window and watch the candy being made. Fruit and liqueur truffles which normally retail for $25 to $35/lb. sell for only $19 here, and they come in nine scrumptious flavors. Filled chocolates that didn't pass inspection are priced at $5.50/lb.

Checks, Credit cards

Brown & Haley

Tacoma: 110 E. 26th A St. (retail store) 593-3067
  1940 E. 11th St. (factory) 593-3000
Hours: Mon-Fri 9:30-6, Sat & Sun 10-6

Did you know that Almond Roca and Mountain Bars are made right in Tacoma? Visit the retail outlet of this nationally-known candy manufacturer for some terrific deals on seconds. Who cares if the shape isn't quite right? Mountain Bars sell for $2.59/lb., and unwrapped Almond Roca for only $2.99. Imperfect assorted chocolates are sold here as well. The factory has big sales to get rid of overstock and novelty items three weeks before Easter, Valentines Day, Christmas and in the middle of June. Watch the Tacoma newspaper for ads or call to get on a mailing list. What a great resource for organizations that sponsor holiday events!

Checks, Credit cards

Baker's Candy Company

Seattle: 12534 Lake City Way 365-1888 *Lake City*
Hours: Daily 8-10

This family-owned business has been around since 1929. Their old-fashioned candies can be found in stores throughout the Northwest and at their Buddy Squirrel retail store in Northgate Shopping Center. Boxed European truffles sell for about $18/lb., dipping chocolate goes for $5.95/lb., and "Buddy's Boo Boo's" — broken chocolates — cost under $4/lb. The factory is located on the lower level of Baker's, a popular restaurant that the family operates in conjunction with the candy counter. Inquire about a volume discount.

Checks

Dilenttante Chocolate, Inc.

Seattle: 2300 E. Cherry 328-1530 *Capitol Hill*
Hours: Mon-Thurs 8-5, Fri 8-6, Sat 10-5

Satisfy that craving for gourmet chocolate by visiting the seconds counter at one of the country's leading candy factories. Everything is 30% to 50% off retail due to slight imperfections in color or shape. Purchase chocolates filled with nuts or cream by the piece, pound, or box. Real chocolate lovers go for the rich tasting cherry cordials and truffles, priced at only $13/lb. New items you might like to sample include biscotti (broken pieces sold by the pound) and taffetti, a flavored Italian nugent similar to taffy. Sometimes seasonal or novelty items show up.

Checks, Credit cards

Hyde's Northwest Candy, Inc.

Seattle: 1916 E. Mercer 322-5743 *Capitol Hill*
Hours: Mon-Fri 9-4

This factory outlet gives you a good deal on "mistakes" as well as regular merchandise that they sell mainly to supermarkets. A 1-lb. bag of imperfect chocolates goes for $3. Prices on divinity, fudge, cashew or peanut clusters, and hard candy run slightly above wholesale. Hyde's is the only candy company in the area that makes candy canes as well as sugar-free caffeine-free candy and chocolates for health food stores. Enter through the warehouse office on the north side of Mercer off 19th.

Checks

Johnson Candy Co.

NEW LOCATION
Tacoma: 1101 S. 10th. *272-8504*
Hours: Mon-Sat 10-6

For over a half-century Johnson Candy Company has been making delicious, old-fashioned hand-dipped chocolates, which are boxed and sold under their own label in drug stores and candy shops all over the Pacific Northwest. You can always pick up a 1-lb. bag of imperfect chocolates for around $5.20 at the retail outlet located in the factory. They also specialize in sugar-free candy and ice mints, which are custom made for weddings, showers and anniversaries. When the factory produces too much, they advertise specials in the local newspapers.

Checks, Credit cards

Northwest Vending Supply

Seattle: 5609 Rainier S. 725-4361 *Rainier Valley*
Hours: Mon-Thurs 9-5

If your kids spend a lot of money on vending machine candy, here's your chance to stock up. Northwest Vending Supply carries over 30 different varieties, ranging from the ever-popular M&M's to gumballs, boston baked beans, red hots, and roasted nuts. They even sell novelty items like capsules with toys inside, which make fun party favors. Everything is sold by the pound or case. Bulk candies average $2.50/lb., which beats the price in grocery stores. Call first so they can pack your order.

Checks

Sutliff's Candy Company

NEW LOCATION
Seattle: 336 N.W. 40th St. 784-5212 *Fremont*
Hours: Mon-Fri 6:30-5:00

Sutliff's makes personalized after-dinner mints for hotels, restaurants, weddings, and anniversaries. One-inch chocolate squares layered with a creamy filling are wrapped in gold foil. When the name or logo printed on the foil doesn't come out quite right or the wrapping doesn't pass inspection, the end results are sold as "miswraps" or "misprints." A 1-lb. bag can be yours for around $6; broken mints and end runs are reduced even more. Senior citizens qualify for a $1.00 discount.

Checks

Ethnic Foods

Golden Pheasant Noodle Co.

NEW LOCATION
Seattle: 1222 S. Weller St. 325-3296 *International District*
Hours: Mon-Fri 8:30-5

This tiny factory is not geared for walk-in trade, so we suggest you call first and place as large an order as possible to make it worth their while. Wonton skins come in 1-lb. bags, and noodles in up to 10-lb. packages at about $1.50/lb. Fortune cookies go for the same price. "Unfortunates" (factory rejects) are even less.

Cash only

Hoven Food Co.

Seattle: 508 S. King 623-6764 *International District*
Hours: Mon-Sat 10-6, Sun 11-5

You can buy fresh soybean products from Hoven, including tofu pudding, deep fried tofu, baked tofu, tofu noodles, and soybean drink. Ten packets of Tofu cost only $6.50, or buy 20 for $11. Hoven gives away by-products from the soybean manufacturing process, which you can use for fertilizer.

Checks

La Mexicana

Seattle: 10020 14th Ave. S.W. 763-1488 *White Center*
Hours: Mon-Fri 9-5

Believe it or not, Seattle has its own tortilla factory where they make over a dozen varieties of flour and corn tortillas daily. For only $1, a price that has remained the same for the last 18 years, you can buy three dozen tortillas. Take home a case and save even more. What you don't use can be frozen for future use. Masa dough for making tamales should be ordered a day in advance. La Mexicana also carries a complete line of Mexican food products which can be purchased by the can or case. They even stock Mexican cookies, candy, and pinatas, which are great fun at kid's birthday parties. Call ahead to find out what's in stock or have them send you a product list.

Checks

Merlino's Fine Foods

Seattle: 5605 Martin Luther King Way S. 723-4700 *Rainier Valley*
Hours: Mon-Fri 10-4

Restaurants and delicatessens buy imported as well as domestic Italian and Asian food products here, and the general public is welcome to take advantage of wholesale prices. Tomato products can be purchased by the case or can. Pastas come in 5-lb to 20-lb cartons, cheese and salami are sold by the loaf. The best buy is on Merlinos olive oil, which they import themselves. For a quick and easy meal, try the frozen pasta entrees. At Christmas time Merlino's even stocks Italian candy.

Checks

Pacific Food Importers

Seattle: 1001 6th Ave. S. 682-2022 *Sodo*
Hours: Tues-Fri 9-5:30, Sat. 10-2

Asian, Middle Eastern, and Mediterranean foods are the specialty at this small outlet owned by a wholesale restaurant supply warehouse. Customers come from ethnic communities all over the state to buy staples, as well as such exotic items as dried eggplant or Malaysian squid in milk. Beans come in 20 different varieties, from Egyptian to Italian fava. Volume packaging keeps prices way below retail. Olive oil is sold by the gallon, tomato paste in 28-oz. cans, spices and grains by the pound out of huge drums. It's hard to beat this importer's prices on cheese, salami and pasta.

Checks

Tsue Chong Co.

Seattle: 801 S. King 623-0801 *International District*
Hours: Mon-Fri 9:30-5:30

Visit the largest Chinese noodle and fortune cookie factory in the Northwest to buy products manufactured under the Rose Brand label. Over a dozen different types of noodles, both fresh and dry, can be purchased here, along with pot stickers, won tone wrappers and egg roll wrappers. For only $2.10 you can buy a 2-lb. package of noodles, which will feed an army! A 1-lb. bag of fortune cookies sells for $2, and a 5-pound bag of "unfortunates" for $5. Customized fortune cookies can be special-ordered with your own message inside. There's a 1-lb. minimum per message, but what a great idea for a business promotion!

Checks

Natural Foods and Health Products

Special growing and handling processes make natural foods more expensive than food produced the conventional way. Be sure to comparison shop the bulk items sold by the gram, ounce, or pound from bins and barrels. One outlet may have especially good grain prices while another beats everyone else's price on seeds. Don't forget to check out the health food products in local supermarkets. Fred Meyer stores with grocery departments have become very competitive in this market.

Consumer Tip

✔ Joining Central Co-op or Puget Consumers Co-op is another way to ensure savings, and you can participate in the running of the business. Each store will gladly explain its policies over the phone. Non-members are welcome to shop but must pay 13% to 15% above the posted price. If you are visiting for the first time, the co-ops will waive the non-member markup.

Central Co-op

Seattle: 1835 12th Ave. 329-1545 *Capitol Hill*
Hours: Daily 9-9

Although the store carries a full-range of health food products, the focus is on organically-grown fresh produce. The selection includes soy, macrobiotic and fresh dairy products, plus a good selection of herbs and spices. Members have voted to eliminate wine, meat, and products containing sugar from their shelves. To become a member, you pay a $5 non-refundable fee and $2 a month up to $60 and then you are a lifetime member. Senior citizens can join for a one-time $5 fee.

Checks

Ener-G Foods

Seattle: 5960 1st Ave. S. 767-6660 *Georgetown*
Hours: Mon-Fri 8:30-5

Ener-G is a manufacturer of foods made especially for people who cannot eat wheat, gluten, eggs or milk products due to food allergies, celia-sprue disease or renal failure. Many of their products are sold in health food stores nationwide. Buying direct from the warehouse will save you anywhere from 20% to 30%, and there is no minimum. Call for a product list and place your order in advance. Shipping is available for a minimal fee. As a special service, the company will compile a list of recipes to meet individual dietary requirements. Enter through the Sam Wylde office.

Checks, Credit cards

Green Earth Nutrition

Renton: 125 Airport Way 226-7757
Hours: Mon-Fri 9:45-6:30, Sat. 9:45-6:00

This spacious store offers discounted prices on a huge selection of health food items. Vitamin supplements average 5% to 15% below retail, and you'll find everyday low prices on vegetables, oils, soups and juices, plus lots of bulk items. Raw milk and acidophilus are always available. Green Earth makes a habit of passing good buys on to customers, but since their low overhead limits advertising, it's best to visit or call frequently to find out about the latest specials.

Checks, Credit cards

Manna Mills, Inc.

Mountlake Terrace: 21705 66th W. 775-3479
Hours: Mon-Fri 10-8, Sat & Sun 10-5

Savings at this large natural food warehouse start at 20% below high-end retail outlets. Because they buy grain by the truckload and mill it on the premises for resale to bakeries, whole wheat flour sells for the lowest price around — only 29¢/lb. Raw almonds are another super bargain at $2.25/lb. Buy wheat, corn, flour, rice or beans by the sack and save even more. The store also stocks vitamins, dairy products, earth-friendly household items and an extensive selection of wheat-free foods. Senior citizens qualify for a 5% discount everyday.

Checks

Nutra Source

Seattle: 4005 6th Ave S. 467-7190 *Sodo*
Hours: Mon-Fri 8:30-5

If you are willing to spend $100 or more, you can buy natural food and health products direct from this warehouse distributor at 15% above wholesale. Call and they'll send you a 1" thick catalog that outlines their ordering policies and lists a huge selection of name-brand products sold in health food stores all over the country. Prices go down even more with larger orders. Free delivery if you purchase $400 worth of merchandise. Just remember, most items are sold by the case or carton.

Business checks, Cashiers checks, or Money orders only

Puget Consumers Co-op

NEW LOCATIONS
Everett: 9121 Evergreen Way 742-1240
Kirkland: 10718 N.E. 68th 828-4621
Seattle: 6504 20th Ave. N.E. 525-1450 *Ravenna*
6522 Fremont Ave. N. 789-7144 *Greenwood*
5041 Wilson Ave. S. 723-2720 *Seward Park*
6514 40th Ave. N.E. 526-7661 *Ravenna*
West Seattle: 2749 California Ave. S.W. 957-8481
Hours: Everett, West Seattle, View Ridge, Kirkland daily 8-10; all other locations daily 9-9

Started in 1960 as a buying club, PCC now boasts 35,000 members, making it the largest food co-op in the country. The inventory is astounding, covering any and everything you'd find in a grocery store, plus lots of literature on how to stay healthy. The organic produce department carries a terrific selection year round. Chicken and fish are delivered fresh daily, along with bakery and dairy products. Packaged, canned or bulk foods purchased by the case or sack lower prices 5% to 10% Membership fee is $8 to join, then $2 every month until the total reaches $60. Those who are disabled or over 65 pay a one-time fee of $2. Membership includes cooking demonstrations, nutrition classes and a monthly newspaper. Call for a brochure and to find out about new store locations.

Checks, Credit cards, Food Stamps

Additional Food Outlets

(See Index for page numbers)

Food Service Warehouses and Grocery Stores

ABC Sales
Big Mike's Factory Outlet
Liquidators Outlet
Sessions Variety

Eggs and Dairy Products

MJ Meats
Twenty Fifth Street Market

Meat, Poultry and Seafood

Green River Cheese and Dairy Products

Sweets and Treats

South Seattle Community College
Wax Orchard

Natural Foods and Health Products

Cascade Coffee
The Cider Shed
Cold Mountain Juice
Hyde's Northwest Candy
Market Spice
Rising Sun
Valley Harvest

Personal Care

Drugs and Sundries

It's easy to save 30% to 50% on sundries because so many name-brand products go on sale on a regular basis, and big chains offer private-label goods that are cheaper than name-brands. Diligent shoppers compare prices by reading the colorful Sunday sale supplements and by using the many coupon books put out by drugstore chains and mass merchandisers. Something different gets marked down every week, so it's best to stock up when you see a bargain rather than wait until you run out. Maximize your savings by combining a coupon clipped off a box or out of a magazine with a store coupon or in-store sales.

My survey and a survey by the Seattle Times in 1993 revealed that prices on prescription drugs can vary as much as 30% from pharmacy to pharmacy, so it pays to shop around. It was also noted that while some druggists may offer rock bottom prices on one drug, they'll charge more on others which means if you're taking several different medications, you may have to visit more than one pharmacy to get the lowest prices overall.

It's easy to comparison shop prescription drugs because state law requires that pharmacies quote prices over the phone. Have the name, dosage and quantity available. If you're on maintenance drugs, purchase as large a quantity as possible since the fee you pay the pharmacists for preparing your prescription is the same whether you buy 30 pills or 100. Most chains and independent drug stores give a 10% discount to seniors, but few in our listings do because their prices are already rock bottom

Generic drugs and over-the-counter medicines can undercut name-brands 30% or more because you're not paying for the high cost of research, development and advertising. Generics are simply copies of brand name medications whose patent has expired. FDA guidelines require that ingredients must be identical if a generic is to be substituted for a name-brand prescription drug. To keep costs down, insurance companies, government agencies and welfare programs now require generics whenever possible.

Some doctors, out of habit, prescribe name-brands instead of generics, so it pays to ask if there is a substitute, keeping in mind that generics are not available or feasible for all prescriptions. Don't be afraid to ask your pharmacist if there is a less expensive drug on the market that could replace the one prescribed. He or she will call your doctor to get the change approved. It's easy to compare prices and ingredients on aspirin, cough syrups, cold remedies, and other over-the-counter medications. because private label generics and name brands are stacked next to each other on drug store shelves.

American Association of Retired Persons (AARP)

NEW LISTING

Seattle: 9750 3rd Ave. N.E. #400 526-7918 *Northgate*

If you are 50 years old or older, for only $8 you can join AARP and save money on prescription drugs plus take advantage of their many other benefits, which include investment programs, low-interest credit cards and free publications, plus discounts on travel, medical supplies, auto, home and health insurance. The closest AARP drugstore is in Oregon, so all prescriptions are sent by mail for a $1 shipping and handling fee, no matter what size the order! Stop by the local AARP office to pick up an application or call and they will gladly send one.

Checks, Credit Cards

Apex Wholesale

Seattle: 521-A 1st Ave. N. 285-2639 *Queen Anne*
Hours: Mon-Fri 8-3

If you don't mind buying in volume, shop here and you'll save 20% to 30% on sundries, toiletries and non-prescription drugs. The $100 minimum may sound steep, but by the time you add up the cost of a year's supply of shampoo, toothpaste, film and batteries, it doesn't take long to spend that amount.

Use in-store catalogs to familiarize yourself with the inventory and pricing structure. Some items must be purchased in the carton or by the dozen. Located in an alley behind Dick's Drive-In, parallel to Queen Anne Blvd.

Checks

Costco Pharmacy

Federal Way: 35100 Enchanted Pkwy. S. 874-4431
Kirkland: 6829 120th Ave. N.E. 822-0414
Lynnwood: 19105 Hwy. 99 774-4210
Seattle: 4401 4th Ave. S. 682-6244 *Sodo*
Silverdale: 1000 Mickelberry Rd. 698-1155
Hours: Mon-Fri 11-7, Sat 10-6

The good news is that non-members can shop at Costco's pharmacy and take advantage of their consistently low prices on prescription drugs. Both my survey and the Seattle Times ranked them among the top resources for saving money on drugs.

Cash, Discover Card

Cost Less

Tacoma: 5431 Pacific Ave. 474-9493
Hours: Mon-Fri 9-6, Sat 9:30-5

Many drugstores in Tacoma advertise low prices, but this one quoted me the cheapest rates of anyone I called in the Puget Sound area, so call them first, even if you live in Seattle, because they will mail anywhere and only charge you postage.

Checks, Bank Cards

Cost Plus RX

Statewide toll-free: 1-800-444-5079
Burien: 17644 1st Ave. S. 244-4106
Tacoma: 204 N. I St. 572-6473
7304 Lakewood Dr. W. 473-7246 *Stanford Court*
Hours: Generally, Mon-Fri 9-6, Sat 9-3

Cost Plus quoted me an incredibly low price on one of the maintenance drugs I surveyed and a very competitive discount price on the others. Free mailing to anyone over 62 unless the prescription is a narcotic or costs more than $100, in which case clients pay UPS shipping charges.

Checks, Credit Cards

Drug Emporium

NEW LOCATION
Edmonds: 23632 Hwy. 99 778-2130
Everett: 7725 Evergreen Way 348-0900
Federal Way: 2030 S. 314th 946-3777
Kent: 25406 104th Ave. S.E. St. 850-0696
Kirkland: 12515 116th Ave. N.E. 820-0440 *Totem Lake W.*
Lynnwood: 3815 196th S.W. 771-5944
Seattle: 818 N.E. Northgate Way 771-5944 *Northgate Village*
Silverdale: 2779 N.W. Myhre Rd. 692-1120
Tacoma: 5401 6th Ave. 752-1400
      7901 S. Hosmer 472-7485
Tukwila: 17348 Southcenter Pkwy. 575-3103 *Parkway Plaza*
Hours: Mon-Fri 9:00-10, Sat 9:00-8, Sun 9:00-7

The family budget got a break when this big national discount chain came to town. Prices on prescription drugs are competitive with other area discounters, plus, the stores offer low prices every day on hundreds of name-brand, hair care and beauty products, vitamins, cleaning supplies, baby needs and over-the-counter remedies. The big inventory of trial sizes are great for travel or testing a product. You can save 35% on cosmetics and 40% on gift wrap, greeting cards, ribbon and stationary. Prices will vary week-to-week on the same item, so it pays to shop often and compare competitors' advertised sales.

Checks, Credit cards

Madison Plaza Pharmacy

NEW LISTING
Seattle: 2201 E. Madison 324-6633 *Central area*
Hours: Mon-Fri 9-7, Sat 9-5

This large neighborhood pharmacy had the cheapest prices overall of the 11 pharmacies the Seattle Times polled when they were comparison shopping commonly used prescription drugs. For $2 or less prescriptions will be shipped anywhere in the U.S. Another good reason to shop here are the everyday low prices on generic over-the-counter medications.

Checks, Bank Cards

The Medicine Man

NEW LOCATION
Everett: 4027-A Rucker Ave. 252-1000
Seattle: 1752 N. Market 789-6804 *Ballard*
  323 N.W. 85th 789-0800 *Greenwood*
Hours: Mon-Fri 9:30-6, Sat 9:30-2

These small drugstores advertise that they'll undersell the big chains on prescription drugs and I'm happy to report that their price quotes did indeed beat the competition. You will also find low prices every day on over-the-counter medications and vitamins, plus a large selection of reading glasses and products for contact lens wearers. Other aggressive marketing tactics include a $5 discount on all prescriptions transferred from another pharmacy with the first refill and free mailing of prescriptions anywhere in the U.S.

Checks, Credit Cards

The Rubber Tree

Seattle: 4426 Burke Ave. N. 633-4750 *Wallingford*
Hours: Mon-Fri 10-7, Sat 10-6

Run by the local chapter of Zero Population Growth, a non-profit organization, this store sells non-prescription contraceptives at 10% to 40% off retail. Call or write for one of their brochures and you can shop by mail. At the store, you'll find free information on all forms of contraception, sexually transmitted diseases, optional parenthood and population issues. The Rubber Tree is the only store of its kind in the country and they've been advocating safe sex since 1975.

Checks

Safeway

NEW LISTING
See yellow pages for locations nearest you

Safeway quoted me low enough prices to earn them a listing in the Super Shopper. Plus, they promised to meet any competitors price, which means saving money on prescriptions will be a lot easier since there are so many Safeway pharmacies in the Puget Sound area. Senior citizens receive a 10% discount on brand names, and 20% off on generics.

Checks, Credit Cards

Cosmetics and Grooming Products

Beauty supply stores are excellent places to shop if you want the best value for your money on hair care, nail and skin products. While the public is welcome at most of these outlets, some items can only be sold to licensed beauticians because products require special salon procedures that are not fully explained on the package. Do not buy anything unless you know how to use it or the staff is able to provide detailed instructions. Consider visiting a beauty school for a professional application before trying a new product yourself.

Prices aren't necessarily lower on merchandise from beauty supply outlets, but the quality is often better because products manufactured especially for professional salons must meet industry standards, plus more time and money is spent on ingredients than on expensive advertising. Salon formula shampoos, conditioners, permanents, hair dyes, rinses, mousses and sprays are more concentrated, PH balanced and better for your hair. Although you won't recognize the labels, some of the best buys are on generic knock-offs of famous brands and large-size containers not usually available in retail stores. Brushes, combs, scissors, rollers, curling irons and blow dryers are made for heavy-duty use, so you know they're going to last. Cosmetics and skin care products favored by professional make-up artists will be a lot less expensive than designer lines sold in department stores.

All beauty supply shops stock well-known hair care lines, but product mix varies from store to store. Some will have a wider variety of makeup or nail supplies, while others may focus on implements or fancy hair ornaments. Also, look for items not normally available at cosmetic counters, like lash and brow tint, ethnic products and formulas made especially for men. Don't be afraid to ask questions since the stores are staffed by trained professionals.

BJ Beauty Supply Inc.

NEW LISTING
Seattle: 2504 S. Jackson 325-7131 *Central area*
Hours: Mon-Thurs 9-6, Fri 9-7, Sat 9-6

> The impressive line-up of hair care products here attracts a lot of customers and the super low prices keeps them coming back. BJ quoted me the cheapest price in town on Paul Mitchell shampoo. They also stock cosmetics, brushes, combs, curling irons, and nail care products, plus many specialty items for African Americans.
>
> ***Checks, Credit Cards***

Brown's Beauty Supply

NEW LISTING
Everett: 7825 Evergreen Way 347-5866
Seattle: 10301 Aurora Ave. N. 523-4407 *North Park*
Hours: Mon-Fri 8-5, Sat 10-5; Everett Thurs 8-8

Although these stores cater to professional beauticians, a special area has been set aside where the general public is welcome to shop. Nail, skin, and hair products abound.

Checks, Credit cards

Discount Beauty Supply

NEW LISTING
Tacoma: 7911 S. Hosmer 475-2043
Hours: Mon-Sat 10-8, Sun 10-6

Located inside Mega Foods, this small shop displays an array of hair care lines that often sell for less here than they do in beauty supply stores. Shampoos and conditioners by Nexus, Paul Mitchel, Sebastian, Skisha, Matrix, Joico, Optimum, and Wave Nouveau fill the shelves, as well as hair dyes, perms, combs, brushes, curlers, and implements.

Checks, Credit Cards

Eejay's Haircutter & Beauty Supply

Auburn: 1210 Auburn Way N. 833-1347
Kent: 25621 104th Ave. S.E. 852-5566
Renton: 17620 140th S.E. 277-1699 *Fairwood Square*
Hours: Generally Mon-Sat 9-6, Sun 12-5

Everything you'd need in the way of hair care products can be purchased here, with Paul Mitchel, Redkin and Joico the best selling lines. Seniors qualify for a 10% discount and residents should watch for discount coupons that appear frequently in the Fairwood Square paper. Eejay's charges low-end prices for salon services, so make an appointment to have your hair cut.

Checks, Credit Cards

Issaquah Beauty Supply & Salon

NEW LISTING
Issaquah: 1620 N.W. Gilman Blvd. 391-1825 *Meadows Shopping Center*
Hours: Mon-Fri 9:30-6, Sat 9-5, Sun 11-4

When the distributor gives them a good deal, Issaquah Beauty Supply passes the saving on to it's customers. They also buy in volume so their prices will be lower than what you would pay at a salon and the selection is fantastic — 27 lines of hair care products, four skin care lines including Aveda, two cosmetic lines, plus an array of implements to keep your hair beautiful year round.

Checks, Credit Cards

K's Beauty Supply & Salon

Everett: 1001 N. Broadway, Suite A-8 258-2866 *College Plaza*
Hours: Mon-Sat 10-6

K's sells perms, dyes, conditioners, gels, shampoos and nail care products to the trade and to the public. Best selling lines include Paul Mitchel, KMS, and Sebastian. You might like to try Sherani, their professional make-up line.

Checks, Credit cards

Kari Lynn's Beauty Supply Inc.

NEW LISTING
Renton: 17817 108th S.E. Ave. 271-9333 *North Benson Center*
Hours: Mon-Fri 10-9, Sat 10-6, Sun 11-5

Everything you'd need for your skin or nails. Hair products by Lanza are popular as well as professional strength nail polish by Opti, priced at $4.99. Kari's stocks make-up by Beverly Taylor, LaFemme, Ci Ci, and Pallido.

Checks, Credit Cards

Karin's Beauty Supply

Bellevue: N.E. 8th and Bellevue Way 454-3443 *Bellevue Square*
Everett: 1203 S.E. Everett Mall Way, Suite Q 347-2884 *Everett Mall Plaza*
Factoria: 3700 128th Ave. S.E. 643-2121 *Loehman's Plaza*
Federal Way: 26110 Pacific Hwy. S. 941-4009
Kent: 25612 S.E. 104th 854-3708 *Kent Hill Plaza*
Lynnwood: 4001 198th S.W. 775-3212
    3105 Alderwood Mall Blvd. 775-9244
Puyallup: 10312 120th St. E. 845-3308 *East Meridian Square*
Renton: 1222 Bronson Way N. 271-7145 *Village Square*
Seattle: 8314 Aurora Ave. N. 526-5861 *Greenwood*
    10017 Holman Rd. N.W. 782-0577 *Art's Shopping Plaza, Crown Hill*
Tacoma: 4502 S. Steele 472-1288 *Tacoma Mall.*
Wooodinville: 14013 N.E. Woodinville-Duvall Hwy. 486-5937
Hours: Generally, Mon-Sat 10-6, Sun 12-5

You can purchase anything here you'd find in a full service beauty salon, including equipment and fixtures. Best selling products are shampoos, perms and conditioners by Paul Mitchell, KMS, Focus 21 and Joico, plus makeup by Janelle, La Femme and CiCi. Prices are competitive with other beauty supply outlets and once a month "something old and something new" goes on sale. The selection is amazing, and the newest products on the market pop up here first.

Checks, Credit cards

Marquis Beauty Products & Salon

Federal Way: 1706 S. 320th 839-5881 *Sea-Tac Village*
Hours: Mon-Fri 10-6, Sat 10-5

Hair care products are the big selling item at this outlet, especially shampoos, hair dyes and permanents. The cosmetic line by Anita of Denmark compares to expensive lines sold in department stores.

Checks, Credit cards

New Attitude Beauty Supply & Salon

NEW LISTING
Kirkland: 12548 120th Ave. N.E. 821-4488
Hours: Mon-Fri 9-8, Sat 10-6, Sun 12-5

With over 25 major lines in stock, you're sure to find just what you need! Paul Mitchell shampoos and conditioners outsell other products. Check out the competitive prices on make-up, hair ornaments, cutting, and styling implements.

Checks, Credit Cards

P.J.'s Beauty Supply

Lynnwood: 18700 33rd Ave. W. 774-1999 *Alderwood Terrace*
Hours: Mon-Fri 9-9, Sat 9-8, Sun 11-6

P.J.'s stocks a little of everything for hair and nails. You can choose from 15 different types of perms, along with an extensive selection of shampoos, tints, dyes, curling irons, and brushes. Low prices make this a popular spot.

Checks, Credit cards

Prestige Fragrance & Cosmetics

Tukwila: 17900 Southcenter Parkway 575-3991 *Pavilion Mall*
Hours: Mon-Fri 9:30-9:15, Sat 9-8, Sun 9-6

Prestige, one of the fastest growing off-price chains in the country, sells internationally-known cosmetics, perfumes and skin care products at 25% to 75% off the normal retail price. Expensive lines such as Charles of the Ritz, Visage, Borghese and Halston are purchased from department store surpluses and stores going out of business, so the stock is always changing. Look for good deals on the designer fragrances and cosmetic kits, which give you a chance to sample a variety of products. Less expensive lines like Revlon and Almay are also carried. Beautifully packaged soap and perfume collections make wonderful gifts. A special section in the store features clearance items starting at 99¢. Watch for monthly sales.

Checks, Credit Cards

Vaar-M Beauty Supply and Salon

Redmond: 17212 Redmond Way N.E. 883-8889 *Bear Creek Village*

Hours: Mon-Fri 9-7, Sat 9:30-6, Sun 11-4

In comparing prices on an array of beauty supplies here, you'll find that a 16-oz. bottle of shampoo costs only $6.95. Hair cutting scissors range from $10 to $60. The store promotes a special line of conditioners and shampoos for swimmers and Redmond residents who build up minerals in their hair from drinking the local well water.

Checks, Credit cards

Grooming Services

Beauty Schools and Community Colleges are great resources for low-cost basic hair care and beauty services. Prices average about half of what you would pay a licensed cosmetologist, and all procedures are supervised by an instructor. Call first to make an appointment, keeping in mind that since these are students, the procedure may take longer than normal. Most beauty schools can provide any service available in a professional salon. Here's a break down on the cost of basic procedures, which will vary depending on the level of the student. Take advantage of low prices to investigate beauty procedures that might normally be beyond your budget.

Cutting: $5-$8. Higher prices include a shampoo and blow dry.
Perms: $20-$30. Prices increase with the length of hair and the procedure used. Spiral perms start at $25.
Artificial Nails: $20-$25, fill-ins: $15.
Manicure or Pedicure: $6-$8
Facial: $8-$12

Other services offered include hair coloring and conditioning treatments, waxing, make-up application, and brow and lash tints. Some schools even do ear piercing. When you visit, remember that you're not only saving money, but also giving the students a chance to practice their craft.

Comparison shopping at the big family oriented discount chains such as Fantastic Sams, Super Cuts, and Hairmasters revealed the following prices:

Haircuts: $10-$15 for adults, $8-$10 for children under 12
Perms: $35 and up.
Some neighborhood beauty shops and barbers can meet these prices.

ABC Nail & Skin College

Bellevue: 14508 N.E. 20th 643-4283
Hours: Tues-Fri 10-8, Sat 10-6

Treat yourself to a day of pampering, while advanced students hone their skills. Prices are a little higher here because of the in-depth training. Facials cost $20. A manicure is $8.50, a pedicure $13.95. Other procedures available include waxing, make-up application, and lash or brow tinting.

Checks, Credit Card

BJ's Beauty & Barber College

Tacoma: 5236 S. Tacoma Way 473-4320
Hours: Mon-Fri 8:30-9, Sat 8:30-5

BJ's offers a full range of beauty services and treats seniors to a discount on sets and shampoos Tuesday through Thursday.

Checks, Credit Cards

Bates Cosmetology

NEW LISTING
Tacoma: 1101 South Yakima 596-1606
Hours: Tues-Fri 10-4:30

Fees are based on a sliding scale depending on whether you have a beginning, intermediate, or advanced student work on your hair, skin, or nails.

Checks, Credit cards

Bellevue Beauty School

NEW LISTING
Bellevue: 14045 N.E. 20th 643-0270
Hours: Mon-Fri 9-4:30, Sat 8-4:30

Haircuts cost only $4.50 to $5.75, perms start at the unbelievably low price of $13 for short hair and $24 for long.

Checks, Credit Cards

Everett Plaza Beauty School

NEW LISTING

Everett: 607 S.E. Everett Mall Way #5 353-8193

Hours: Tues-Sat 9:30-5

This is the only beauty school listing for Everett residents. Senior citizens who visit Tuesday through Thursday receive 20% off on all services.

Checks

Evergreen Beauty & Barber College

NEW LISTING

Lynnwood: 3815 196th 776-9178

Hours: Tues-Thurs 9:30-9, Fri-Sat 9:30-5

Men's and Women's haircuts start at $8. Seniors can visit any day except Saturday for a 20% discount on all hair, skin, and nail services.

Checks

Gene Juarez Academy of Beauty

NEW LISTING

Federal Way: 2222 S. 314th 839-4000 *Hillside Plaza*

Seattle: 10715 8th Ave. N.E. 365-6900 *Northgate*

1514 6th Ave. 622-6611 *Downtown*

Hours: Tues-Sat 9-3:30

Students who train here often end up at the very successful local chain of salons started by Gene Juarez, which are among the top-rated in the country. Prices are higher than at other beauty schools and almost double at the downtown location, which is an advanced training center where many of the students are already employed in Gene Juarez salons. Haircuts cost $15, perms start at $45, manicures run $10, pedicures, including a foot massage, $15. A full set of nails will cost you $45. Discount coupons for the Northgate location appear frequently in the Northgate Journal.

Checks, Credit Cards

Greenwood Academy

NEW LISTING

Seattle: 8501 Greenwood N. 782-0220 *Greenwood*

Hours: Tues-Fri 9:30-9, Sat 8:30-5

When you visit, treat yourself to the "ultimate facial" which includes a soothing mask. Sounds heavenly! Seniors stop in Tuesday through Thursday for a 20% discount.

Checks, Credit Cards

Kent Beauty College

NEW LISTING
Kent: 25725 101st S.E. 854-5500
Hours: Tues-Sat 9:30-4

A full range of skin, hair, and nail care is available here. No waxing or brow tinting, however. Senior discount Tuesday through Thursday.

Checks, Credit Cards

Kirkland Beauty School

NEW LISTING
Kirkland: 10702 N.E. 68th 822-6013
Hours: Tues-Sat 8:30-4:00

Here's a terrific deal for eastside residents! Anyone who visits on Tuesday gets 10% off any service. On Wednesday and Thursday, senior citizens take advantage of the 20% discount.

Checks

Mr. Robert's Beauty School

NEW LISTING
Tacoma: 5205 S. Tacoma Way 472-2500
Hours: Tues-Sat 9:30-5

Low prices on basic cuts ($3.95) and perms ($19.95) keep the customers coming back. Seniors save 20% Tuesday through Thursday.

Checks

New Beginnings

NEW LISTING
Auburn: 435 E. Main 939-2480
Hours: Tues-Sat 9-5

Auburn residents who haven't discovered Mr. Lee's are paying too much for hair care and beauty services. He offers senior citizens 20% off Tuesday through Friday.

Checks

Paul Mitchell Academy of Cosmetology

NEW LISTING
Seattle: 14352 Lake City Way N.E. 363-8555 *Lake City*
Hours: Tues-Thurs 9-9, Fri-Sat 8-5

This is the only beauty school I found that does body wrapping and bikini line waxing. If you're interested in experimenting with a new look, a make-up application costs only $8.95. Senior citizens visit on Tuesday and Thursday for a 20% discount.

Checks, Credit Cards

Renton Beauty School

NEW LISTING
Renton: 2828 Sunset Lane N.E. 226-5855
Hours: Tues-Sat 9-4

> On Wednesday and Thursday senior citizens receive a 20% discount on any and all hair and beauty procedures.
>
> *Checks*

Cosmetology departments at the following community colleges are open to the public. South Seattle gives seniors a 20% discount on Tuesday and Thursday. At Seattle Central and Shoreline the discount is good every day. No credit cards accepted.

Clover Park Votec

Tacoma: 4500 Steilacoum Blvd. S.W. 589-5623
Hours: Mon-Fri 7:45-3:30

Everett Community College

Everett: 1110 N. Broadway Ave. 388-9339
Hours: Mon-Fri 8:30-4

Seattle Central Community College

Seattle: 1500 Harvard 587-5477 *Capitol Hill*
Hours: Tues 11-4, Wed 11-7, Thurs & Fri 9:30-4

Shoreline Community College

Seattle: 16101 Greenwood Ave. N. 546-4631
Hours: Mon-Fri 9:30-4

South Seattle Community College

Seattle: 6000 16th Ave. S.W. 764-5814
Hours: Mon-Fri 9-3:30

Dental Services

Community colleges offer the general public an opportunity to save money on dental fees while students training to be dentists and hygienists learn their profession. All work is overseen by a licensed instructor and most procedures will take longer than they do at a dentist's office. Dental hygiene schools require that you visit three times. Don't forget that appointments have to be scheduled around school breaks and you may sometimes have to wait a month from the time you call until your appointment. Dental schools are usually closed during summer quarter. I haven't listed the University of Washington Dental School because when I called they had a back up of 400 people!

The Seattle King County Dental Association suggests that you shop around because fees will vary depending on the dentist and the location of his office.

Clover Park Votec

NEW LISTING
Tacoma: 4500 Steilacoum Blvd. S.W. Bldg. 4 589-5632, adults, 589-5713, children
Hours: Mon-Fri 8-12 adults, Mon-Fri 1-6, children

General dentistry is taught here and only low income families qualify for services, which cover everything but braces. Routine exams start at $35 for adults, $10 per visit for children.

Checks

Lake Washington Technical College

NEW LISTING
Kirkland: 11605 132nd. Ave. N.E. 828-5616
Hours: Thurs-Fri 8-2

Since students study to be dental hygienists, the only thing they do is clean teeth. There is no fee for the first appointment, $20 for the initial exam, and on the third visit, $47 to have your teeth cleaned. No children accepted.

Checks

Pierce College

NEW LISTING
Tacoma: 9401 Farwest Dr. S.W. 964-6694
Hours: Mon-Fri 9-5

A screening and workup is free. X-rays cost $6 to $20, cleaning $12 and up, fillings, $18 to $36. Pierce College takes children starting at age two, so this is a good place to save on protective sealants for their teeth.

Checks

Renton Technical College

NEW LISTING

Renton: 3000 N.E. 4th St. 235-2297

Hours: Wed & Fri 8-12:30

Renton Votec teaches general dentistry so services include everything from cleaning to root canals. No braces or children under 16. A general exam plus X-rays costs $15. Fillings are $120 and crowns around $160.

Cash

Shoreline Community College

NEW LISTING

Seattle: 16101 Greenwood Ave. N. 546-4711

Hours: Mon, Wed, Thurs 8-12, Fri 1:30-5

There is no charge for the first exam. Cleaning, which includes X-rays, costs $30 to $45. Add $20 for a full mouth X-ray. Senior citizens get $5 off. The school is usually booked a month in advance so schedule your appointment as soon as possible.

Checks

Additional Personal Care Outlets

(See Index for page numbers)

Drugs and Sundries

ABC Sales
Big Mike's Factory Outlet
Canned Foods Grocery Outlet
Castle Cash & Carry
Sessions Discount Variety

See dollar stores and 99¢ stores under Mass Merchandise Discounters.

Cosmetics and Grooming Products

ABC Sales
Apex Wholesale
Canned Foods Grocery Outlet
Big Mike's Factory Outlet
Drug Emporium
Sessions Discount Variety
Six Star Factory Outlet

See dollar stores and 99¢ stores under Mass Merchandise Discounters.

Home Building and Remodeling

T he Puget Sound area is a great place to live if you like to do your own home repairs, remodeling or redecorating. Rumor has it that prices may be lower here than anywhere else in the country due to the influx of so many giant warehouse operations battling it out for their share of the market. Rivals Home Base, Home Depot and Eagle Hardware all carry a vast array of merchandise and guarantee the lowest prices possible, which makes for convenient one-stop shopping. Ernst and Fred Meyer superstores even get into the act sometimes with super low prices on loss leaders.

Building Materials and Hardware

Boeing Surplus

Kent: 20651 84th Ave. S. 393-4060
Hours: Tues-Fri 11-6, Sat 9-4

Customers come from out of state just to spend the day browsing through this incredible surplus outlet. A huge warehouse contains thousands of new and used items left over from the construction of airplanes and the running of Boeing's corporate offices. The outside yard overflows with cast-off building materials and scrap iron. Even company vehicles are sold

115

on the grounds. A semi-truck unloads goods daily, so inventory changes constantly.

Businesses shop for furniture, office supplies and computers. Manufacturers pick up steel drums, electrical equipment, motors, fasteners, cutting tools, sheet metal, aluminum, plastic and rubber components which can also be used for remodeling and shop projects. Free wood can be picked up 24 hours a day at the corner of 206th St. and 84th Avenue South. Everything is sold "as is where is", thus, no returns. (I'm still trying to decide how to recycle airline seats!)

Checks

Captain Sam's

Seattle: 410 2nd Avenue Extension S. 624-1478 *Pioneer Square*
Hours: Mon-Fri 10-5, Saturdays 10-3

Captain Sam's, named after a cat that died over 15 years ago, specializes in vintage lighting fixtures, plumbing supplies, hardware, doors and windows salvaged from old houses and buildings. This is where many items from the Music Hall ended up, from ornate moldings to theater seats. As long as you don't mind the mess, a thorough search should turn up a glass globe for that antique light fixture, parts to repair an old toilet, or a carved door to add a little character to your home. Even the set decorator for Northern Exposure shops here. Be forewarned: nothing is priced. Exchanges accepted.

Credit card

Chinook Door

Tacoma: 1515 S. Tacoma Way 472-9614, 241-1832
Hours: Mon-Fri 8-4:30

Buy a prehung door from the distributor and cut out the cost of a retail markup. Scrap wood goes in a dumpster where people pick it up for kindling and gardening stakes.

Checks

Discount Lumber

NEW LISTING
Marysville: 14821 Smokey Pt. Blvd. 653-4010, 486-3379
Hours: Mon-Fri 7-6, Sat 8-5

Look for everyday low prices on basic building supplies such as 1/2" plaster board and 2" studs. Discount Lumber also stocks a lot of shop and economy grade lumber. Their policy states "If it's not on sale, a manager's special, or quoted on a bid, you automatically receive a 10% discount."

Checks, Credit Cards

Door Barn

NEW LISTING
Edmonds: 23631 Edmonds Way 776-1137
Hours: Mon-Fri 8-5:30, Sat 9-4

Purchase "A" grade doors, fresh from the mill, at discounted prices. "B" grades start at 30% off retail, with over 2,000 styles to choose from. The best buy is inventory that has been marked down simply because it's overstock, or special orders that never got picked up. The day I called, the store had just received 20 sets of French doors in perfect condition that the factory decided not to make any more.

Checks, Credit Cards

The Door Store

Tacoma: 3110 Ruston Way 752-1900, 1-800-252-1900
Hours: Mon-Fri 8-5, Sat 9-4

Save on interior or exterior doors at this distributor who boasts the largest selection of solid wood doors in the state. Seconds, which have cosmetic flaws, are the best value. Buy five or more first-quality doors and get a break on price. Watch for big sales three times a year

Checks, Credit cards

Eagle Hardware & Garden

NEW LISTING
Bellevue: 11959 Northup Way 646-9031
Bremerton: 4220 Wheaton Way 377-9052
Federal Way: 35205 16th Ave. S. 838-2233
Mt. Vernon: 1717 Freeway Dr. 424-5868
Puyallup: 301 37th Ave. S.E. 841-5669
Seattle: 2700 Rainer Ave. S 760-0832 *Rainer*
Tukwila: 101 Andover Park E. 243-5470
Hours: Mon-Fri 7:30-9, Sat 7:30-7, Sun 9-7

This locally owned warehouse chain burst on the scene in 1992 and quickly claimed a following because they stock "more of everything," especially small, hard-to-find items. The hardware department alone contains over 8,000 fasteners! The selection of building supplies is impressive, with lumber and tools for any project imaginable. Women like Eagle because of its spacious aisles, attractive displays, expansive nursery and big, home decor departments, which includes more lighting fixtures and toilet seat covers than any other warehouse operation. Service-oriented and geared to do-it-yourselfers, all stores offer free workshops on weekends, a resource center filled with books, brochures and videos plus trained personnel who will be glad to answer questions. The cut shop can cut anything. Delivery within King County for $25. Lenient return policy. Lowest prices guaranteed.

Checks, Credit Cards

The Door Store/Frank Lumber

NEW LISTING
Marysville: 1046 Cedar St. 658-0362
Seattle: 17727 15th N.E. 362-2311 *North City*
Hours: Mon-Fri 8-6, Sat 9-4

One of the largest inventories of doors in the Northwest from basic 6-panels to French doors, double doors, woodscreen doors, dutch doors and leaded glass doors, plus lots of odd sizes and seconds. A factory first retails for $108 while "B" grades go for $59.

Checks, Credit Cards

Home Base

NEW LOCATION
Kent: 18230 E. Valley Hwy. 251-9400
Kirkland: 11831 120th Ave. N.E. 821-1161
Lynnwood: 17300 Hwy. 99 742-7900
Silverdale: 9577 Ridge Top Blvd. N.W. 698-0527
Tacoma: 1913 S. 72nd St. 472-6767
Hours: Mon-Fri 6-9, Sat 7-8, Sun 8-8

Home Base, a favorite hangout for builders and contractors, is a great resource for those who like to save money by shopping at no-frills cavernous warehouses. Although the emphasis is on lumber, hardware, tools, electrical supplies and plumbing, you'll find any and everything you need for a remodeling or building project, plus garden and nursery supplies, decorative items and patio accessories. Home Base boasts the largest selection of Black and Decker tools around. Departments are staffed by trained personnel who will gladly give advise to do-it-your selfers. Delivery service costs $25 for every 25-miles from the store nearest you. If you find an identical item advertised at a lower everyday price, Home Base will beat that price by 10%. Refunds with receipt.

Checks, Credit Cards

Home Depot

NEW LISTING
Seattle: 2701 Utah Ave. S. 467-9200 *Sodo*
Tacoma: 7050 Tacoma Mall Blvd. 474-9600
Tukwila: 6810 S. 180th St. 575-9200
Hours: Mon-Fri 6-9, Sat 7-9, Sun 7-7

This is the nation's largest warehouse home improvement chain, with very aggressive marketing and pricing strategies. Stores are larger than Home Base and Eagle Hardware, with long aisles stacked to the ceiling with tools, lumber, hardware, plumbing, electrical and building supplies plus anything you'd need to renovate the interior of your house. When Home Depot opened their first store in January of 1993, Eagle had to lower some of their prices to be competitive, so, this is the first place you should visit to comparison shop.

Get on their mailing list for monthly catalogs to familiarize yourself with Home Depot's inventory and pricing. Staff includes professional contractors, plumbers and painters who give advice and conduct daily how-to clinics.

Delivery costs $25 within a 50-mile radius. If you're not satisfied with your purchase, Home Depot will repair it, replace it or refund your money, no questions asked. Lowest prices guaranteed. Look for new stores in Federal Way and on 200th and Aurora in Seattle.

Checks, Credit Cards

Jones Glass and Used Materials

NEW LISTING
Tacoma: 1912 S. Wilkenson 272-4351
Hours: Mon-Fri 9-4, Sat 9-2

Window glass goes for rock bottom prices here. Salvaged building supplies include bath tubs, doors, pipe, bricks, and windows in good to not-so-good condition.

Checks

Kiski Cabinets

Edmonds: 782-8227
Hours: By appointment only

Bill Kiski, a wholesale broker, reps a deluxe line of kitchen cabinets used in homes that have been featured in the Seattle Times and Architectural Digest. There is no retail showroom since most of his clients are contractors, interior decorators and apartment owners, but call for an appointment and he'll be glad to show you sample doors and photos of kitchens.

Checks

Lighting Supply, Inc.

Seattle: 2729 2nd Ave. 441-5075 *Downtown*
Hours: Mon-Fri 8-5

Here's a great place to save money on lighting fixtures, but don't expect a big fancy showroom since this is a low overhead operation that deals mainly with contractors, architects and decorators. Although most of the inventory is standard lighting equipment commonly found in commercial and residential buildings, there's a huge library of catalogs from which to order anything not in stock. Check out the prices on light bulbs by the case. Returns accepted.

Checks, Credit cards

McLendon Hardware, Inc.

NEW LOCATION
Puyallup: 5420 112th St. E. 536-6560
Renton: 710 S. 2nd 235-3555
Sumner: 1111 Fryar Ave. 863-2264
White Center: 10210 16th S.W. 762-4090
Woodinville: 17705 130th N.E. 485-1363
Hours: Daily 7:30-7:30

McLendon's has the look and feel of an old-fashioned general delivery store, but in a huge warehouse setting,which isn't surprising since the local, family-owned business started in Renton as just that! Rumor has it that Eagle modeled their inventory after McLendon's, which numbers an astounding 100,000 items — more than any of the big warehouses. Merchandise may not be as neatly displayed, but prices are competitive and you'll find things in this combination lumber yard, hardware store, home center, and nursery that no one else carries, plus they offer "down home" service. McLendon's is the only warehouse I went into where someone actually came up to me and asked if I needed help! Twice a month the store advertises hundreds of bargains. If you don't live in the area, call to get on their mailing list. Senior citizens qualify for a 15% discount. All returns accepted.

Checks, Credit Cards

Mutual Materials

Bellevue: 605 119th Ave. N.E. 455-2869
Hours: Mon-Fri 7-5

Bricks, tile and clay products manufactured by Mutual and Interpace are used to build skyscrapers, houses, fireplaces, chimneys and patios. The price is the same whether you buy one or 1,000 bricks. Although the majority of customers are contractors and masons, do-it-yourselfers stop in for small projects. Tools and mortar mixes are also stocked, and the helpful staff will answer questions. This is the main office and largest yard for Mutual, which has other retail locations in Auburn, Everett, Kenmore and Tacoma.

Checks

North City Lumber/Frontier Lumber

NEW LISTING

Everett: 8811 36th S.E. 334-8035 *Old Lemaster Yard*
  715 91st N.E. 334-8035 *Frontier Village*
Seattle: 1221 N.E. 175th 362-6200 *Shoreline*
Hours: Mon-Fri 7-5, Sat 9-1

Ninety-five percent of this lumber yard's customers are contractors but you don't have to be a contractor nor do you have
to buy in volume to take advantage of the low prices.

Checks, Credit Cards

The Old Hobby Shop

Lynnwood: 17707 Hwy. 99 743-1003
Hours: Tues-Sat 9:30-5:30

For years this second hand shop has been the clearing house
for overstock and unclaimed merchandise from the largest
aluminum window manufacturer in the state. Prices depend
on size and condition, but savings average 20% to 50%, with
over 7,000 windows to choose from. New windows qualify for
government subsidized weatherization programs. A small
selection of leaded glass and old wood windows is scattered
about. Seven day return policy.

Checks

Pacific Industrial Supply

Seattle: 2960 4th Ave S. 682-2100 *Sodo*
Hours: Mon-Fri 8-5, Sat 9-3

Loggers, boat owners, commercial fisherman and contractors
shop here for new and used equipment of all kinds, including
fittings, hydraulic hoses, cylinders, pumps and valves, plus
motors, wood and metal-working tools, and industrial
machines. A big warehouse in back called the "wire rope shop"
contains chains, cable, pulleys, rope and hoists in every size
imaginable. Merchandise is mainly surplus and salvaged
goods, which keeps prices way below retail. Reasonable return
policy.

Checks, Credit cards

Pacific Iron's Building Materials

Seattle: 2230 4th Ave. S. 628-6256 *South of Kingdome*
Hours: Mon-Fri 8-5:30, Sat 9-5:30, Sun 10-3

You'll find tools, windows, hardware, moldings, laminates,
particle board, fiberglass roofing, metal sheeting, pipe and
chain, plus a big selection of doors and kitchen cabinets. Metal
and acrylic glass is cut-to-order, free-of-charge, with floating

hot tub covers a specialty. An odd assortment of household items passes in and out of this narrow, crowded warehouse. Factory close-outs, discontinued, or freight-damaged goods keep prices below wholesale and limited to stock-on-hand. 90-day return policy.

Checks, Credit cards

Rhine Salvage

NEW LISTING
Tacoma: 1124 112th E. 531-7223
Hours: Mon-Fri 8-4:30, Sat 8:30-2

These guys buy anything that's usable after a building has been torn down and sell it to you. Lumber, which comes in all sizes, is sometimes in quite good condition.

Checks

Read Products, Inc.

Seattle: 3615 15th Ave. W. 283-2510 *Interbay*
Hours: Mon-Fri 8-5

If you are interested in saving 30% to 40% on cabinets, major kitchen appliances, plumbing fixtures, and floor and window coverings, then visit this contractor's show room, where you will find lots of samples and catalogs to look through. Brand name appliances include Viking, Thermador, Whirlpool and Sub-Zero. Located just south of the Ballard Bridge. Restocking charge for returns.

Checks

Seattle Building Salvage, Inc.

Seattle: 202 Bell St. 448-3453 *Downtown*
Hours: Tues-Sat 10:30-5:30

Looking for a claw foot bathtub, leaded glass windows, or antique faucet to add a little character to your home? Seattle Building Salvage restores old doors, windows, hardware, plumbing and lighting fixtures to their former glory. Some items go for half of what you would normally pay. The owner, who is an electrician, offers cut rates on repairing old light fixtures.

Checks, Credit cards

Sherman Supply

Seattle: 2456 1st Ave. S. 624-0061 *Sodo*
Hours: Mon-Sat 8-5

I'm told this is the place to go if you're setting up a sprinkler system. Sherman's sells plumbing, irrigation, and industrial supplies, some of which come from salvage operations. The store is crammed with rope, hoses, pipes, and valve fittings of

all sizes, plus motors, compressors, blocks, winches, etc. They
also stock florescent lighting fixtures. Senior citizens qualify
for a discount. Ten day return policy.

Checks, Credit cards

Timber Windows

NEW LOCATION
Mukilteo: 7929 44th Ave. W., Unit G 745-9665
Hours: Mon-Fri 8-4:30, sometimes Sat

"Boneyard glass" is what this window factory calls its' odd
sizes and unclaimed stock. Sometimes wood frame windows
end up in the sale pile. Savings can amount to 60%, and all glass
carries a guarantee. Call ahead to find out what's in stock.

Checks

Town and Country Distributors

NEW LISTING
Kirkland: 12828 N.E. 124th St. 823-2110
Hours: Mon-Fri 8-6, Sat 9-3

Town and Country stocks hundreds of doors and a large selection of trimwork at contractors prices. Interior 6 panel doors
start at $50. Two-inch primed casing costs only 11 cents a foot.
Buy a B grade door that has a minor blemish or needs a little
sanding and save 30% more. Shelving systems are also available.

Checks, Credit Cards

Warehouse Kitchen Sales

NEW NAME
Auburn: 233 D Street N.W. 1-800-422-7046
Hours: Mon-Fri 8-5, Sat 9-2

A dealer/distributor, in business for over 22 years, who opens
their showroom to the public. There's a huge display of
kitchen cabinets from five different manufacturers, in dozens
of wood and laminate styles. Compare prices on appliances by
Frigidaire, Jen Air and Dacor, as well as floor coverings by
leading brand names.

Checks, Credit Cards

Well Home Program

NEW LISTING
Seattle: 6532 Phinney Ave. N. 789-4993 *Phinney Ridge*

Home owners who like to do their own maintenance and
remodeling should check out this wonderful program sponsored by the Phinney Ridge Neighborhood Association. Do-it-
yourselfers can take classes, rent tools, get on-site

consultations or buy recycled building materials for a nominal fee. Staff also gives free advice, maintains a reference library, refers people to reputable contractors and custom-builds low-cost storm windows. Call for a brochure.

West Coast Door Factory Outlet

NEW LISTING
Tacoma: 3102 S. Pine 572-8333
Hours: Tues-Sat 9-5

A bonafide factory outlet for the biggest door manufacturer in the South end. Everything in stock is seconds, so you can get a quality wood door at below wholesale prices. Selection covers every room in your house, interior or exterior, from solid wood to raised panels, glass fronts and bifolds.

Checks, Credit Cards

Wholesale Door Company

NEW LISTING
Snohomish: 1316 Bonneville Ave. 568-0515, 1-800-562-3930
Hours: Mon-Fri 8-5

Wholesale Door Company prehangs doors for contractors. Stop by to see what they have left over from jobs. Some doors are seconds, others are in perfect condition. There's always a lot of discounted molding available. No returns.

Checks

Tools

Pawn shops and tool rental stores often have used or like-new tools for sale at substantial savings. If you know what you want, call to find out what's available.

Aircraft Parts Exchange (A.P.E.)

Kent: 13812 8th S. 242-4059
Hours: by appointment only

A.P.E. buys and sells surplus and salvaged equipment out of an old dairy barn. The owner says he carries or can get "anything under the sun mechanical." If you're in the market for hydraulics, machinery, hardware or tools, give him a call.

Checks

Aronson-Campbell Industrial Supply, Inc.

Seattle: 5300 Denver S. 762-0700 *Georgetown*
Hours: Mon-Fri 8-5

Tools here are sold mainly to contractors, carpenters and tradespeople, so the quality is better than commercial brands found in hardware stores. Prices, however, tend to be a little higher. Drill presses, band saws, miter boxes, sanders and grinders by Bosch, Delta and Porter Cable carry long-term warranties. The large showroom features a lot of in-store specials on tools, machinery, abrasives and shop supplies. Call and they will send you a comprehensive product catalog. Returns accepted on everything but sale merchandise.

Checks, Credit cards

Black and Decker

NEW LOCATION
Seattle: 421 S. Michigan 763-2010 *Georgetown*
Tacoma: 2602 S. 38th 473-6040
Hours: Mon-Fri 8-5, Sat 9-2

Stop by Black and Decker's service and parts center to check out the inventory of blemished or reconditioned power tools and small kitchen appliances, all of which come fully warranted. 30-day return policy.

Checks, Credit Cards

Coast Tools, Inc.

Seattle: 8926 Roosevelt Way N.E. 527-4474 *Northgate*
Hours: Mon-Fri 8:30-5:30, Sat 9-2

This shop sells industrial-quality electrical and hand tools at way below list price, especially those needed for fine woodworking projects. Major lines include Makita, Bosch and Ryobi. Get on the mailing list to find out about periodic specials and their annual Christmas sale. Returns accepted.

Checks, Credit cards

Greenshield's Industrial Supply

Everett: 710 N. Broadway 259-0111
Hours: Mon-Fri 8-5, Sat 8-12

Greenshield's discounts small portable electrical tools by Proto and Milwaukee 25% to 30%. Proto is manufactured by Stanley and comparable to Craftsman, a line put out by Sears. Savings will vary on other lines, which include automotive tools. Anything not in stock can be special ordered.

Checks, Credit Cards

Hardwick's Swap Shop

Seattle: 4214 Roosevelt Way N.E. 632-1203 *U-District*
Hours: Tues-Sat 9-6

Hardwick's is a fun place to visit because it looks like an old-fashioned general store with merchandise piled in every nook and cranny, some of which I'll swear has been there since they opened in 1932. Noted for their big selection of new and used tools, plumbing and electrical supplies, the store attracts machinists, carpenters, plumbers, mechanics, and gardeners looking for obscure or hard-to-find items.

The other half of the premises overflows with household goods, glassware, furniture, bric-a-brac and whatever the two Hardwick brothers can get a good deal on, making this a favorite haunt of students furnishing their first digs. Much of the merchandise is new, mainly close-outs, samples, and factory liquidations, but Hardwick does pay cash for used wooden furniture, dinette sets, housewares, beds, office furniture, tools, and hardware. Trade-ins accepted on electrical tools. Variable return policy.

Checks, Credit cards

Milwaukee Electrical Tools

NEW LISTING
Seattle: 5419 Maynard S. 762-8430 *Georgetown*
Hours: Mon-Fri 8-4:30

If you know what you want, call Milwaukee and they will check their 22 service centers around the country to see if they have any reconditioned tools available. Nothing is stocked in the store since this is a repair center.

Checks, Credit Cards

Pacific Air Tool

Seattle: 7400 2nd Ave. S 762-3550 *South Park*
Hours: Mon-Fri 8-4:30, Sat 8-12

Pacific Air always has a good supply of rebuilt or used air tools in stock at substantial savings. They also rent tools. Restocking charge for returns.

Checks

Porter-Cable

Renton: 268 S.W. 43rd St. 251-6680
Hours: Mon-Fri 7-5

How would you like to pay close to wholesale for tools that were simply taken out of the box for display or used for a demo by sales reps? Inventory includes drills, screwdrivers, sanders, and a big selection of saws. 30-day return policy.

Checks, Credit Cards

Skil Corporation

Seattle: 101 S. Branden 762-1127 *Georgetown*
Tacoma: 1610 Center 572-7107
Hours: Mon-Fri 8-5

Benchtop tools will be cheaper here than at regular outlets, especially if you buy blemished or reconditioned models, which still qualify for the one-year warranty. Look for good deals on wood working saws. Skil also rents tools.

Checks, Credit Cards

Tacoma Screw Products Annex

Tacoma: 2001 Center St. 572-3444, 1-800-562-8192
Hours: Mon-Fri 8-5, Sat 9-1

The building industry shops at Tacoma Screw's eight stores for hardware, tools, fasteners and equipment. Everything sold at the Annex is discounted because it's old merchandise or over stock. Best buys are on the specials, which change frequently. Call to get on their mailing list or to request a catalog. Returns accepted.

Checks, Credit cards

Tool Town

NEW LOCATIONS
Des Moines: 23639 Pacific Hwy. S. 878-1148
Everett: 2302 Broadway 259-2590
Kirkland: 12700 N.E. 124th St. 821-3007
Seattle: 652 Elliott Ave. W. 281-1166 *West of Seattle Center*
  19811 Aurora Ave. N. 542-0910 *Aurora Village*
Tacoma: 1601 Center St. 572-3693
Hours: Mon-Fri 9-6, Sat 9-4

This local chain relies on volume buying and low overhead so they can offer everyday low prices on all kinds of tools and shop equipment. Industrial lines by Milwaukee and Mikita are carried along with such well-known brand names as Black and Decker. Imports may be cheaper but the quality may not stand the test of time. Tool Town also stocks a large selection of specialty automotive tools. Watch the Little Nickel for advertised specials. Return policy subject to manager's discretion.

Checks, Credit cards

Tool and Woodworking Co.

NEW LISTING
Tacoma: 1215 Center St. 272-4343
Hours: Mon-Fri 8-5, Sat 9-1

Check out the ever-changing inventory of used woodworking tools and machinery, which includes a lot of specialty saws. Watch for frequent sales on brand names such as Delta.

Checks

Western Tool Supply

NEW LOCATION
Kent: 8613 S. 212th St. 395-3102
Woodinville: 16110 Woodinville/Redmond Rd. 488-7222
Hours: Mon-Fri 8-5, Sat 9-2

If you plan on investing in industrial-grade tools, this is a good place to comparison shop since Western is part of a seven-store chain based in Oregon, and has one of the best selections around. Inventory is geared to contractors and cabinet makers, so you'll always find good buys on portable power tools, fasteners, abrasives and shop supplies. Call to get on the mailing list for promotional catalogs. Big sales in August and March. Return policy varies.

Checks, Credit cards

Your Tool House, Inc.

Renton: 155 Rainier Ave. S. 255-1216
Hours: Mon-Fri 8:30-5:30, Sat 9-5

If you like to repair cars or motors, this wholesale/retail distributor cuts prices on industrial-grade hand tools used by mechanics and machinists. Even tools by leading brand names are discounted. Three day return or exchange policy.

Checks, Credit cards

Floor Coverings

The average consumer buys or replaces carpet in at least one room of their home every seven years. The good news is that the price of carpet has not increased as dramatically as other household commodities and competition is fierce among the many dealers who populate the Puget Sound area. However, comparison shopping is hard when carpet is private labeled, and quotes include the cost of pad and installation. If a retailer advertises free pad and installation, the cost has been added into the price of the carpet. A good pad runs approximately $3/yard and installation about the same, so subtract $6 from the per yard cost to figure out what you're really paying for the carpet.

According to an industry spokesman, $20/sq. yard is the price you should pay to ensure a good quality residential carpet. I think you can get a lot better deal than that by shopping around. Just remember, the best way to judge a carpet is by the feel and the density of the yarn, not by the price alone. The Better Business Bureau puts out a pamphlet, "Tips on Buying Carpets and Rugs." For a copy, send a business size, self-addressed, stamped envelope to the Better Business Bureau, 2200 6th Avenue, Suite 828, Seattle, WA 98121.

Since the last edition of the Greater Seattle Super Shopper, a number of new outlets have sprung up specializing in remnants, seconds, and thirds, which is where the real savings lie. More and more frequently you can find remnants and roll ends big enough to carpet a living room or a whole house. Prices can fall as much as 50% below retail on first quality goods. Some seconds have been rejected by the factory simply because the dye lot didn't match the color sample. Others, called "mill pull-ups," may be carpet that has been installed and then pulled up after a short period of time, either because the color wasn't right or the factory didn't catch a flaw. Sometimes the carpet wasn't even tacked down. "Thirds" is carpet with a serious defect, such as a backing that won't adhere, making it the perfect choice for garages and basements. A few carpet dealers have even started selling used carpeting, which means you can save money and recycle at the same time. It's often possible to find pieces in excellent condition, especially if they come from low traffic areas in offices or hotels where carpets are vacuumed daily.

Consumer Tip

✔ When you visit a remnant store, you'll see lots of carpet samples lying around, some of which are quite large. The small rectangular pieces make great entry way rugs, car mats or carpeting for pet areas. The larger samples and scrap remnants left over from jobs can be used in boats, motor homes, vans, and for area rugs. One dealer even told me people buy his small remnants to make scratching posts for their cats!

4 Day Carpet

NEW LISTING
Seattle: 900 Broad St. 343-7628 *Seattle Center*
Hours: Wed & Thurs 9-8, Fri & Sat 9-6

The owner uses his connections as a former mill rep to get terrific buys on roll ends from local contractors plus seconds and pull-ups from the mill. He's also one of the few dealers around who specializes in "thirds" and used carpet, which can be unrolled if you want to see what kind of condition it's in. The day I visited the warehouse had a lot of used carpet from Boeing and Microsoft, some of it like new, priced at $1 to $3/sq. yd. Used carpet pad was only $1/sq. yd.

Checks, Credit cards

Anita's Interiors

NEW LISTING
Tacoma: 3418 Pacific Ave. 1-800-287-3386, 472-3386
Hours: Mon-Fri 8-5:30, Sat 10-2

There's no one by the name of Anita here but you will find a small, service-oriented company that takes a low mark-up on carpet, vinyl, window coverings and wallpaper. The owner, a very knowledgeable, courteous gentleman, buys direct from leading manufacturers and re-sells at what he considers a fair price, whether it's for commercial accounts or for the general public. The quote he gave me for carpet installation was lower than any one else.

Checks, Credit cards

Bayside Supply Co.

NEW LOCATION
Everett: 2934 Broadway 259-4994, 1-800-554-4410
Hours: Mon-Fri 8-5:30, Sat 8-5

This is the largest mill-direct factory outlet in the Northwest! Builders, contractors, and home owners flock to Bayside's 12,000 sq. ft. warehouse for bargain-priced floor coverings. Carpets by Mohawk, Philadelphia and Salem are stacked floor to ceiling, with discontinued styles, off-colors, remnants, seconds, and special promotions the main focus. Buy a full roll and get a discount. The best buy is commercial grade carpet like you'd find in offices and apartments, which is great for high traffic areas.

Bayside also carries counter top materials, hardwood flooring and window coverings. Installer's tools are available for do-it-yourselfers, along with friendly advise from the staff. If you're interested in higher quality carpet, visit Bayside's upscale retail division, Broadloom Northwest, located at 2601 Colby. Call for a brochure.

Checks, Credit cards

Carpeteria

Tukwila: 17720 Southcenter Pkwy. 575-1687, 1-800-339-9700
Parkway Plaza
Hours: Mon-Fri 9-9, Sat 9-6, Sun 10-6

With 73 stores on the West Coast, Carpeteria has the buying power to purchase directly from the mills. Their low-end carpet starts at $9.99/sq. yd., including pad and installation. They carry most major brands, including commercial-grade carpet for offices. A large selection of area rugs, window coverings, vinyl and wood floor coverings completes the inventory. Discount for seniors.

Checks, Credit cards

Carpet Exchange

Bellevue: 12802 Bel-Red Rd. 455-8332
Federal Way: 30820 Pacific Hwy. S. 839-2142
Lynnwood: 5501 196th S.W. 771-1477
Seattle: 1251 1st Ave. S. 624-7800 *South of Kingdome*
Silverdale: 3200 N.W. Randall Way 692-7732
Tacoma: 6818 Tacoma Mall Blvd. 474-9034
Hours: Generally, Mon-Fri 9-9, Sat 9-6, Sun 11-5

These locally owned stores stock more carpet than any other dealer in the state. You'll find a wide range of first quality name brands for every budget, and management claims they can beat anyone's prices. The Seattle warehouse carries the largest selection of discontinued styles and colors, plus hundreds of roll ends. I saw some exceptional buys on big area rugs. Check out the prices on vinyl, wood and tile floor coverings as well. Senior discount.

Checks, Credit cards

Carpet Remnant Outlet

NEW LOCATION
Issaquah: 1875 N.W. Poplar Way 391-7383
Tukwila: 16600 West Valley Hwy. 251-6860
Hours: Mon-Fri 10:00-6:00, Sat 10:00-5:00

Remnants at this no frills operation, owned by Long's Home Furnishings in Issaquah, average 40 sq. yds, which is large enough to carpet a whole room. Roll ends as big as 130 sq. yds. have been known to show up. Prices run $3 to $4/sq. yd. on carpet that normally retails for $12/sq. yd. The stores stock lots of the large 22" by 54" samples, which make great hallway or entry way runners. Vinyl remnants are also available. Three day return policy.

Checks, Credit cards

Color Tile and Carpet

Bellevue: 121 106th N.E. 455-5135
Bremerton: 3324 Wheaton Way 373-1458
Burien: 105 S. 152nd St. 243-3766
Federal Way: 31007 Pacific Hwy. S. 941-3316
Lynnwood: 4232-A 196th S.W. 775-5477
Renton: 134 Rainier Ave. S. 271-4550
Seattle: 809 N.E. Northgate Way 365-2950 *Northgate*
Tacoma: 2602 S. 38th St. 473-2611
Hours: Mon-Fri 8-8, Sat 9-6, Sun 10-5

As the nation's largest retailer of floor coverings, Color Tile offers not only an extensive selection of tiles made exclusively for them, but carpet, vinyl and wood floor coverings by leading brand names as well. In the last few years they have added wallpaper and blinds. Frequent sales and close-outs yield some terrific buys. You can also purchase the materials necessary to install any of their products. Color Tile even rents a ceramic tile cutter. Liberal return policy. 10% discount to seniors.

Checks, Credit cards

Consolidated Carpet Warehouse

NEW LOCATION
Bellevue: 14150 N.E. 20th 641-4552
Kent: 310 N. Washington 852-7100 *Kmart Plaza*
Lynnwood: 4601 200th S.W. 774-3303
Seattle: 5935 4th Ave. S. 762-6270 *Georgetown*
  200 N. 85th St. 789-7737 *Greenwood*
Hours: Mon-Fri 9-8; Kent Mon-Fri 9-6; All stores Sat 9-6, Sun 11-5

Prices on carpets and vinyl floor coverings are low here because much of their 2,000 roll inventory consists of mill closeouts purchased below wholesale. Remnants are cut from full rolls to ensure a fast turnover. New items arrive regularly. The main warehouse on 4th Ave. S. has the largest selection.

Checks, Credit cards

Direct Carpet Sales

Lynnwood: 18503 Hwy. 99 778-5057
Seattle: 11724 Lake City Way N.E. 364-9061 *Lake City*
Hours: Mon-Fri 9-8, Sat 9-6, Sun 11-5; Seattle, Mon-Fri 9-7

Direct Carpet Sales buys in volume from mills and passes the savings on to its' customers. Prices are in the medium range, and service is first rate. Roll ends sell for up to 40% off regular prices, with the best selection at the warehouse in Lynnwood. Vinyl and window coverings are also discounted. Get on the mailing list to find out about sales. Discounts for seniors.

Checks, Credit cards

Floors To Go

Renton: 336 Burnett Ave. S. 271-7133
Hours: Mon-Fri 10-6, Sat 10-5, Sun 12-5

A low-budget, low-pressure operation that offers some of the best deals around on name-brand carpet and vinyl floor coverings. Hundreds of manufacturers are represented in their warehouse, where you'll also find lots of remnants for bathrooms or small kitchens. No terms are available, and cash will probably get you a better deal.

Checks, Credit cards

M. Rolled Carpet

NEW LISTING
Auburn: 3108 "A" St. S.E. #A 735-4479
Hours: Mon-Fri 9-6, Sat 9-5

This retail store buys discontinued and overstock carpet by the roll and sells it for remnant prices, starting at $4.99/sq. yd. Some rolls measure 150 feet long, making this a favorite stop for builders and contractors. Large vinyl remnants and hardwood flooring can be purchased as well.

Checks, Credit cards

Major Brands

Seattle: 2418 1st Ave. S. 623-3550 *South of Kingdome*
Hours: Mon-Fri 9-6, Sat 10-4

Major Brands is a good place to comparison shop for name brand vinyl, ceramic and hardwood floor coverings. The store does a thriving business in plastic laminate because they stock four major lines at prices that put the competition to shame. The selection of vinyl tile and sheeting is still one of the best around. The back room houses a limited assortment of paints. Landlords qualify for a discount. Reasonable returns.

Checks, Credit cards

Midlake's Floors & Interiors
NEW LOCATION
Bellevue: 345 160th Ave. N.E. 454-3941
Hours: Mon-Fri 9-5:30, Sat 10-4

Midlake showcases more expensive decorator floor coverings. Visit the warehouse located in back of the showroom for a terrific buy on carpet remnants by high-end lines such as Wood Craft and Galaxy. Sizes vary but some rolls are quite large for remnants. Vinyl floor coverings and tile left over from jobs are also discounted.

Checks, Credit cards

Miller's Interiors, Inc.
Bellevue: 1811 130th Ave. N.E. 363-4788
Kent: 18439 E. Valley Hwy. 251-0674
Lynnwood: 15615 Hwy. 99 743-3213
Seattle: 7726 15th Ave. N.W. 783-4888 *Ballard*
Hours: Mon-Fri 8:30-5:30, Sat 11-5 (Bellevue and Kent locations by appointment only)

Millers advises you to "buy where the builders and decorators buy." Their carpet is custom-made at the mill under their own label and purchased in carload lots, which makes their prices competitive with other "discount" outlets in the area. Behind the main store in Lynnwood is a large warehouse where roll ends are sold at 50% off. Miller's also sells ceramic tile, formica, hardwood floors and Corian.

Checks, Credit cards

The Remnant King
Everett: 4117 Rucker Ave. 259-4922
Seattle: 800 N.W. 65th 789-7553 *Ballard*
Hours: Everett: Mon-Thurs 10-6, Seattle: Tues-Thurs 10-7, Both stores: Fri & Sat 10-5; Sun 1-4

Carpet remnants here come larger than at other stores — some measure 60 feet long. Prices range from $4 to $12 on name brand carpet that normally retails for $12 to $35/sq. yd. Look for some especially good deals on wools and pretty florals. Vinyl flooring remnants are also available. A brother/sister team runs this store with friendly, conscientious service. Mom works on Sundays.

Checks

Remnants to Go

NEW LISTING
Burien: 145 S.W. 152nd 433-0550
Lynnwood: 15115 Hwy. 99 743-6930
Seattle: 12505 Lake City Way N.E. 361-6260 *Lake City*
  2420 1st Ave. S. 382-1253 *Sodo*
Hours: Mon-Sat 10-7, Sun 10-5

"Big or small, we have it all," is the motto at this local chain,
which means hundreds of different sizes, some big enough to
carpet a whole house! The huge selection includes Berbers and
plushes, residential or commercial, and indoor/outdoor carpet.
Staff tells me that customers buy their vinyl flooring remnants for shelf liners since it lasts forever.
Checks, Credit cards

Remnant World Carpets

NEW LISTING
Auburn: 4040 Auburn Way N. 850-7979
Hours: Tues-Fri 10-6, Sat 10-5

The husband and wife duo who run this small, low overhead
outlet specialize in carpet for people on a budget, concentrat-
ing more on price than on quality. The largest remnant, a 12'
by 30' roll end, sells for only $199. Even 6-lb. bond padding is
cheap at $1.99/sq. yd. And they quoted me great prices on
designer solarium vinyl floor coverings. Comparison shop at
the two major chains located on either side of Remnant World
and you'll appreciate their low pricing. Installation tools and
videos are available for do-it-yourselfers.
Checks, Credit cards

The Rug Barn

NEW LOCATION
Tacoma: 4326 S. Tacoma Way 475-6402
Hours: Mon-Fri 10-6, Sat 10-5

Although the Rug Barn specializes in discontinued styles,
close-outs and rollends, they also sell seconds, thirds and used
carpet. Brand-new, first-quality styles start at $6/sq. yd. and
the factory seal is still intact on some rolls. Used carpet from
condos, offices, and apartments or private homes sells for
$3/sq. yd. or less, the same price it was 10 years ago when
these guys were the only ones in the Puget Sound area recycling carpet. The really ugly stuff they'll pay you to haul away.
Vinyl flooring by the roll or remnant is also available. Carpet
can be exchanged if you change your mind after unrolling it at
home. Pay cash and get a discount.
Checks

Sea-Tac Distributors/L & W Distribution

NEW LISTING
Tukwila: 1027 Andover Park E. 575-2852
Hours: Mon-Fri 7-4:30, Sat 7-11:30

Sea-Tac Distributors buys used polyurethane carpet padding, ships it out for recycling, and resells it to builders and installers. Remanufactured, prices start at half the cost of new padding. Roll ends are even less. L&W Distribution was born when the owner decided to expand into carpeting. The only line he reps is Philadelphia, the largest carpet manufacturer in the country. Shop here and save 20% to 30% on Monsanto, Stainmaster or Sculpture that normally retails for $8 to $18/sq. yd. Located behind the buildings facing Andover Park East.

Checks

Seattle Carpet Broker

NEW LISTING
Renton: 228-0454
Hours: By appointment only

Avoid high pressure salesmen and go through Gary Jensen, a broker who runs his business out of his home and maintains a warehouse nearby. Totally installed, with a 6-lb. pad, he can deliver a good quality carpet for $11.99/sq. yd. Gary tells me that it's best to know what you want when you come in, and people ordering high-end carpet save the most.

Checks, Credit cards

Seattle Carpet Center

NEW LISTING
Seattle: 416 Elliot Ave. 285-7500 *Lower Queen Anne*
Hours: Tues-Sat 9-6

Buy new or used commercial grade carpet direct from a general contractor. The warehouse contains mill ends, seconds and used carpet, which starts at $2/sq. yd. New carpet can be special ordered from samples.

Checks, Credit cards

Sun West Carpets

Seattle: 501 Dexter Ave. N. 625-1536 *East of Seattle Center*
Hours: Mon-Fri 8:30-4:30

A brokerage business, Sun West sells floor and window coverings to interior decorators, builders and the public at 10% above cost. Choose from hundreds of samples representing top-quality, nationally known manufacturers. Orders come directly from the factory to an adjacent warehouse where carpet and vinyl remnants are sold.

Checks, Credit cards

Tile For Less

NEW LISTING

Kirkland: 12305 120th Ave. N.E. 820-4400 *Totem Hill Plaza*
Silverdale: 9990 Mickelberry Rd. N.W. 698-4052
Tacoma: 1901 S. 72nd 471-0271 *Tacoma Place*
Hours: Mon-Fri 10-6, Sat 9-5, Sun 12-4

Started locally by a group of friends, this mini warehouse serves as an outlet for manufacturer's close-outs, production overruns and special purchases, all priced at $2 or less. Inventory may be basic stock but with over 200 styles to choose from, you're sure to find just what you need to perk up the bathroom, kitchen, or patio. Marble tiles sell for $5 to $6/sq. ft. User-friendly services include free loan of tools and a video on how to install tile.

Checks, Credit cards

Van Dam Floor Covering

NEW LISTING

Marysville: 4229 76th St. N.E. 653-3233, 653-2210
Hours: Mon-Fri 8-5, Sat 10-4

Because Van Dam deals with builders, they sell mainly basic, commercial grade floor coverings, counter tops, and window coverings that end up in rentals and apartment houses. Carpet averages $7.95/sq. yd., $13.95 installed. Visit their remnant warehouse for some terrific buys or order better quality residential goods from their showroom.

Checks, Credit cards

Windsong Industries, Inc.

NEW LISTING

Seattle: 118 N. 36th 545-7302 *Fremont*
Hours: Mon-Fri 8:30-4 or by appointment

This is a small wholesale showroom run by two brothers who deal mainly with commercial and public works clients. Stop by to look through their many floor and window covering samples and they'll give you a competitive bid on any job you want done. One corner is stacked with remnants left over from jobs.

Checks, Credit cards

Paint and Wallpaper

The first place you want to check for bargains on paint is the "boneyard," a special section set aside in retail paint stores, where mismatched colors, overages on special orders, and unclaimed custom tints are sold. If you're painting a large area, you might be able to "batch" mistints, like paint manufactures do, by combining several similar colors. Contractors often use batched exterior paint, which usually comes out a grey color, as a primer.

Consumer Tips

✔ The chemical content determines the price of paint, so be sure to compare prices based on ingredients.

✔ Latex is cheaper than acrylic and works fine for interior paint jobs, but if used in large amounts on exteriors, will eventually cause the paint to fade and chalk.

✔ Exterior paint should have a high acrylic base to do the best job, especially in our area where its water shedding properties are so important.

Farwest Paint

Kirkland: 12545 116th N.E. 821-1334
Tukwila: 4522 S. 133rd 244-8844
Hours: Mon-Fri 7:30-5, Sat 9-1

Buy your paint direct from a local manufacturer who's been around since 1925, and not only will you save money, you'll get a product designed specifically for the Northwest's damp climate. Plus, they give you a 25% discount on the rental of a pressure washer and airless sprayer. The stores stock a complete line of commercial and residential paint as well as stain, brushes, rollers, paint thinner, stripper and spray equipment. Once or twice a year the factory in Tukwila has blow out specials on mis-tints, factory batches and close outs.

Checks, Credit cards

Rodda Decor Center

NEW LOCATION
Bellevue: 1034 116th N.E. 451-1666
Federal Way: 1626 S. 310th St. 941-9717
Issaquah: 635 N.W. Gilman Blvd. 392-7511
Kent: 25615 104th S.E. 859-5115
Lynnwood: 18811 28th Ave. W. 672-0231

Puyallup: 11907 Meridian S.E. 840-2111
Redmond: 16717 Cleveland St. 881-5583
    14850 N.E. 24th St. 861-5449
Seattle: 5055 4th Ave. S. 767-6043 *Sodo*
    3633 Stoneway N. 547-7405 *Wallingford*
Tacoma: 6249 Tacoma Mall Blvd. 472-7286
Hours: Mon-Fri 7:30-9, Sat 8-6, Sun 11-4

This Portland-based paint manufacturer offers one-stop shopping for interior and exterior paint geared to the Northwest climate. Pay $16/gal. for paint that normally retails for $20 or more. Stock interior colors were only $12.19/gal. the day I called. The best value is their "Master Painter" made especially for contractors. All stores carry mis-tints but you have to ask for them. There's also a big selection of wall paper and blinds that go for exceptionally low prices. Classes on decorator wall finishes are offered for a fee. Something different goes on sale every month. 30-day return policy.

Checks, Credit cards

Standard Brands

Lynnwood: 21558 Hwy. 99 774-8861
Tacoma: 4824 S. Tacoma Way 475-8444
Hours: Mon-Fri 9-9, Sat & Sun 9-5:30

Standard Brands manufactures their own paint, which keeps prices lower than national brand names. Mismatched colors and batched paints go for up to 75% off the regular price, with large quantities often available. The company will meet or beat any competitor's price on their big selection of tile and vinyl flooring. Carpets vary in price from high-end to bargain basement remnants. Watch for good deals on specialty items like marble tiles, artificial turf, and indoor/outdoor carpeting. Window or wall coverings can be purchased from stock or special ordered.

Standard Brand stores boast a big art supply department where brushes, paint and canvas sell for less than anywhere else. Budding artists can even sign up for art classes at the Lynnwood store. Sales are promoted via bulk rate mailings. Every three months wall paper gets marked down 50%. Twice a year floor coverings are cleared out at cost. The helpful sales staff caters to do-it-yourselfers. 30-day return policy.

Checks, Credit cards

Wallpaper To Go

NEW LOCATION
Bellevue: 14339 N.E. 20th St. 747-0150
Lynnwood: 19417 36th Ave. W. 774-9646
Tacoma: 2901 S. 38th St. 472-9679
Tukwila: 17540 Southcenter Parkway 575-4035 *Parkway Plaza*
Hours: Mon-Fri 9-7, Sat 10-6, Sun 12-5

Beautiful rooms begin at this national chain, which caters to do-it-yourselfers. You'll find over a thousand patterns in stock, ranging from fun vinyls to sophisticated foils as well as many more that can be special ordered. Instructional videos and books can be "checked out" with a refundable deposit, or you may sign up for free wallpapering clinics. Close-outs and discontinued styles are usually available at 50% to 75% off the original price. Window coverings can also be custom-ordered at reasonable prices. Watch for big sales in March and October.

Checks, Credit cards

Window Coverings

Comparison shopping window coverings is easy because you can get price quotes over the phone — a real time saver for the dedicated bargain hunter. Visit a nearby window covering showroom and decide exactly what you want or call and see if they will send a brochure, price list, or samples. Some companies prefer to send a sales reps with samples who will give an estimate free-of-charge. Remember that price quotes do not include installation. If you are purchasing a lot of window coverings, don't be afraid to ask for a discount.

Comsumer Tips

✔ Because they are both fashionable and inexpensive, aluminum mini-blinds are still the most popular form of window covering today. However, just like everything else, they vary in quality. Levoler, the leading brand name in this market, makes five different grades of mini blinds, with the top of the line style priced at 30% more than the low-end product, which is what some mass merchandisers and warehouse operations stock. Just remember, an eight-gauge metal blind will be a lot stronger than a six-gauge.

✔ Some manufacturers keep prices down by limiting their color selection to basics as opposed to the 100-plus fashion colors offered by major lines.

✔ In the last few years, more people have been buying pleated fabric shades because of their energy efficiency.

Allied Custom Drapery Stores, Inc. & Window Wares

NEW LOCATIONS
Everett: telephone only: 337-0581
Kent: Allied Custom Drapery; 21620 84th Ave. S. 872-5710
Mill Creek: Window Wares; 15712 Mill Creek Blvd. 771-4900
Tacoma: telephone only: 564-0404
Hours: Mon-Fri 9:30-6, Sat 10-5

These jointly owned companies guarantee the lowest prices available on draperies that are custom-made in their workroom located in the back of the Kent store, plus they give big discounts on blinds, duettes, or verticals from all the leading brand name manufacturers. Save even more money and time by calling first to find out if they have any unclaimed stock that will fit your windows.

Checks, Credit cards

American Drapery & Blinds

NEW LOCATIONS
Federal Way: 31248 Pac. Hwy. South 964-0413
Lynnwood: 20101 44th Ave. West 670-1270
Redmond: 7990 Leary Way 861-1804
Renton: 700 S. 3rd St. 226-5920
Seattle: 1555 Northwest Market 781-4993
Hours: Mon-Fri 9-7, Sat 9-5

It pays to window shop at American, a local, family-owned operation since 1972 that custom-makes blinds and draperies for businesses as well as the general public at their big work room in Renton. Turnaround time is usually three days with loaner draperies available for those who need something sooner. Mini-blinds go for half the price of leading brand names, which are also discounted. Bargain hunters check out the hundreds of unclaimed blinds and draperies at the Renton location, plus the big selection of overruns, off-color items, wrong sizes and special purchases.

The Renton store also sells drapery fabric by the yard for below retail prices to do-it-yourselvers, who love the plentiful supply of remnants and close-out fabrics.

Checks, Credit cards

Colorel

NEW LOCATION, NEW NAME
Redmond: 2560 152nd Ave. N.E. 867-5365
Federal Way: 31840 Pacific Hwy. S. 941-9482
Lynnwood: 19725 40th Ave. W. 778-4693
Kent: 7681 S. 180th St. 251-0989
Tacoma: 2913 S. 38th St. 473-5440
Hours: Mon-Fri 10-6, Sat 10-5, Sun 12-5

Need window coverings fast? Order your mini-blinds, pleated shades or verticals by noon on Monday or Thursday and you can pick them up the next day because the factory is located in Kent. Mini-blinds are made from an 8 gauge aluminum, which means quality compares to that of leading brand names. Check the Redmond and Kent stores for a big selection of "Oops" blinds, which is what the company calls mis-measured window coverings.

Checks, Credit cards

Discount Window Coverings/Naber Services

Seattle: P.O. Box 81191 (98108) 762-8206
Hours: Mon-Fri 9-5

Discount Window Coverings does not have a retail showroom because they sell mainly to commercial accounts. Call and they will send samples and a brochure, or set up an appointment with a representative who will consult with you in your home free-of-charge. Choose from leading brand names such as Levolor, Hunter Douglas, Louver Drape, Kirsch, Del Mar and Verosol. Levolor Macho Shade, a new line the company recently acquired, features motorized shades for hard to reach windows and sky lights.

Checks, Credit cards

Factory Direct Draperies

Seattle: 8300 Aurora Ave. N. 525-7932 *Greenlake*
Hours: Mon-Sat 9:30-5:30

Visit this showroom to get decorating ideas and compare prices on their extensive display of window treatments. Be sure to check out the bargains on custom-made draperies that were not picked up or didn't quite meet specifications. Sometimes blinds and shades are available at drastically reduced prices. If you want to try your hand at making draperies, you'll find an excellent selection of fabrics.

Checks, Credit cards

Wessco

Seattle: 3208 15th W. 285-5455, 1-800-878-8787 *West Interbay*
Hours: Mon-Fri 9-6, Sat 9-3

Call Wessco for a low bid on window coverings. They'll mail free samples and worksheets, so you can do your own measuring. Pay in full upon ordering, and the blinds will be sent by UPS from the factory to your home. If you prefer to visit the showroom, helpful staff will show you their outstanding selection, which includes top-of-the-line manufacturers. Satisfaction guaranteed from this service-oriented firm.

Checks, Credit cards

Additional Home Building and Remodeling Outlets

(See Index for page numbers)

Building Materials and Hardware

Hardwick's Swap Shop

Floor Coverings

B&M Liquidators
Design Center Northwest
Eagle Hardware
Home Depot
Home Base
Read Products
Standard Brands

Tools

AAA Liquidators
Boeing Surplus
Eagle Hardware
Greenshield's
Home Base
Home Depot
McLendon Hardware
Pacific Industrial Supply
Pacific Iron
Old Technology Shop
Well-Home Program

Paint and Wallpaper

Anita's Interiors
Chubby & Tubby
Color Tile
Design Center Northwest
Eagle Hardware
Home Base
Home Depot
McLendon's Hardware

Window Coverings

Anita's Interiors
Bayside Supply
Carpeteria
Color Tile
Design Center Northwest
Direct Carpet Sales
Eagle Hardware
Home Base
Home Depot
Read Products
Rodda Decor Center
Sun West Carpet
Wallpaper to Go

Home Furnishings

Furnishing a home is expensive, especially if you're starting from scratch. But, with a little creativity and time, smart shoppers can create rooms straight out of "House Beautiful" without paying full retail price! Visit stores in your area or the many off-price retailers located near Southcenter to familiarize yourself with what's available. Write down the manufacturer's name and style number, if you want to call brokers, discounters, and factory outlets for price quotes. Some retail stores have even started blacking out the style number to prevent people from doing this!

Consumer Tips

✔ When purchasing major appliances or furniture, don't be afraid to negotiate a lower price, especially if you pay in cash.

✔ Shop in January when furniture stores traditionally have their biggest sales; floor samples and discontinued styles are usually the best buys.

✔ Keep your eyes open year-round for great bargains on furniture and appliances that have been scratched or dented during shipping. Major flaws can easily be hidden if you shove them into a corner or against a wall.

Furniture

One of the easiest ways to save money if you're on a limited budget is to buy used furniture. Rental furniture clearance centers offer current styles, and, by law, all rental furniture must be cleaned and sanitized before it can be sold or rented again. National, Cort, Grantree, Continental, and People's all have rental stores scattered around the Puget Sound area that you can visit to check out what kind of furniture will be available at their clearance centers.

Another place to look for better quality used furniture is at office furniture liquidators who sometimes get beautiful custom-made sofas, chairs, tables and decorative items from corporate offices and executive suites that go for a fraction of their original value.

Although there are a lot of second hand stores that sell furniture, the few that have been listed in the Super Shopper carry better quality newer merchandise, as opposed to vintage or antique. That doesn't mean diligent shoppers won't find a super buy at thrift shops in general. The advantage of older furniture, especially wood pieces, is that it's usually better made. The disadvantage, of course, is that price depends on condition and sometimes all it takes is a little sanding or paint to restore something to it's former glory.

Abodio Outlet Store

NEW LOCATION
Tukwila: 790 Andover Park E. 575-2041
Hours: Mon-Sat 10-6, Sun 12-5

If you're a fan of Abodio's distinctive high-tech lifestyle home furnishings, visit the crowded "bargain backroom" at this location, where returns, discontinued, and damaged merchandise sells for 30% to 70% off retail prices. Inventory changes constantly but there's always basic white bookshelves, desks, end tables and dressers in stock. Housewares and decorative items turn over faster. Put your name on the mailing list for advance notice of big sales held in September and March. All sales final.

Checks, Credit cards

All Aboard Second Hand Inc.

NEW LISTING
Seattle: 6500 3rd N.W. 784-8090 *Ballard*
Hours: Tues-Sat 11-6

Crowded into this small corner shop is a lot of wood furniture, mainly book cases, tables, vanities, chests of drawers and chairs ranging from brand new to 50 years old in good to excellent condition. Prices start as low as $25.

Checks, Credit cards

Antique Liquidators

Seattle: 503 Westlake N. 623-2740 *East of Seattle Center*
Hours: Mon-Sat 9:30-5:30

Although antiques have been excluded as a separate category because determining what is a "bargain" is such a subjective task, I couldn't pass up mentioning the favorite haunt of professional dealers, amateur collectors, and yours truly. Browse to your heart's content through three floors of furniture dating from 1890 to 1930. Stately wardrobes, ornate hall trees, Victorian sideboards and country hutches are packed into every nook and cranny of this no-frills warehouse. New shipments arrive continually. The high turnover and owner's willingness to negotiate keep prices low.

Checks, Credit cards

apt. art

NEW LISTING
Seattle: 905 E. Pike 322-8488 *Capitol Hill*
Hours: Mon-Wed 10-5, Thurs-Fri 10-7

Part gallery, part consignment shop showcasing budding artists and a fascinating mix of furniture and decorative accessories from vintage to post modern. The day I dropped in the small, two story shop, contained a classic black leather Charles Eames chair and ottoman, a dining set that came over on the Oregon trail, and a glamorous, super-long sectional sofa from the 1950's that originally belonged to a silent film star. Smaller items, from oriental rugs to lamps, end tables, and collectibles are tastefully displayed throughout the store. The owners only take merchandise that is in good condition and affordable. Consignors get 50% to 60% off the selling price. Call to get on the mailing list for monthly artist's showings. All sales final.

Checks, Credit cards

B & M Liquidators

NEW LISTING
Lynnwood: 13815 Hwy. 99 743-9100
Hours: Mon-Sat 10-5

Liquidation merchandise from hotels, motels, and offices, some of which is in excellent condition, ends up at B&M. Mattresses, mirrors, headboards, and lamps are super cheap. Used carpet costs only $2.99/sq. yd. Office furniture varies from basic chairs for $7.50 to desks, file cabinets, typewriter stands and chalk boards. No returns.

Checks

The Bon Marche Clearance Center

Tukwila: 17000 Southcenter Pkwy. 575-2164
Hours: Mon-Fri 10-9, Sat 10-6, Sun 12-5

Those more comfortable shopping established retailers can stop by the Bon's clearance center for good deals on furniture and electronics, mainly TVs, stereos and VCRs. Merchandise consists of floor models, returns, overstock, discontinued and damaged goods. The big line-up of upholstered furniture often includes some very stylish pieces. Staff says mattresses sell like hotcakes. A variety of smaller items, from area rugs to typewriters, telephones and small household appliances, comes and goes. Full warranties on electronics. 30-day return policy.

Checks, Credit cards

Bushell's Auction House

NEW LISTING
Seattle: 2006 2nd 448-5833 *Downtown*
Hours: Preview Mon 8-7, Fri 12-5, Auction Tues 10-3

A tremendous variety of furniture, appliance and household goods flows through Bushell's doors since they liquidate estates, businesses and personal belongings for banks as well as private individuals. There's no minimum bid, so, depending on how many dealers are in the audience, antiques and good quality second hand furniture often goes for dirt cheap prices. Some items look brand new or have never been used. Decide before hand exactly how much you want to pay and don't get caught up in the excitement of competitive bidding. Everything is sold as is, so check it out carefully before you raise your hand.

Checks

Coho Supply Inc.

NEW LOCATION
Kent: 8504 S. 228th 623-5480
Puyallup: 15011 Meridian E. 848-9359
Hours: Mon-Fri 8-6, Sat 10-5

A big, beautiful showroom filled with better-quality lighting fixtures in every style and price range, including gorgeous chandeliers. Also a good place to buy light bulbs by the case. Anything not in stock can be special ordered from catalogs. Staff will quote prices over the phone on specific model numbers. Coho caters to builders as well as home owners, so they also stock major appliances and locks.

Checks, Credit cards

Continental Furniture Clearance Center

Seattle: 2200 Western Ave. 441-0531 *Downtown*
Hours: Mon-Sat 9-5:30, Sun 12-4:30

Continental Furniture uses this big warehouse to clear out new and used inventory from their retail stores, rental businesses, and model homes. Choose from complete room groupings, individual pieces, accessories and office furniture, all priced according to their condition. You'll always find a big selection of sofas. Anyone over 62 years of age gets a 10% discount and free delivery in Seattle. All sales final.

Checks, Credit cards

Coy's Furniture Sales

NEW LISTING
Tacoma: 9813 Pacific Ave. 537-9234
3921 100th S.W. 588-6850
Hours: Mon-Sat 10-6, Pacific Ave. Sun 12-6

Coy's claims they're one step up from St. Vinney's because so much of what they sell is used and "abused," mainly from army surplus, government auctions and hotels or motels upgrading their decor, which is why they always have so many beds. The day I called the owner was bidding on a lot from the Red Lion Inn. Mattresses are rebuilt and sofas in really bad condition get recovered and priced at one-third of what they would cost new. Some of the inventory is factory liquidations and goods damaged in shipping. Places like this often yield some terrific deals. Three-day exchange on new items, no returns on used.

Checks, Credit cards

Cort Furniture Rentals Clearance Center

Tukwila: 1230 Andover Park East 575-4119
Hours: Mon-Fri 10-5, Sat 10-6, Sun 12-5

Cort's motto is "You save more because we rented it before." Walk to the back of this rental store to peruse three rooms filled with attractive, contemporary style furniture in excellent to not-so-good condition, from model homes, apartments and offices. I saw sofas for under $300, end tables for $50 and kitchen chairs for just $15. During periodic clearance sales prices dip below wholesale. All sales final.

Checks, Credit cards

Decorative Interiors

NEW LISTING
Bellevue: 1919 120th Ave. N.E. 641-1917
Hours: Sat 10-5, Sun 12-4 Call for an appointment during the week or evenings

Visit this storage warehouse and you'll save big time on beautiful, designer-quality solid pine, maple and cherrywood furniture originally displayed in showrooms and model homes. Complete room settings in Queen Anne, traditional and shaker styles include elegant formal dining sets, classic sleigh beds, gorgeous master suites, lighted china cabinets and buffets, plus giant TV armoires worth thousands of dollars. No returns. Located behind West Court Beauty Supply.

Checks, Credit cards

Design Center Northwest

Seattle: 5701 6th Ave. S. 762-1200, 1-800-497-7997 *Georgetown*
Hours: Mon-Fri 1-5

Join the Design Center's exclusive Visions program for access to the Northwest's premier home furnishings showrooms, normally only open to professional decorators. Samples of exquisite objets 'd art, fine furniture, elegant decorative accessories, sumptuous fabrics, and rugs come from manufacturers and designers around the world. Free membership includes an orientation video that familiarizes you with the building and its resources, a guided tour, home design workshops, consultation with a professional decorator at reduced rates and notification of special events, plus the opportunity to purchase direct from the sales representatives. Once a year in February, the Northwest Society of Interior Designers sponsors a fabulous sample sale at the Design Center. Call 763-8799 to get on their mailing list.

Checks, Credit cards

Discount Furniture Outlet

NEW LISTING
Clearview: 18026 Hwy. 9 487-2830
Hours: Mon-Sat 12-7

This is a low overhead operation that may not look like much, but bargain hunters will love the prices. Most of the sofas, chairs, mattresses, beds, and oak furniture come from local manufacturers. Pick out what style you want and the factory makes it up. By the way, Clearview is a little town north of Woodinville.

Checks, Credit cards

Dixon's Nothing New

NEW LISTING
Seattle: 1528 12th Ave. 322-0553 *Capitol Hill*
Hours: Mon-Sat 10-6

Situated on the corner, Dixon's is loaded with current-style, second hand furniture at unbelievably low prices considering that much of it is in excellent condition. The impressive selection includes anything you'd find in a regular furniture store, plus some better quality older stuff. I spotted a Duncan Phyfe mahogany dining table for $165, a Bauhaus sectional in great shape for $395 and a Bentwood rocker for $35. The owner buys whatever he can resell at a good value, stating "Our prices are firm and fair." All sales "as is," no returns.

Checks, Credit cards

For Yu Furnishings

NEW LOCATION
Bellevue: 2299-A 140th Ave. N.E. 865-9886 *Evans Plaza*
Hours: Mon-Sat 10-6

Here's a very exclusive consignment shop that specializes in fine-quality designer furniture and decorative items. On a recent visit I found a classic Ethan Allen dresser with mirror for only $595, an unusual L-shaped sectional by Stearns and Foster priced at one-third of the retail value, and an elegant Dania glass table with eight chairs going for $1,499. The owner only accepts current style name-brands or unique pieces in perfect condition. Prices start at half-off retail but drop even lower after 30 days, which means it pays to visit often. Consignors receive 50% to 60% of the selling price. Get on the mailing list if you don't want to miss seasonal sales, especially their famous White Elephant sale. No returns.

Checks, Credit cards

Grantree Furniture Rental Clearance Center

Tukwila: 13400 Interurban S. 246-6882
Hours: Mon-Fri 10-7, Sat 10-6, Sun 11-6

Good quality home and office furniture from Grantree's four rental stores, including close-outs and discontinued stock, sell for affordable prices here. All used furniture has been cleaned and repaired so much of it is in showroom condition. I found an attractive three-cushion sofa priced at $250, recliners for $170 and coffee tables as low as $40. All sales final.

Checks, Credit cards

Greenbaum's Home Furnishings Clearance Center

NEW LOCATION
Bellevue: 905 Bellevue Way N.E. 455-1707
Woodinville: 18815 139th Ave. N.E. 487-8900, ext. 3960
Hours: Mon-Sat 10-6, Thurs 12-6, Bellevue open Fri 'til 9, Sun 12-5

Save 35% to 70% every day on traditional style furniture by Drexell, Pennsylvania, Heritage, and Thomasville. Inventory, which always includes a lot of sofas and chairs, varies from overstock, closeouts and special orders in perfect condition to floor samples and goods damaged in shipment from Greenbaum's five retail stores. For those having a hard time finding it, the entrance to the Bellevue store is behind Pier I Imports. All items U-haul priced and sold "as is."

Checks, Credit cards

Hunter's Furniture Outlet

Tacoma: 588-8897
By Appointment Only

After owning a furniture store for ten years, Hunter decided to eliminate the high cost of a retail operation by arranging for customers to visit a big wholesale showroom filled with furniture just like you'd see at department stores. As a broker, Hunter only charges 15% above cost, which means you can save 35% on items that may never go on sale. No financing, no returns.

Cash, Credit cards

J.C. Penney's Clearance Furniture Annex

Tukwila: 17200 Southcenter Pkwy. 575-4792
Hours: Mon-Sat 9:30-5:30, Sun 12-5

J.C. Penney's takes deep discounts on overstock, discontinued, damaged, and unclaimed special-orders at their clearance center, where furniture is crammed into a big room. There's always an outstanding assortment of recliners and mattresses. Sometimes, decorative items and unclaimed window coverings turn up. Prices average 50% off but during monthly sales advertised in the newspapers, many items are marked way below cost. New merchandise arrives daily, so there's a fast turnover. All sales final. Located on the north side of Penney's distribution center.

Checks, Credit cards

John's Furniture

Tukwila: 512 Strander Blvd. 241-6263
Hours: Mon-Fri 9-6, Sat 10-6, Sun 11-8

The emphasis at John's is on solid oak furniture (no particle board), most of which comes from a local factory that operates the store. The spacious two story building contains oak bookcases, entertainment centers, roll top desks, dining room and bedroom sets, plus an impressive assortment of bunk beds upstairs. Many items go for 30% or more below suggested retail price. There's also a good selection of attractive sofas and loveseats that complement the oak settings. Three day return policy on oak, all sales final on upholstered pieces.

Checks, Credit cards

King of Oak

NEW LISTING
Lynnwood: 4520 200th St. S.W. 672-3094
Snohomish: 1010 2nd St. 568-1533
Hours: Mon-Fri 10-7 (Lynnwood open until 8), Sat 10-6, Sun 11-6

Oak furniture lovers take note! This low overhead, high volume operation handles the biggest inventory of top quality solid oak furniture in the Northwest. The Snohomish store is the size of a roller skating rink! The huge inventory includes contemporary as well as classic Victorian styles for the whole house, plus kids bedroom sets, all by leading brand names. An arrowback chair that normally retails for $79.99 costs only $48 here. Savings add up even faster on roll top desks, china cabinets, dining room sets and entertainment centers. All sales final unless prior arrangements have been made.

Checks, credit cards

Lamps Plus

NEW LISTING
Lynnwood: 3611 196th S.W. 775-4320
Tukwila: 16839 South Center Parkway 575-9110
Hours: Mon-Fri 10-9, Sat 10-6, Sun 11-6

A lighting superstore with thousands of lamps in hundreds of styles, including spectacular chandeliers. As the largest specialty retail lighting chain in the country, Lamps Plus not only buys factory direct from well-known lines such as Stiffel, but they also manufacture table lamps exclusively for their stores in styles that cost twice as much at other outlets. The classic ginger jar lamp sells for $19.95 every day. Big inventory reductions in January and March. 15-day return policy.

Checks, Credit cards

National Furniture Liquidation

NEW LOCATION
Kent: 24823 Pacific Hwy. S. 839-3640
Hours: Mon-Fri 10-7, Sat & Sun 9-6

Where else could you buy a sectional for only $99? Stock is mainly used furniture from National's many local rental stores plus new furniture for budget-minded customers. Staff takes pains to restore items to like-new condition. Stores in Everett, Tacoma, Seattle and Bremerton always have a small selection of rental furniture for sale. Check the telephone book for exact locations. Everything is sold "as is."

Checks, Credit cards

Oak Barn Furniture

Tukwila: 17600 W. Valley Hwy. 251-9345
Hours: Mon-Fri 10-8, Sat 10-7, Sun 11-6

If you like the furniture you see in the Oak Barn's stores in Tukwila, Lynnwood and Tacoma, then visit their clearance center located in the backroom of their mega-store. Close-outs, returns, overstock and freight-damaged merchandise sells for up to 70% off the retail price. Look for terrific buys on oak dining sets, which are made especially for the stores, as well as sofas, chairs, mattresses, and decorator accessories. Management says "If you don't like our prices, make us an offer." No returns.

Checks, Credit cards

Oak Furniture Outlet

NEW LISTING
Burien: 151st & Ambaum Way 431-0457
Hours: Mon-Fri 10-7, Sat 10-5, Sun 12-5

Visit this big out-of-the-way no-frills location for bargains galore on quality oak furniture. The 10,000 sq. ft. cement block building houses a complete line of classic to contemporary styles, from Amish-made to Twawain imports. Many items sell for the same price they were 10 years ago. Anything not in stock can be special ordered. Check out the clearance corner where factory seconds and consignment pieces from manufacturers end up. Blow-out sale in February, tent sale in June. Exchanges within 7 days.

Checks, Credit cards

Off Center Furniture Warehouse

Tacoma: 2926 S. Steele St. 627-2862
Hours: Mon & Fri 10-8, Tues-Thurs, Sat 10-6, Sun 10-5

A lot of stores advertise discount prices, but few can compete with the quality and prices found here. Furniture and accessories for the whole house, from bunk beds to grandfather clocks, come from well-known manufacturers like Dixie, Stanley and People Loungers. These are current styles, not closeouts or seconds, so you can compare prices elsewhere. A bona fide warehouse setting and word-of-mouth advertising keep the overhead down. The owners guarantee the best deal around on oak furniture. Three day return policy.

Checks, Credit cards

Omnibus Furniture Gallery

NEW LISTING
Seattle: 5605 University Way N.E. 522-1200 *U-District*
Hours: Mon-Sat 9-4:30

A peek through the window reveals an eclectic collection of museum-quality antiques along with unusual modern one-of-a-kind pieces that attracts not only decorators, but the set director of Northern Exposure. However, a trip to the huge storage warehouse in back, where overflow and less expensive items are kept, can yield some fantastic finds for those on a budget. Selection ranges from sofas, leather chairs, and dinette sets, to mattresses, rugs, book cases and complete bedroom sets, all of which come from estate liquidations and private sales. The owner, an estate appraiser who has been at this same location for over 30 years, can tell you a fascinating story about every piece of furniture in the place. All sales final.

Checks, Credit cards

Oriental Furniture Warehouse

Seattle: 1111 Elliott Ave. W. 286-3139 *Northwest of Seattle Center*
Hours: Tues-Sat 10:30-5, Sun 12-4

East meets West. Decorate your home with quality stately furniture and accessories imported from Taiwan, China, Hong Kong and Korea. Beautiful one-of-a-kind pieces in rosewood, teak and black lacquer range from modern to traditional. The selection of parchment and gold-painted panel screens was impressive the day I visited. Decorative items include nesting tables, porcelain vases, lamps, fish bowls and figurines. Get on the mailing list for a sneak preview of new arrivals and sales. Seven-day return policy.

Checks, Credit cards

People's Furniture Rental

Tacoma: 6818 Tacoma Mall Blvd. 474-5501, 800-922-1231
Hours: Mon-Fri 10-7, Sat 10-5

Bargain hunters head for People's back room, where rental furniture is sold. Sofas start as low as $90. Add a matching chair and pay around $150. Dinette sets run around $100 to $150. Look for good buys on coffee tables, lamps and mattresses. The best time to shop is the beginning of the month since that's when most rental furniture comes back. No returns.

Checks, Credit cards

Sansaco

NEW LISTING
Tukwila: 5950 S. 180th 575-0811
Hours: Mon-Fri 10-8, Closed Wed, Sat 10-6, Sun 11-5

A sea of furniture greets you at the door of this huge 30,000 sq. ft. bare-bones warehouse. Prices are moderate to high on top quality traditional styles from over a dozen leading brand names, with an emphasis on Lexington and American Drew. Sofas and chairs dominate in a multitude of attractive but subdued colors and textures, including leather. Oak dining sets, china cabinets and bedroom furniture ring the crowded room. I noticed lots of table lamps the day I visited. No returns.

Checks, Credit cards

Sears Furniture and Appliance Outlet

NEW LISTING
Seattle: 1st S. & Lander 344-4827 *Sodo*
Kent: 26020 104th Ave. S.E. 854-9300 *East Hill Plaza*
Hours: Mon-Fri 9:30-9, Sat 9:30-8, Sun 10-6

Sears liquidates returns, re-conditioned, damaged, and discontinued furniture and major home appliances at the outlet store in Kent and on the third floor of the Sodo store. There's lots to choose from and, depending on condition, discounts vary from 20% to 50%. Appliances carry one year warranties. 10-day return policy.

Checks, Credit cards

United Buy & Sell Furniture

NEW LISTING
Fife: 3605 20th E. 926-1950
Lynnwood: 16929 Hwy. 99 745-2660
Seattle: 3849 1st Ave. S. 624-1292 *Sodo*
Tacoma: 8726 S. Tacoma Way 581-2101
　　5950 N. 9th 565-8188
Hours: Mon-Fri 10-9, Sat 10-6

Just as their TV commercials proclaim, United Buy and Sell is indeed a no-frills, low cost warehouse operation focusing on affordable low-end lines such as Master Craft, Sunline, Klauser and Shaw. Recliners are by Bassett, mattresses by Posture Beauty, Englander and King Koil. The emphasis seems to be on mainstream formal dinette sets, bedroom sets and overstuffed living room furniture. Scattered about are a few surprisingly contemporary-looking pieces. No returns.

Checks, Credit cards

Household Appliances

Consumer Tips

✔ When shopping for appliances, whether it's a refrigerator or a toaster, be sure to use the Consumer Reports magazine and Buying Guide for comparison shopping. Their in-depth research and unbiased analysis will help you get the best value for your money.

✔ Because of space limitations, I have only listed a few of the many places in the Puget Sound area that sell used major appliances, which are a good option for those on a limited budget. Check out the yellow pages for additional listings and when you visit, keep the following tips in mind:

✔ Used appliances aren't necessarily reconditioned or rebuilt. Some came into the store in perfectly good condition simply because the owners remodeled their kitchen or wanted to update their appliances.

✔ Pick a reputable dealer who has been in business for a long time and make sure he has the inventory and parts in stock to make repairs.

✔ Price is based on physical condition, as opposed to age, and a visual inspection should tell you how much the appliance has been used.

✔ Check what kind of warranty comes with the appliance.

✔ Remember: Old refrigerators, freezers, and dishwashers are not as energy-efficient as new ones, so they will be more expensive to operate.

✔ The King County Solid Waste Division puts out a great brochure entitled "Guide to Recycling Major Appliances in King County" that lists over 50 businesses and organizations that buy, sell, and recycle used appliances. Call 296-6540 for a copy.

Action Small Appliance Service

Bellevue: 1500 145th Place S.E. 643-9806
Seattle: 2125 2nd Ave. 448-2020 *Downtown*
Hours: Mon-Fri 8:30-5, Most Sat 9-1

Although Action's main business is repairing small appliances, both stores stock seconds and factory reconditioned appliances by Braun, Sunbeam, Hamilton Beach, Kitchen Aid and Toastmaster. Since my last edition they've added espresso and coffee makers by Krups, small cooking stoves and lanterns by Coleman. Inventory may be limited but everything is marked 20% to 40% below retail with factory warranties still in effect. No returns.

Checks, Credit cards

Albert Lee Appliance

Seattle: 1476 Elliott Ave. W. 282-2110 *Lower Queen Anne*
Hours: Mon-Fri 9-6, Sat 9-4

The Albert Lee family has been in business at this location for three generations so they must be doing something right! The big showroom is filled with an incredible selection of major appliances by over half a dozen leading manufacturers, as well as high-end commercial gas ranges and energy conservation models from Germany. Although everything is purchased by the carload and sold at builder's cost, look for exceptional savings on General Electric.

Checks, Credit cards

American Meter and Appliances

Seattle: 1001 Westlake N. 282-4488 *Northeast of Seattle Center*
Hours: Mon-Fri 9-6, Sat 9-5

To find this store, look for the big blue and yellow building with the cartoon painted on the side of a woman hanging the wash out. Because American sells a lot of appliances to apartments, the best buys are on refrigerators, stoves, and dishwashers in the low to medium price range. Or maybe you'd like to invest in a coin-operated washer or dryer built for heavy duty use? Check out the separate area set aside for used appliances from apartment buildings, all of which have been reconditioned and come with 90-day warranty.

Checks, Credit cards

Appliance Distributors

NEW LISTING
Tukwila: 14639 Pacific Hwy. S. *244-6955*
Hours: Mon-Fri 10-8, Sat 10-6, Sun 11-5

Shop here for a terrific deal on repossessed appliances that are two months to two years old, including top-of-the-line commercial models. Some sell for less than cost even though they're in like-new condition. The store also carries a lot of freight-damaged and showroom samples plus a few reconditioned appliances.

Checks, Credit cards

Dave's Appliance Rebuild

Seattle: 1601 15th Ave. 324-3270 *Capitol Hill*
Hours: Mon-Fri 9-5:30, Sat 10-2

For almost 20 years Dave has been buying, selling and trading used appliances. There's a constant turnover since landlords and property managers are his best customers and suppliers. Refrigerators average $129 to $299, and stoves about $150, but prices are always negotiable. New and used parts available.

Checks, Credit cards

J & S Sewing and Housewares

Renton: 2836 N.E. Sunset Blvd. 255-8900, 1-800-634-0300
Hours: Mon-Fri 9-6, Sat 10-5

Home sewers alert: Because J&S sells sewing machines to Home Economic departments in over 60 schools, used sewing machines from school trade-ins make up a big part of their inventory. Some machines are only two years old, and have hardly been used. Shop the beginning or end of the school year for the best selection. You can also mail order sewing supplies, small appliances, dishes, and pots and pans like those used in Home-Ec departments. 30-day return policy.

Checks, Credit cards

Judd & Black Clearance Store

NEW LISTING

Kenmore: 7016 N.E. Bothell Way 485-9755
Hours: Mon-Thurs 9-6, Fri 9-7, Sat 9-5

Judd & Black serve as a clearance center for four major appliance stores. Close-outs, overstock and damaged goods sell for 30% to 70% below retail. There is something in every price range with over a dozen brand names to choose from, including top of the line commercial appliances by Thermador, Sub Zero and Viking. Merchandise is one-of-a-kind. No returns.

Checks, Credi cards

King & Bunny's Discount Appliance and TV

Renton: 4608 N.E. Sunset Blvd. 277-0600
Hours: Mon-Fri 9-7, Sat 9-6, Sun 12-5

This dinky little red store may not look like much, but King and Bunny, the husband and wife team who run it, sell more Whirlpool appliances per square foot than any other dealer in the country at prices that put the competition to shame. Scratch and dents are cleared out in July during the annual sidewalk sale. King, a man who believes in taking care of customers, says, "If you don't like it, bring it back."

Checks, Credit cards

Major Brand Appliances

Federal Way: 34419 Pacific Hwy. S. 838-7056
Hours: Mon-Fri 9-6, Sat 9-5

A rental and sales operation with one of the largest inventories of used appliances and parts that you'll ever see, including reconditioned ranges, refrigerators, washers, dryers, freezers and disposals from two to ten years old. I counted 80 refrigerators alone! Ninety day warranty on parts and labor. Senior citizens and property managers get a discount. Exchanges only.

Checks, Credit cards

Pickering Appliance & TV

Renton: 909 S. 3rd 226-3232
Hours: Mon-Thurs 8:30-6, Friday 8:30-8 Sat 8:30-5

If you want to save money on brand new appliances, try Pickering. They have a separate room jam packed with freight-damaged or scratch 'n' dent ranges, refrigerators, washers and dryers, as well as some in perfect condition from model homes and incorrect orders. Satisfaction guaranteed from this small, down-home retailer.

Checks, Credit cards

Remington Shaver Factory Service

Seattle: 1909 4th Ave. 682-1522 *Downtown*
Hours: Mon-Fri 9-4

Prices on new electric shavers are competitive with most discount stores. Save even more by purchasing a factory return that was simply taken out of the box for display. If your old shaver is in good condition, bring it in for $10 off on a trade-in. The store also sells name-brand cutlery, sporting goods, knives and sewing scissors. Chefs and cooking school students get a discount if they purchase three or more knives.

Checks, Credit cards

Sarco (Seattle Appliance Repair Company)

Kirkland: 220 Kirkland Ave. 827-5739
Seattle: 2416 2nd Ave. 441-5977 *Downtown*
Hours: Seattle, Mon-Fri 8-5, Sat 9-1; Kirkland, Mon-Fri 10-6, Sat 9-2

When your iron, toaster, vacuum cleaner or coffee maker breaks down, bring it in to be fixed or buy the parts here and do it yourself. The limited but wide-ranging selection of blemished and factory rebuilt small appliances changes constantly, but you can always find a good buy on name-brand electric shavers, and used rebuilt Hoover vacuum cleaners, which sell for $49.99.

Checks, Credit cards

Seattle Home Appliance Center

Bothell: 10042 Main St. 485-0551
Hours: Mon-Fri 10-6, Sat 10-5

Not only does this store regularly liquidate demos and scratch 'n' dent models for major suppliers, but every year, a few weeks after school is out, they have a fantastic sale on General Electric washers, dryers, ranges and refrigerators that have been used for instructional purposes in local public schools. Appliances are only a year old, in like-new condition, with warranties still intact. Seattle Home Appliances also sells rebuilt appliances, employing two full-time technicians who put units in perfect working order. Warranties vary depending on the brand. 10% discount on parts to senior citizens. 30-day return policy.

Checks, Credit cards

Sewing Machine Service Co. Inc.

Renton: 315 Main Ave. S. 255-8673
Hours: Mon-Fri 8:30-5:30, Sat 8:30-4:30

SMS carries one of the largest inventories of used industrial and household sewing machines in the Northwest. Amongst the 100 plus models, serious seamstresses will find everything from specialized equipment for tailors and garment manufacturers to heavy duty machines that will sew sail cloth and upholstery fabric. Customers are welcome to bring sample fabric in and try out any machine. Rentals available as well.

Checks, Credit cards

Silo

Bellevue: 14315 N.E. 20th St. 746-6080 *Ross Plaza*
Everett: 811 S.E. Everett Mall Way 355-7390
Federal Way: 31621 23rd Ave. S. 941-6810
Lynnwood: 18833 28th Ave. W. 771-2282
Seattle: 10409 Aurora Ave. N. 527-5000 *Greenwood*
  809 N.E. 45th St. 545-3506 *U-District*
Silverdale: 10796 Myhre Place N.W. 692-0775
Tacoma: 2951 S. 38th St. 475-7001
Tukwila: 17550 Southcenter Pkwy. 575-1012 *Parkway Plaza*
Woodinville: 17638 140th Ave. N.E. 481-5885
Hours: Mon-Fri 9-9, Sat 10-9, Sun 12-6

The most visible and aggressive off-price retailer on the West Coast selling name-brand appliances, electronic and audio/video equipment, Silo buys in huge quantities and sells at incredibly low markups. Prices tend to fluctuate since they're constantly having sales, so I recommend you use the frequent advertisements for comparison shopping or call for price quotes. If you find somebody selling the same item for less (floor models don't count), Silo will reimburse the difference plus 10%. Every once in a while a discount chain will have a special promotion that beats Silo's prices. Refund in 7 days, exchanges within 30 days.

Checks, Credit cards

Kitchen and Restaurant Equipment

Most of the listings in this category refer to businesses that sell equipment and supplies to the food service industry, which means you'll be rubbing shoulders with people who own restaurants, taverns, bakeries, delis, convenience stores, and catering services. Restaurant-supply emporiums sell everything from fixtures, appliances, cookware and dishes to paper products, bar mixes and cleaning supplies, plus a lot of items not available on the retail market.

Prices will not necessarily be lower than those at a department store or kitchen shop, but it stands to reason that toasters, mixers and coffee makers built to withstand heavy daily use will be a better long-term investment than those designed for the consumer market. A brand-new commercial-grade gas range will last a life time. And, you can keep costs down by purchasing these appliances used.

Serious chefs will love the quality of professional-grade stainless steel cookware as well as the selection of gadgets. Oversize utensils, glassware, pots and pans are both decorative and practical. Restaurant china and flatware can be surprisingly handsome as well as durable.

It would be impossible to include all the restaurant supply houses listed in the phone book so I suggest you check in the yellow pages under "Restaurant Supplies" for other locations.

AAA New & Used Restaurant Equipment

Kent: 7835 S. 212th 872-7474, 622-2525
Hours: Mon-Fri 9-5:30

Whether you want to open a full scale restaurant or simply outfit your kitchen with commercial-grade cookware, this is a good place to start. The huge, no-frills showroom houses everything you'd ever need, including aprons. Shop the used department and save 25% to 85%. The friendly staff probably won't let you leave without purchasing one of their best selling items — a $2.00 rubber scraper that lasts forever. Exchanges only.

Checks

Bargreen-Ellingson, Inc.

Seattle: 1275 Mercer St. 682-1472 *East of Seattle Center*
Tacoma: 6626 Tacoma Mall Blvd. 475-9201, 838-3515
Hours: Mon-Fri 8-5, Sat 9-1

Window shop at Bargreen-Ellingson, one of Seattle's premier restaurant supply houses, then go downstairs to check out their clearance center, where everything from major appliances to china sells for much less. Although some of the merchandise is used or damaged, the majority is close-outs and discontinued styles in perfect condition. The basement store is called ABC Used Restaurant Equipment. Enter outside from the parking lot. Returns accepted.

Checks, Credit cards

Best Equipment Sales

NEW LISTING
Kirkland: 13723 100th Ave. 624-4242
Hours: Mon-Fri 8-5

Best has any and everything you'd need to set up a restaurant, bakery or deli on a shoestring budget because much of what they sell is used. There's always a good selection of smaller housewares, utensils, cookware, and china. Appliances come with a 60 to 90 day warranty. Two-week return policy.

Checks

Budget Sales

NEW LISTING
Seattle: 1534 1st S. 621-9500 *Sodo*
Hours: Mon-Fri 8-5

Budget Sales specializes in used and reconditioned appliances from restaurants, bakeries, caterers, and convenience stores, much of which is in excellent condition. Guarantees vary depending on the item.

Checks

Dick's Restaurant Supply

Seattle: 2963 1st Ave. S. 382-0160 *Sodo*
Hours: Mon-Fri 8:30-5

Much of the inventory in this gigantic 20,000 sq. ft. warehouse is used, with gas ranges and commercial appliances the best selling item. Although cutlery, utensils, pots and pans may be new, customers still tell Dick his prices are cheaper than the competition. Look for big savings on slightly flawed china. Used equipment is guaranteed but sold as is. Returns accepted on new items.

Checks, Credit cards

Checks, Credit cards

Kitchen 'n' Things

NEW LISTING

Seattle: 2322 N.W. Market St. 784-8717 *Ballard*
Hours: Mon-Sat 10-6, Sun 12-5

> Why wait for a sale when this specialty store offers a 20% discount every day on stainless steel knives and kitchen gadgets by J.A. Henckels and Chicago Cutlery.

Checks, Credit cards

Medalia's Restaurant Equipment

NEW LISTING

Seattle: 1112 N. 98th 523-8835 *Greenwood*
Hours: Mon-Fri 9-5:30, Sat 9-1; Weekend hours extended May through September to include Sundays

> Ever notice that store on Greenwood with all the school desks sitting out front? The main focus at Medalia's is on used restaurant equipment, mainly appliances, although some of the china, cookware, and glassware may be new. During the summer months the owner, a congenial fellow who has been at the same location for 25 years, sells furniture purchased by the truck load from school auctions. For $7.50 parents can even buy old-fashioned flip-top desks for the kids. All sales "as is."

Checks

Restaurant Mart

Seattle: 2851 Eastlake E. 322-4900 *East Lake Union*
Hours: Mon-Fri 8:30-5, Sat 9:30-4

> Maybe you've seen their commercials on late night television! Restaurant Mart, which has been in the same location for 66 years, sells as much to the general public as they do to the food and beverage industry. New appliances and kitchen ware are always 20% below list price. Glassware and china can be purchased by the dozen, but you'll save 25% more if you buy by the case. Bar mixers, under the Restaurant Mart label, cost a lot less here than at the grocery store. Exchanges only.

Checks, Credit cards

Beds and Linens

Alternative Futon Co.
NEW LISTING
Seattle: 715 Dexter Ave. 286-1760 *East of Seattle Center*
Hours: Mon-Thurs 11-8, Fri 11-6, Sat 11-5

The owner delivers a top quality product at wholesale prices because he makes it himself and zeros in on the two most popular styles: a basic tri-fold for $134 and a sofa bed for $324, which normally sells for $500. Frames are built from solid oak or mahogany, instead of pine, and futons measure 8" thick to ensure comfort. Covers come in 15 different colors but you can bring your own fabric in and the workroom will stitch it up for you. Returns accepted.

Checks

Bald Bob's Mattress Outlet and Futon Warehouse
NEW LISTING
Bellevue: 13310 Bel-Red Rd. 643-7378
Monroe: 17150 162nd St. S.E. 794-1137, 1-800-982-5250
Hours: Mon-Fri 10-7, Sat 10-6, Sun 12-5

Talk about low overhead! The Bellevue store, located in the same building as JB Factory Carpets, was once an underground parking lot while the huge 20,000 sq. ft. metal building in Monroe sits in front of the state prison! Bald Bob has, without a doubt, the lowest prices in the Northwest on premium quality mattresses by famous brand names, because he buys overstock, floor samples, factory mistakes and store cancellations for 50¢ on the dollar. Mattresses range from exclusive pillow tops to extra-plush styles by leading manufacturers such as Restonic, Ther-a-pedic, and Spring Air. Bob also stocks the largest selection of futons, frames and covers in the state since he buys from five different manufacturers, including top names like Shamiana. Variable return policy.

Checks, Credit cards

Beds, Bunks & Mattresses
NEW LOCATION
Tacoma: 4004 100th St. S.W. 582-3483 *Lakewood*
Hours: Mon-Sat 10-5:30, Sun 11-4

Bring the kids when you shop this off-price outlet, where you'll find the largest selection of bunk beds in the state. Ther-a-pedic mattresses, which the owner purchases in volume because he thinks they're the best buy for the money, come in any size or style, with lots of different frames and headboards to choose from. Although the store stocks some bedroom furniture, anything can be ordered from the many catalogs on hand. Super low prices have kept the doors open since 1917. All sales final.

Checks, Credit cards

Bedzz Mattress Outlet

NEW LOCATION
Silverdale: 3276 N.W. Plaza Rd. 698-8900
Tacoma: 2602 Bridgeport Way 565-1565 *University Plaza*
2520 E. 38th St. 475-7500
Hours: Mon-Sat 10-5, Sun 12-5

Folks in Tacoma will find over 50 models on display, one of the biggest selections in Western Washington. With the focus on better quality lines, this is the only dealer I know of in the Northwest that discounts Stearns and Foster, the premier mattress manufacturer in the country. Low overhead keeps prices lower than department stores and factory close-outs show up frequently. Frames and some headboards available.

Checks, Credit cards

Bedspread & Linen Warehouse

NEW LOCATION
Factoria: I-90 & I-405 747-1115 *Loehmann's Plaza*
Woodinville: 17311 135th Ave. N.E. 481-7676
Hours: Mon-Sat 10-6, Sun 12-6, open Wed & Fri nights until 8, Woodinville, Mon-Sat 10-5

Everything is first-quality, current-style merchandise by well-known manufacturers, as well as designer lines by Laura Ashley and Eileen West. Anything not in stock can be special-ordered. The stores also carry bathroom accessories and gift items. Discount coupons are sometimes given out with purchases or included in Value Pack mailers. Call to get on the mailing list. Seven-day return policy.

Checks, Credit cards

Bur-Bank Domestics, Inc.

Seattle: 2213 15th Ave. W. 282-1551 *Ballard*
Hours: Mon-Fri 8:30-5

If you need a large supply of linen, visit this wholesale distributor. They sell basic stock from JP Stevens, Cannon and Fieldcrest to institutions, mass merchandisers and drugstores, along with baby lines by Regal, Campbells, and Carters, mainly JamaKins, T-shirts and bedding. The showroom also dis-

cases come packaged by the dozen. Other items can be purchased individually. Orders that amount to less than $100 are subject to a 10% service charge. Returns accepted.

Checks

Discount Waterbeds

Bellevue: 11010 N.E. 3rd Place   455-4314
Hours: Mon-Fri 11-8, Sat 11-6, Sun 12-5

This is the only waterbed store listed in the Super Shopper because they offer the best prices and friendliest service in town, which is probably why they've been in business for 17 years. Although the store appears to be a small house, you'll be impressed when you see the large inventory of conventional and flotation beds inside. Quality oak furniture is made especially for the company, as well as waterbed sheets that really fit and stay put. Discount Waterbeds is the only place that offers a 30-day in-home trial for a nominal fee, gives credit on account for customers you refer to them, and encourages visitors to scribble messages on the walls. Mailing list for sales and catalogs.

Checks, Credit cards

The Foam Shop

NEW LOCATION
Bellevue: 12121 Northup Way 861-1827
Seattle: 5315 Roosevelt Way N.E.   525-2301 *U-District*
Hours: Seattle Mon-Fri 10-6, Sat 10-5; Bellevue Mon-Thurs 11-8, Fri 11-6, Sat 11-5

The friendly staff will cut foam in any shape or size, with 12 densities and 18 levels of firmness to choose from. Bring in your cushion or pillow covers and they'll stuff the new foam snugly in place, free-of-charge. The stores also custom-sew covers from your fabric or theirs and custom-build wood bed frames. Shredded foam costs only $2.25 a pound, the cheapest price of all the foam shops I called.

Checks, Credit cards

Frame Works Wholesale

NEW LISTING
Redmond: 15015 N.E. 90th, Bldg. #3 883-7440
Hours: Sat 10-4

Every Saturday seconds and overstock from this pine futon frame manufacturer go on sale along with futons. Although some frames are returns that have been repaired, they all come with a one year warranty. No returns.

Checks, Credit cards

Futon Factory Outlet

Seattle: 13555 Aurora Ave. N. 367-5575 *Haller Lake*
Hours: Generally, Mon-Fri 11-7, Sat 10-6, Sun 11-5

Inventory changes constantly, but you can count on big discounts because they sell overstock, damaged and liquidation goods from their own and other local factories. Stock varies form basic styles for $189 to the most expensive item in the store, a deluxe double-size futon and solid oak frame for $389. All covers sells for $49.95, half the normal retail price, and they reverse from a print to a solid. Original hand-painted designs by a local artist can be purchased for $79.95. Exchanges only.

Checks, Credit cards

Futon of North America Warehouse

Seattle: 810 Dexter 286-8559 *Northeast of Seattle Center*
Hours: Daily 10-5:30

This futon manufacturer is the oldest and largest in the Puget Sound area. Visit the small area that has been set aside in their warehouse to pick up a good deal on discontinued and irregular futons, frames, covers and pillows from their 10 retail stores. Enter in back of the warehouse on 8th Street. No returns on as is merchandise.

Checks, Credit cards

Jen-Cel-Lite Corp.

Seattle: 953 E. Union 322-3030 *Capitol Hill*
Hours: Mon-Sat 9-4

The factory across the street makes insulation, bedding and sleeping bags for local nationally-known retailers Roffe, REI and L.L. Bean. Overstock, seconds, discontinued merchandise and anything left over from the manufacturing process ends up in this little outlet store. Comforters and sleeping bags average $25. Kids sleeping bags go for $12. Other finished products include baby bags, pillows (down, cotton or polyester filled) and pet beds left over from catalog sales. Home sewers will flip when they see the prices on material and notions. Quilted fabric sells for $2/yd, batting 50¢ a yard and stuffing 25¢/lb. For $2 you can fill a big plastic bag with fabric scraps out of the bargain bin. All sales final.

Checks

Luxury Linens/Burlington Coat Factory

NEW LOCATION
Edmonds: 2411 Aurora Ave. 776-2221
Tacoma: 10405 Gravely Lake Dr. 588-3595 *Lakewood Mall*
Tukwila: 17900 Southcenter Pkwy. 575-3995 *Pavilion Mall*
Hours: Mon-Sat 10-9:30, Sun 11-6

A wonderful resource for famous-name linens and accessories for the bathroom, bedroom and kitchen. The impressive selection includes best selling basics by Cannon, Springmaid and Fieldcrest as well as the latest styles from designer lines by Laura Ashley, Bill Blass and Battenburg, all priced at 20% to 50% below retail. Although all the major off-price chains contain a linen department, Burlington stocks the most extensive inventory of them all. Returns within seven days for credit or exchange.

Checks, Credit cards

Mattress Plus

NEW LOCATIONS
Lynnwood: 3614 196th S.W. 776-0999
Redmond: 15230 N.E. 24th 641-3230
Tacoma: 5100 S. Tacoma Mall Blvd. 472-9389
Tukwila: 17310 Southcenter Pkwy. 575-8560 *Parkway Plaza*
Hours: Mon-Fri 10-8, Sat 10-6, Sun 12-5

Top quality mattresses by Restonic, Ther-a-pedic and King Koil, which is endorsed by the International Chiropractic Association, sell for discount prices every day because the owner buys by the truckload and passes the savings on. Anything not in stock can be special ordered. Free frame and free delivery with all purchases. 10% discount to seniors. Mailing list for special sales. Returns accepted.

Checks, Credit cards

Mattress Warehouse

NEW LISTING
Tukwila: 223 Andover Park E. 243-1616
Hours: Thurs-Mon 11-6

Mattress Warehouse can sell top quality brand name mattresses by Sealy, Simmons, Serta and Spring Aire at 50% off department store prices because most of their inventory is factory seconds, which means the fabric or color has a slight imperfection that will never be seen once the bed is made-up. Mattresses come in all sizes and price ranges, from a queen-size set for $150 to a deluxe king-size wool pillowtop for $749 that normally retails for around $2,000. The 13,000 sq. ft. no-frills showroom also holds bedroom furniture, leather or upholstered sofas and chairs. No returns.

Checks, Credit cards

Pacific Coast Feather Company

NEW LISTING
Seattle: 1964 4th Ave. S. 624-1057 *Sodo*
Hours: Sept. through March only: Sat 10-3

Pacific Coast makes pillows, comforters, feather beds, slumber sacks and body pillows with natural and synthetic fillings for Eddie Bauer, Lands End and department stores. Closeouts, seconds, and discontinued styles are sold through the warehouse outlet every Saturday when the factory is in production. Call to get on the mailing list for fantastic monthly sales in the fall when specific items get marked down even more. All sales final.

Checks

Pacific Linen

NEW LOCATION
Bellevue: N.E. 8th & 156th 562-9801 *Crossroads*
Bothell: 17130 Bothell Way N.E. 365-1413 *Lake Forest Park*
Federal Way: 2130 S. 314th Street 941-8085
Lynnwood: 2701 184th St. S.W. 774-7700 *Pacific Linen Plaza*
Puyallup: 3500 S. Meridian 841-4220 *South Hill Mall*
Seattle: 13510 Aurora Ave. N. 364-5350 *Haller Lake*
Silverdale: 10876 Myhr Place N.W. 692-7007
Tacoma: 5401 6th Ave. 756-2141
Hwy. 16 & Union Ave. 572-4445
10401 Gravelly Lake Dr. S.W. 584-1122 *Lakewood Mall*
Tukwila: 17855 Southcenter Parkway 575-0576
Hours: Generally, Mon-Sat 10-9, Sun 11-6

Everything you need from basic necessities to fashionable decorator items for the bed, bath, or kitchen can be found on the shelves of this very successful local chain, which now operates 49 stores in eight states. Prices average 30% less than what you would pay for the same item in department stores because Pacific Linen buys nationally-known brand names direct from the mill in huge quantities. Inventory includes a big selection of beds, including futons. I counted 39 in Bellevue, the largest store at 20,000 sq. ft. Assorted housewares and gift items are available at all the stores. Watch the newspaper for monthly promotions and shop the

housewares and gift items are available at all the stores. Watch the newspaper for monthly promotions and shop the clearance store in Lynnwood on Highway 99. Very generous return policy, 60-day price protection.

Checks, Credit cards

The Well-Made Bed

Bellevue: 990 102nd Ave. N.E. 455-3508 *University Bookstore Complex*
Seattle: 1427 Western Ave. 343-5066 *Downtown*
Hours: Mon-Fri 10-6, Sat 10-5, Sun 12-5

White sale prices are in effect year round at these small shops, but don't be fooled by their size. Even though they only stock king and queen-size sheets in dozens of different styles, any size or pattern put out by a leading manufacturer can be special ordered. As a matter of fact, the store has access to over 400 patterns, which can be viewed via pillowcases and pictures. Matching comforters, dust ruffles and shams are also available, as well as custom-made comforter covers. During "Change Your Bed" sales in January and July everything in the store is marked down 20%. Mailing list for new arrivals. Seven-day return except on special orders.

Checks, Credit cards

Here's a list of mattress manufacturers in the area that sell directly to the public: Many of these companies will renovate or rebuild mattresses, and some specialize in odd-size bedding for boats, RV's and trucks.

Arty's Custom-Bilt Mattress & Upholstery

Tacoma: 5415 S. Puget Sound 474-4800
Hours: Mon-Fri 8-5, Sat by appointment

Case Littell

Seattle: 8214 Greenwood Ave. N. 782-3131 *Greenwood*
Hours: Mon-Sat 9-5, Mon & Wed open until 8

Eastside Mattress Co.

Redmond: 7858 Leary Way 885-2156
Hours: Mon-Fri 10-6, Sat 10-4

Everrest Mattress

NEW LOCATION
  Lynnwood: 21101 Hwy. 99 776-8180
  Seattle: 1907 15th Ave. W. 284-9531 *Ballard*
  Hours: Seattle Mon-Fri 8-5, Sat 9-4; Lynnwood Mon-Fri 10-6,
  Sat 10-5, both stores Sun 12-4

Imperial Mattress Co.

  Seattle: 462 N. 34th St. 632-2240 *Fremont*
  Hours: Mon-Fri 8:30-5, Sat 10-1

Restmore Mattress & Furniture Factory

  Tacoma: 1541 Market 272-2429
  Hours: Mon-Fri 8-6, Sat 9-1

Sleep-Aire Mattress Co.

  Bellevue: 13120 Bel-Red Road 454-0310
  Kent: 25447 Pacific Hwy. S. 839-6003 *Midway*
  Silverdale: 9800 Silverdale Way N.W. 692-6207
  Seattle: 19022 Aurora Ave. Ave. N. 546-4195 *Richmond
  Highlands*
    6110 Roosevelt Way N.E. 523-3702 *Roosevelt*
    2444 1st Ave. S. 682-4063 *Sodo*
  Hours: Mon-Fri 9:30-6, Bellevue Mon-Fri 9:30-9, Silverdale
  and Sodo open Mon & Fri til 8, 1st & Roosevelt open Mon &
  Fri until 9, All stores Sat 9:30-6, Sun 12-5

China, Crystal and Silver

Anderson's China, Crystal & Silver
NEW LISTING
Issaquah: 1480 N.W. Gilman Blvd. 1-800-541-1241, 392-4462
Issaquah Meadows Shopping Center
Hours: Mon-Sat 10-6

Anderson's can save you 20% to 40% on world-famous table settings and decorative items, from popular well-known names like Mikasa, Lenox, Royal Doulton, Wedgewood, Gien, Haviland, and Pickard. The store is 4,200 sq. ft., so there are lots of patterns to choose from. The "no-fault-breakage guarantee" ensures that if you break something, you can replace it for 50% off the retail price. Be sure to get on the mailing list. Complimentaray gift wrapping. Mailing for a fee. Exchanges only.

Checks, Credit cards

China, Silver & Crystal Shop
Seattle: 2809 2nd Ave. 441-8906, 1-800-759-5817 *South of Seattle Center*
Hours: Mon-Fri 9-5:30, Sat 10-5

What a find for wedding and anniversary gifts! The dazzling array includes over 700 china patterns from classic dinnerware to elegant designer sterling and stainless flatware by Reed and Barton, Oneida, Lunt and Buccellati and many more. Even storage cases and cleaning products are discounted. Get on the mailing list for bi-monthly newsletters announcing special events and money-saving coupons or hold out for big sales in January and July when prices plummet to cost on some items. The helpful staff will quote prices, take phone orders, and arrange shipping anywhere in the U.S. 30-day return policy except on special orders and clearance items. Exchanges only on bridal gifts.

Checks, Credit cards

Kokesh Cut Glass Co.
Seattle: 301 N.E. 65th 527-4848 *Latona*
Hours: Tues-Fri 11-5, Sat 10-1

This is a great place to purchase custom-engraved crystal in the $15 to $35 price range for wedding or anniversary gifts. Choose from a big selection of beautiful stemware, bowls, pitchers, vases, salt and pepper shakers or sugar and creamers, all priced below retail. The owner says people even purchase engraved crystal for trophies and corporate gifts. Monogrammed tumblers and champagne glasses are the most popular items. Discounts for organizations who buy in quantity. Exchanges.

Checks, Credit cards

Kusak Cut Glass Works

Seattle: 1911 22nd Ave. S. 324-2931 *Mt. Baker*
Spring sale: starts third week in March, lasts 9 days
Fall sale: starts third Thursday in October, lasts 11 days

Visit Kusak's magnificent showroom during their famous semi-annual sales when overstock and irregulars priced from $5 to $500 sell for 20% to 50% below retail. The exquisite handblown, handcut crystal-ware is made on the premises in a European tradition established 75 years ago by the founder of this family-owned business. The spring event features stemware and vases. In the fall everything goes on sale, making this the perfect time to shop for Christmas gifts. First quality chandeliers dripping faceted Austrian crystals sell for 30% less at both sales. Call to get on the mailing list.

It is only during these sales that, for a nominal fee, Kusak will repair chipped and broken crystal by other manufacturers. Repairs on Kusaks glassware can be done anytime of the year. The showroom is open year round but customers pay retail prices. Custom engraving and guided tours are also available. Exchanges only.

Checks, Credit cards

Pictures and Frames

Bargain Picture Framing
NEW LISTING
Lynnwood: 2827 196th S.W. 774-5577
Hours: Mon-Fri 10-5:30, Thurs until 7

All custom framing is discounted 35% except a loss leader package that offers customers rock bottom prices on a basic metal frame (black or gold), glass, matting and labor. Watch for 50% off coupons in Val-Pak, a bulk mailing packet of discount coupons from local businesses.

Checks, Credit cards

The Beard Outlet
NEW LISTING
Bellevue: 12005 N.E. 12th 451-9844
Hours: Mon-Fri 9-7, Sat 9-6, Sun 10-5

Overstock, damaged and discontinued frames as well as molding from Beard's Frame Shops end up here at half off retail. "Fall off frames" have been made from molding left over from custom orders and do-it-yourself jobs. Save 50% to 70% on posters, art books and framed art recycled from Beard's 30 plus Northwest retail stores. No custom orders available at the outlet but they are set up for do-it-yourself framing. Credit on exchanges.

Checks, Credit cards

Cass Contemporary Art
NEW LISTING
Bellevue: 555 116th Ave. N.E. #118 646-6666
Hours: Mon-Fri 8-4 by appointment

Some people could look at this as an investment, others as a way to collect fine art at affordable prices. Cass sells limited edition prints by contemporary artists such as Robert Rauschenburg, Andy Warhol, James Rosenquist, and Claus Oldenburg to galleries all over the country. The public is welcome to buy at wholesale prices, which average $100 to $3,000. All prints are signed and numbered and Cass has 15 years experience behind them, so you know they are legit. No returns.

Checks, Credit cards

Cut-The-Corner Frame Shop

Tukwila: 17900 Southcenter Parkway 575-8272 *Pavilion Mall*
Hours: Mon-Fri 9:30-9:00, Sat 9:30-9, Sun 11-6

Cut-the-Corner offers creative custom picture framing at do-it-yourself prices. Average cost is $60 to frame a 24" x 36" picture using quality materials, which the owner guarantees will last for 150 years. A large collection of framed and unframed original works, limited-edition prints, posters and graphics sell for at least 20% below retail.

Checks, Credit cards

L.A. Frames

Renton: 309 S. 3rd 228-1693
Hours: Mon-Fri 9:30-6, Sat 10-5

With the largest selection of ready-made frames in the Northwest, you're sure to find just the right setting for your work of art or family photo. Don't forget to check out the half-price rack. Poster frames are always 40% off. For odd sizes, save money by having a staff person cut the frame, mat, and glass so you can do-it-yourself. Art students get a 10% discount on drawing and painting supplies. Posters and limited edition prints are also available.

Checks, Credit cards

Trans Accents

NEW LISTING
Seattle: 630-3119
Hours: Mon-Fri 9-5 By appointment only

Representatives of this Georgia-based companay come to your home or office with catalogs filled with examples of fine art for your walls, which they custom frame and hang for you. The selection varies from limted edition lithographs to reproduction art, etchings, paper castings, and fabric collages priced from $50 to $1,000. Mono-prints can be hand-painted to match your decor.

Checks, Credit cards

Additional Home Furnishings Outlets

(See Index for page numbers)

Furniture

Best
Beds, Bunks and Mattresses
Direct Buying Service
Discount Waterbeds
The Foam Shop
Hardwick's Swap Shop
Liquidators Outlet
Mattress Warehouse
Medalia's
The Repo Store
Sessions Discount Variety
The Ultimate Outlet

Household Appliances

47th St. Photo
AAA Liquidators
Big Mike's Factory Outlet
Best
Black and Decker
Bon Marche Clearance Center
Bushell's Auction House
Chubby and Tubby
Coho Supply
Direct Buying Service
Future Shop
Liquidators Outlet
Read Products
The Repo Store
Sears Outlet
Warehouse Kitchen Sales

Pictures and Frames

Super Star Outlet
Univalco

Kitchen and Restaurant Equipment

Best
Bon Marche Clearance Center
Chubby and Tubby
Liquidators Outlet
The Repo Store

Beds and Linens

B&M Liquidators
Bon Marche Home World
Bon Marche Clearance Center
Coy's Furniture Sales
Discount Furniture Outlet
The Down Factory
J.C. Penny's Clearance Furniture Annex
Marshall's
Ross Dress for Less
Sears Outlet
T.J. Maxx
United Buy and Sell

China, Crystal and Silver

Best
Dahnken of Tacoma
Marshall's
Ross Dress for Less
T.J. Maxx

Plants, Flowers and Greenery

W ith a multitude of nurseries, greenhouses and plant shops, the Puget Sound area is a mecca for plant lovers. Most of these businesses rely on quality, service and selection to generate sales rather than discount prices. Quality is the key issue here, because plants must be in good condition to survive. Beware of plants that go on sale because they may harbor insects or disease or be severely root bound from being in the container too long.

Nurseries and Plant Shops

Prices will probably be lower on bedding and house plants at mass merchandisers such as Ernst, Payless, Fred Meyer, and K-Mart, but quality will vary considerably. And don't forget Chubby and Tubby or the newest competition in this category: Eagle Hardware and Home Depot, with their well-stocked nurseries and garden centers.

If you have a green thumb, you can pick up some great buys at plant rental companies when they're clearing out overstock or inventory that needs a little TLC. Check the yellow pages under plants for a leasing company near you and call to see if they have something available.

Many nurseries bring customers in at the beginning of the growing season with loss leaders and have a big clearance sale at the end of the season. Furney's, Molbak's, and Sky, three of the larger, better known nurseries, have mailing lists that announce new arrivals and sale events. The first week in July, Molbaks hosts their popular yearly "2 for 1" sale of annuals and perennials. They also offer a 10% discount every Tuesday and Thursday to those over 62.

If you want to save money, visit one of the many nurseries located in outlying rural communities where land costs are lower. You might like to take along the Retail Nursery Map, a list of 70 nurseries published by the Washington State Nursery and Landscaping Association. Call 1-800-672-7711 for a free copy. Another handy aid is the "Speciality Nursery Guide," which includes a detailed map and a list of 37 small nurseries located between Stanwood and Puyallup that feature rare and unusual plants. Copies are available through libraries or send a stamped, self-addressed #10 envelope to Speciality Nursery Association, 11907 Nevers Rd., Snohomish, WA 98290.

Baker & Chantry Orchids

Woodinville: 18611 132nd N.E.   483-0345
Hours: Mon-Sun 10-5

"Growing orchids is not a hobby," says the owner, "it's an incurable disease!" If you're fascinated by the royalty of the flower world, get on the mailing list for this specialty nursery's quarterly sales. You can pick up a price list, and the knowledgeable staff will answer any questions.

Checks

Edmonds Community College

Lynnwood: 20000 68th Ave. W. 771-1500
Annual sale

During the second or third weekend of May, the Horticulture Department hosts a fund raiser in the greenhouse. Specialty nurseries throughout the area contribute unusual perennials, bedding plants and flowering baskets which usually sell for less than they would at retail outlets. The event also includes free lectures and workshops. Call to get on the mailing list.

Checks

The Greenery

NEW LISTING
Seattle: 4620 Leary Way N.W. 781-2406 *Ballard*
Periodic Sale: Second Saturday of every month, 9-4

Once a month, The Greenery rotates their rental plants by selling off old inventory, some of which is in quite good condition. Prices vary from 25% to 70% below retail and there's always a good selection of interior and exterior plants, especially fuchsias.

Checks, Credit cards

Growing Green Interiors

NEW LOCATION
Des Moines: 2959 1st Ave. S. 622-6543
Hours: Mon-Thurs 8-5, Fri 8-12

Growing Green sells, leases and maintains indoor foliage. In May and September, the company turns over its stock at wholesale prices. Call at the beginning of the month for the exact date.

Checks

Kimura Nursery

Redmond: 3860 N.E. Bellevue-Redmond Rd. 881-6508
Hours: Mon-Fri 7-5, Sat & Sun 9-5

Visit Kimura's three lush greenhouses for low everyday prices on small indoor and outdoor plants. They specialize in bonsai, ficus trees, dracaena, kentia and bamboo palms. In April and October, Kimura and Interior Plant Design, their leasing company, sell off rental plants and nursery overstock. Staff takes the time to rejuvenate rental plants before the sale. Call to get on the mailing list and you'll receive a discount coupon to use during the sale.

Checks, Credit cards

Rosso Wholesale Nursery Co.

NEW LISTING
Kent: 6404 Ellis S. 763-1888
Hours: Mon-Fri 8-5, Sat 9-4

A wholesale nursery open to the public, which means you go out in the field and dig up what you want. The surprisingly large 10-acre spread in Kent includes green houses filled with container stock as well. In the spring, prices on annuals, perennials, hanging baskets, and rhodies are hard to beat.

Checks, Credit cards

South Seattle Community College

West Seattle: 6000 16th Ave. S.W. 764-5323 *Garden Center*
Hours: Mon-Fri 9:30-3:30 (closed in the summer)

Students interested in landscape design and horticulture grow house plants in the fall and winter, and bedding plants, shrubs and trees in the spring, which are sold through the Garden Center on campus. The school sponsors a big sale in the middle of May. Call for the specific dates.

Checks

Tropical Foliage

Renton: 210 Wells Ave. S. 277-0922
Hours: Mon-Fri 10-5, Sat 10-3

Visit the "plant orphanage" at the largest indoor plant shop in South King County and "adopt" a plant at close to cost. Most of them have been leased to commercial accounts and are in need of tender loving care. Tropical Foliage carries a good selection of plants brought in from Hawaii, Florida and Southern California.

Checks, Credit cards

Washington Pottery Co.

Tukwila: 13001 48th Ave. S. 243-1191
Hours: Mon-Fri 8-4:30

Washington Pottery Co. makes and sells red clay pottery and planters to nurseries, garden shops and mass merchandisers. Drive out to their factory store and pay up to 50% off retail for the same items. Seconds are terrific buys, and sometimes the defects are hardly noticeable. Pottery shards, which can be used for drainage in the bottom of pots, are free as long as you're willing to shovel them into a container.

Checks

Benefit Sales

Seasoned gardeners often turn up some great deals at annual sales sponsored by various community or charitable organizations. Here's a list of the most popular established sales. Watch the newspapers or contact the organizations for specific dates.

Arboretum Foundation

Seattle: 325-4510
Spring, Fall and Holiday Sales

Children's Hospital Guild Association

Seattle: 526-2153
Spring Sale

Master Gardeners

Seattle: 296-3440
Spring Sale

Northwest Horticultural Society

Seattle: 527-1794
Summer Fern Festival and Fall Sale

Seattle Tilth Association

Seattle: 633-0451
Spring Sale

Volunteer Park Conservatory

Seattle: 684-4743
Fall Sale

Free Services
and Publications

Amateur landscape gardeners and houseplant lovers should take advantage of the following free services and publications:

The Center For Urban Horticulture and Washington Park Arboretum publish a newsletter that includes a calendar of events for plant sales, public lectures and garden tours. Call 543-8800 or 685-2692 to receive a free copy.

The Cooperative Extension, a partnership between Washington State University, the U.S. Department of Agriculture, and local counties offers over 500 bulletins and fact sheets on all aspects of gardening, farming, food preservation and pest management. For information call: King County, 296-3900 or 1-800-325-0165, Snoqualmie County 338-2400, Pierce County 591-7180.

Master Gardeners teach classes in gardening and pest management. They also give advice at plant clinics, special events, and over the telephone. Call 296-3440 Monday through Friday 10 am to 4 pm to talk to a master gardener.

King County Dial Extension provides 400 taped telephone messages on gardening, pest management and food preservation. Call 296-3425 for a brochure that lists the many different taped messages.

Florists

Many grocery stores have floral departments, which offer not only the convenience of 24-hour-a-day, one-stop shopping, but also prices that beat the going rate at florists. Inventory usually includes fresh cut flowers sold in bouquets or singly and flowering potted plants. Some stores take special orders and put together arrangements with 24 hours notice. Safeway, with their huge buying power, has the lowest prices overall because they buy their fresh cut flowers direct from local growers instead of from wholesale distributors. You'll find the best selection at the superstores, especially those located in Edmonds, Lynnwood, Bothell, Kenmore, Woodinville, Cottage Lake, and on 153rd and Aurora.

Flowers Plus

Tacoma: 5600 6th Ave. 756-0909
Hours: Mon-Fri 9-7, Sat & Sun 9-5

With a huge selection of fresh cut flowers at discount prices, Flowers Plus attracts people who like to save money by putting together their own arrangements. Enter the big walk-in cooler and you'll be surrounded by a profusion of color. Daisies, iris, carnations, snap dragons, gladiolas, lilies, and alstromeria bloom year round here. Red roses sell for 99¢ a stem in season, Carnations 69¢. Staff will help you create a floral arrangement from fresh, dried or silk flowers to suit any occasion. Bring your own vase or buy one in the store.

Checks, Credit cards

Florists

Rose Hearts

Lynnwood: 6925 216th S.W. 774-7673 *Goodwin Business Park*
Hours: Mon-Thurs 6:30-4, make an appointment for pick-up

Need a lot of roses for a special occasion? Buy them in bulk from Rose Hearts, a wholesaler that has dozens of roses air-freighted in daily from California to sell at grocery stores and convenience stores. Although walk-in trade is not a big part of their business, they will sell a bundle of 25 roses for around $10. Prices go up in the fall and winter, but even then no one will be able to beat their prices.

Checks

While it is almost impossible to comparison shop floral arrangements, the following stores quoted me consistently low prices on a bouquet of one-dozen long-stemmed red roses:

Pacific Rose House

Tacoma: 9313 S. Tacoma Way 584-1995

Pacific Flower Market

Federal Way: 33600 Pacific Hwy. S. 874-0977

The Rose Corner

NEW LISTING

Seattle: 10901 Aurora Ave. 361-5051 *Greenwood*
17560 Aurora Ave. 542-3033 **Shoreline**

Southcenter Flower Market

NEW LISTING

Tukwila: 16415 Southcenter Parkway 575-4648

Son-Shine Flower Market

NEW LISTING

Renton: 16407 S.E. Renton-Issaquah 235-7021

Christmas Trees

For years, Chubby & Tubby stores in Seattle have sold Christmas trees at unbelievably low prices. In 1993, every tree in stock was $5, and that included tax! The best trees go quickly, so try to be there when the truck arrives.

Many people enjoy the tradition of cutting their own tree at Christmas time. Not only is it fresher and less expensive than one purchased in city lots, but the whole family can participate in a fun outing.

Early in the holiday season, watch for articles and advertisements in the local newspapers on U-Cut Christmas tree farms. The Puget Sound Christmas Tree Association Inc. puts out a great brochure that lists over 50 "choose and cut" Christmas tree farms, which is available at libraries, banks, convenience stores and grocery stores during the holiday season. If you can't find a brochure, call the Country Extension offices for information. King County Dial Extension (296-3425) sets up a special hotline after Thanksgiving on U-Cut Christmas tree farms. For information year-round, you can write to the Puget Sound Christmas Tree Association, 15703 22nd Ave. E., Tacoma, WA 98445.

Each farm sets its own prices, which will vary with the quality of the tree. A 6-ft. Douglas fir will normally cost $30 to $35 pre-cut, while a U-Cut farm may charge half that. Most farms supply saws and twine, while others provide hot drinks, hay rides, Santa Claus and treats for the kids.

For those interested in a more rugged outing, the National Forest Service issues a limited number of Christmas Tree permits yearly. Call (206) 775-9702 for more information.

Additional Plants, Flowers and Greenery Outlets

The following businesses have consistently good prices on nursery plants. Check the Index for page numbers.

Country Farms
Chubby & Tubby
Eagle Hardware
Home Base
Home Depot
McLendon Hardware

Office Needs

O ne of the easiest ways home-based or small businesses can improve their profit margin is to buy office supplies in quantity when they go on sale. Another is to rent furniture or purchase used furniture. The recent rash of businesses closing, down-sizing and merging has resulted in a flood of office furniture just waiting to be recycled. Not only will you find desks, chairs and file cabinets to meet your basic needs, but a lot of surprisingly attractive items that can be adapted for home use, such as sofas, upholstered chairs, coffee tables, and bookshelves. Sometimes expensive custom-made pieces from corporate offices are available at a fraction of their original cost. Remember, you don't have to own a business to shop at an office furniture store.

Office Furniture, Machines and Supplies

Acme Office Furniture

Seattle: 1230 1st Ave. S. 682-6565 *Sodo*
Hours: Mon-Fri 8:30-4

Acme sells new, used and abused office furniture. They keep prices low on new merchandise by buying overstock and discontinued styles. Used furniture goes for less than wholesale, and there's a big selection. Most items are in good condition since the owner does furniture cleaning and repair work for other companies.

Checks

Amtech Business Systems Inc.

NEW LISTING

Tacoma: 11114 Pacific Ave. S. 531-3202, 1-800-660-3648
Hours: Mon-Fri 8:30-6, Sat by appointment

Quality new and used office furniture and copiers are sold here. The big selection of refurbished used office-grade copiers and fax machines by Sharp comes with a 90-day parts and labor warranty, the same as on brand new models. Used fax machines start at $295. Office-grade copiers will be more expensive initially, but in the long run you'll save because they use toner instead of costly cartridges and they're built to withstand heavy daily use. Used furniture sold "as is."

Checks, Credit cards

Auburn Discount Office Products

NEW LISTING

Auburn: 602 Auburn Way N. 833-1845
Hours: Mon-Fri 8:30-5:30, Sat 10-4

A general office supply store with a big selection and low prices every day. New and used furniture is also available. Open an account and save another 10%. Free delivery in the Kent/Federal Way area on any order over $25.

Checks, Credit cards

Avanti Sports

NEW LISTING

Seattle: 4518 University Way N.E. 547-3558 *U-District*
Hours: Mon-Sat 11-6

Students and yours truly shop here for basic office supplies, which tend to spill out into the hallway and represent a business the owner was in before he took up selling off-price tennis and volley ball equipment. Save 50% or more on basics like scotch tape, pens, steno pads, file folders, film and sundry items picked up from drug stores going out of business. Telephones, typewriters and typing tables even show up. Returns accepted.

Checks, Credit cards

Bank and Office Interiors Inc. Warehouse Outlet

Seattle: 5990 1st Ave. S. 768-8000 *Sodo*
Hours: Mon-Fri 8-5

This huge warehouse services the well-known B&I store down the street, which specializes in interior decor for offices. Merchandise is generally high-quality, and best buys are on used and damaged goods from trade-ins and rentals. Call to make an appointment with a salesman, who will come over from the main store to wait on you. Weekend appointments can be arranged. Big sale at the end of the year. No returns.

Checks, Credit cards

Budget Office Furniture

Seattle: 2244 1st Ave. S. 447-0393 *Sodo*
Hours: Mon-Fri 8:30-5:30, Sat 11-4

As part of a large buying group, Budget can afford to sell leading brand name office furniture at 30% to 45% off list price year round. Selection includes anything you'd need to outfit a bare bones office, executive suite or full scale work center. Call and they'll send you a full-color catalog, with prices. Those on a tight budget can check out the big inventory of used office furniture downstairs. Trade-ins are welcome. Staff guarantees friendly service, free coffee and popcorn. Flexible return policy.

Checks, Credit cards

Bellevue/Seattle Office Furniture Inc.

Bellevue: 13219 N.E. 20th St. 641-8500
Seattle: 3035 1st Ave. 728-5710 *South of Seattle Center*
Hours: Mon-Fri 8-5

Discounts vary from 10% to 40% on everything from floormats to pictures for the wall. Bargain hunters head for the basement in the Seattle store, where used furniture and factory seconds reside, or they get on the mailing list to find out about special promotions and half-yearly sales in July and December. Return policy varies.

Checks, Credit cards

Choices Northwest

NEW LISTING
Auburn: 326 8th S.W. 735-0878
Hours: Mon-Fri 9-5

Choices Northwest sells new, used and refurbished office panel systems to corporate giants like Weyerhauser as well as small businesses who want to save money. Refurbished panels are painted and re-upholstered to look brand new. Clients can choose any color or fabric they desire. Space planning and installation are also available.

Checks

City Office Furniture

NEW LISTING
Seattle: 2030 8th Ave. 587-5335 *Downtown*
Hours: Mon-Fri 9-6, Sat 10-5

City Furniture claims their prices on used furniture beat everyone else's and there's plenty to choose from in this crowded warehouse-like setting. The store also manufacturers wood desks and ergonomic chairs, so seconds and overstock end up here. All sales final.

Checks, Credit cards

Crawfords Office Furniture and Office Supplies

NEW LISTING
Seattle: 435 Westlake N. 623-4210 *East of Seattle Center*
Hours: Mon-Fri 8:30-5

Celebrating 70 years in business, Crawford's 18,000 sq. ft. store showcases new and used furniture. The upstairs houses an incredible selection from trade-ins and buyouts at competitive prices. Staff says file cabinets go quickly. Call for a catalog to compare prices on office supplies, machines, computer paper and basic furniture.

Checks, Credit cards

Discount Office Furniture

NEW LISTING
Tacoma: 3916 100th S.W. 582-9026
Hours: Mon-Fri 9-6, Sat 10-5

Because Discount Office Furniture works on a low mark-up, they can offer you big savings on anything you'd need to outfit an office. La-Z-Boy executive chairs sell for 40% off list price. The day I called the owner quoted me $149.99 for a 30" x 60" double pedestal laminated desk and $159.99 for a 4-drawer legal-size file cabinet. Returns accepted

Checks

Ducky's Office Furniture

NEW LOCATION
Seattle: 1111 Mercer St. 623-7777 *Downtown*
Hours: Mon-Fri 8:30-5:30, Sat 10-4

The owner puts some fun into the boring business of shopping for office furniture by posting "whacky" signs on his colorful building like "Duck into our place and you'll go quackers over the prices." The enormous inventory varies from "el cheapo" to expensive lines, both new and used, with file cabinets and ergonomic chairs their best selling items. Prices are incredibly low because of low overhead and volume buying. Posted prices apply to cash-only purchases. Rentals available. Umbrellas, calendars, T-shirts and other items carry out the duck motif. Returns accepted.

Checks, Credit cards

Foster Office Equipment

NEW LISTING
Burien: 426 S.W. 153rd 243-5900
Hours: Mon-Fri 8-6, Sat 10-4

Good quality at good prices is the motto here, be it furniture, office supplies or equipment. Although used typewriters, mainly IBM Selectrics, are always in stock, for basic typing needs staff recommends the new "made in the U.S." Nakajima typewriter, because of it's long life and extended warranty. Visit the basement where you'll find used and slightly damaged furniture at super low prices. Returns accepted.

Checks, Credit cards

Foster's Used Office Furniture

Kent: 840 S. Central 854-9482
Hours: Mon-Fri 9-6, Sat 10-4

Low overhead keeps prices down on new and used furniture at Foster's. The big warehouse is filled with terrific buys on desks, credenzas, chairs, tables, file cabinets, safes and computer furniture, plus a limited selection of office supplies and equipment. Most of the used merchandise comes from banks. Everything is reconditioned before it goes out on the floor, so many items look brand new. The store also re-upholsters office furniture for other businesses.

Checks, Credit cards

H.D. Baker

NEW LISTING
Tacoma: 915 Center St. 272-7644, 1-800-888-3226
Hours: Mon-Fri 8-5

Check out this well-established family-owned business for savings on a wide variety of office needs including paper products, typewriters, calculators, copiers and telephones. Call to receive a quarterly sales catalog.

Checks, Credit cards

Northwest Office Furniture Sales Inc.

NEW LISTING

Seattle: 2440 1st Ave. S. 682-2331 *Sodo*

Hours: Mon-Sat 8:30-5

As one of the largest liquidators on the West coast, Northwest buys and sells used office furniture by the truck load. The astounding array is crowded into three floors and much of it comes from banks and corporate offices, which means you can buy steel case desks, file cabinets and panel systems as well as contemporary furniture that looks like it came from a designer showroom. I saw beautiful glass tables, leather sofas, and upholstered chairs. Most sales "as is."

Checks

Office Depot Inc.

NEW LISTING

Bellevue: 100 108th N.E. 453-2900

Federal Way: 34950 Enchanted Park Way S. 661-2900

Lynnwood: 5710 196th St. S.W. 771-2582

Redmond: 15301 N.E. 24th St. 747-9019

Seattle: 1751 Airport Way S. 587-2582 *South of Kingdome*

13501 Aurora Ave. N. 364-2404 *Haller Lake*

Tacoma: 3330 S. 23rd. St. 572-6595

Tukwila: 290 Andover Pkwy. E. 248-2582

Hours: Mon-Fri 8-9, Sat 9-9, Sun 11-6

Individuals, small businesses and big corporations shop side-by-side at this 300 store nation-wide chain, which guarantees the lowest prices every day on a complete range of quality, name-brand office supplies and machines. Look for big savings on bulk disks, as well as recyled paper for your copier, computer or fax machine. Prices average 40% to 50% below retail on computers by IBM, Apple, Canon, Panasonic, Texas Instruments, Packard Bell and other leading manufacturers. Discounts on some items go as low as 70%. To compare prices, stop by a location near you and pick up a free catalog or call to get on their mailing list and you'll receive special offers plus a magazine for small businesses. Free delivery on orders of $140 or more, except furniture, within local trading area. 30-day return policy.

Checks, Credit cards

Office Furniture Express

NEW LOCATION
Bellevue: 1910 32nd 747-5577
Hours: Mon-Fri 9-5, Sat 10-3

Merchandise runs the gamut from budget-priced to high-end, which means you can pay $129 to $1,000 for a desk. Discounts will vary but you'll always find a good deal in their used department. Flexible returns.

Checks, Credit cards

Office Solutions Inc.

Tacoma: 1908 Pacific Ave. 383-4505
Hours: Mon-Fri 8:30-5:30

With hundreds of items stored on five floors, this is one of the largest office furniture companies in Western Washington. New merchandise, ranges from generic to designer lines, and averages 40% below retail. Overstock, floor models and discontinued lines come from a top Seattle/Tacoma dealer. Look for bargains galore on used furniture, which makes up about half of the inventory. Mailing list for special promotions. Returns accepted.

Checks, Credit cards

Office Max

NEW LISTING
Bellevue: 14515 N.E. 20th 641-1418
Lynnwood: 18420 33rd. Ave. W. 775-7510
Seattle: 2401 Utah Ave. S. 467-0071 *Sodo*
Hours: Mon-Fri 8-9, Sat 8-8, Sun 12-6

Formerly Biz Mart, these nationwide superstores offer one-stop shopping for all your office needs. Compare prices on over 10,000 products via a big in-store catalog or call 1-800-688-MART to have one mailed to you free-of-charge. Look for everyday low prices on leading brand name computers, fax machines, electronics and software, as well as paper supplies and office furniture. Four drawer letter-size file cabinets are super cheap. All stores contain a full-service print shop where custom engraving and custom-made rubber stamps can be ordered. Sign up for the free Advantage card and get volume rebates, reduced delivery fees, discount coupons, and advance notice of sales. Watch for big sales during tax time, the Christmas holidays and back-to-school promotions. And also watch for new stores to be open soon in both Tukwila and Federal Way. 30-day return policy.

Checks, Credit cards

Office Furniture Recyclers

NEW LISTING
Bremerton: 4207 Wheaton Way 792-1103
Hours: Mon-Fri 9-6, Sat 10-4

The big selection of used office furniture includes chairs, couches, lamps and book cases that would be great in a living room as well as corporate office. Office supplies, which range from paper clips in bulk to file folders and 3-ring binders, are super inexpensive since they come from store and office liquidations.

Checks, Credit cards

Office Furniture Co-op

NEW LOCATION
Bellevue: 13310 N.E. 16th 562-1710
Hours: Mon-Fri 9-5:30, Sat 10-3

Wow, does this place look like a money-saver for Eastsiders! The 10,000 sq. ft. warehouse/showroom displays new and used furniture which includes a lot of close-outs, freight-damaged and liquidation goods at dirt cheap prices. Styles run the gamut from traditional to furniture fit for a CEO. Shelving units, drafting stools and computer tables are best selling items. Call for price quotes. Flexible return policy.

Checks, Credit cards

R & S Office Source

Seattle: 1221 E. Pike 323-5966 *Capitol Hill*
Hours: Mon-Fri 9-6

A low-overhead operation that deals mainly in used office interiors from rental returns and business liquidations. The 2nd floor is jam packed with traditional as well as contemporary styles at bargain basement prices. The store also specializes in solid wood dinette sets with Windsor chairs which sell for $250. Staff attempts to give budget-minded customers the lowest price possible. Save big bucks by renting used furniture or take advantage of their trade-in policy.

Checks, Credit cards

The Repo Store

NEW LISTING
Tacoma: 512 S. 112th 531-1339
Hours: Mon-Sat 9-5

An old 17,000 sq. ft. grocery store filled with commercial equipment and furniture from restaurants, offices, and businesses that didn't make their payments. I was impressed with the big inventory of computers, copiers, typewriters, adding machines, and telephone systems, all of which are in working order. All sales "as is" and final.

Checks

Viking Discount Office Products

Los Angeles, CA : 1-800-421-1222
Hours: Mon-Fri 7-7, Sat 7-4

Viking is the largest mail order office supply company in the country. Call for colorful free catalogs, which come out six to eight times a year, with frequent sale supplements in between. Not only are prices fantastic, but delivery is free with orders of $25 or more. My accountant purchases everything from furniture to calculators to post-its from their extensive line of products. Returns accepted.

Checks, Credit cards

Winter's Office Furniture

Seattle: 6169 4th Ave. S. 763-2677 *Georgetown*
Hours: Mon-Fri 10-4, Sat 10-12

Check out Winters' for bargains on used, close-out and damaged office furniture, especially basic file cabinets, desks and chairs. They are also one of the few places where you can buy used warehouse equipment, mainly lockers and shelving. New office furniture, which makes up one third of their inventory, starts at 20% off list. Flexible return policy.

Checks, Credit cards

Computer Hardware and Software

The key to buying a computer is to know what you want before you set foot in the store. If you are planning on using it for more than simple word processing or basic accounting, the rule of thumb is to double what you think you will need in terms of hardware capability. When asked if they would like more features and more power, most new computer users answer "yes" to both questions after only two years of experience.

To give you an idea of current prices, read the ads in the business section of local newspapers, especially on Sunday, and pick up a copy of the "Puget Sound Computer User," a monthly tabloid distributed free-of-charge at Safeway, Albertson's and computer stores in the greater Seattle area. Subscriptions are mailed free to businesses that send a request on their letterhead. Informative articles, a calendar of events, listings of user groups, advertisements by big discounters, and a classified section make this newspaper a must for bargain hunters. The paper also sponsors a modem-linked electronic bulletin board and publishes a comprehensive user-directory in January.

Comparison shopping will reveal that most systems are priced within a few hundred dollars of each other due to fierce competition amongst the 100-plus dealers in the Puget Sound area. Visit Bellevue, where over a dozen computer stores make up "Computer Row" on N.E. 20th which turns into Northrup Way.

When it comes to buying a computer, service and support after the sale are more important than saving a few bucks, which is why it pays to shop with a reputable dealer. The best recommendation is word-of-mouth, so talk to someone who has recently purchased a computer, or has some experience in the marketplace. Good questions to ask a dealer are how long have they been in business, what kind of warranty do they offer and do they have the facilities and technicians to service your machine. Stores that sell leading brand names aren't necessarily going to give better service than the many small manufacturers of IBM clones in the Puget Sound area who offer factory-direct prices. If all you need is an entry-level computer that won't require much dealer support, Costco, Office Depot, and Office Max sell low-end generic models.

Used equipment may be the answer for those on a budget or for beginners who aren't interested in the latest applications. The market is flooded with used machines from rentals, the upgrading of offices, and people trading in old models for new ones. Look for a good deal on used computers in the classified section of major newspapers or at computer repair shops where unclaimed equipment goes for a song. Also, check with computer dealers for user groups who buy, sell and trade among themselves.

AM Computer Swap Meet
Periodic Sales
Everett: April & October
Kitsap: August & November
Kent: March, July, Sept. & December
Phone: 874-8711

Buyers and sellers converge at this unique event, where over 100 vendors rent space. While the majority of them are small retailers selling brand-new merchandise at discount prices, used equipment from individuals and businesses cleaning out their offices show up as well. Call for a brochure listing location, dates, and information for renting space.

Ballard Computer
NEW LOCATIONS
Kirkland: 8525 120th Ave. N.E. 822-7000
Mt. Vernon: 1615 Buck Way 424-6000
Seattle: 5424 Ballard Ave. N.W. 781-7000 *Ballard*
Tacoma: 6111 Tacoma Mall Blvd. 471-0700
Tukwila: 331 Tukwila Parkway 246-0700
Hours: Mon-Sat 8-8, Sun 10-6

A major local mass market retailer, Ballard Computer offers discounts not only on a tremendous variety of hardware and software from leading brand names such as McIntosh, Compaq, and Hewlitt Packard, but technical support via a hot line and an on-site repair center as well. Watch the newspapers ads for ever-changing specials, loss leaders and their big scratch 'n' dent sale. If you know what you want, call and they'll send you a product sheet. Ballard boasts one of the largest selections of laptop computer in the Northwest. Classes and extended warranties are available for a fee. Novices need not fear entering this user-friendly store. Returns accepted.

Checks, Credit cards

Bit by Bit

NEW LISTING
Redmond: 2715 152nd Ave. N.E. Bldg 6 881-5353
Hours: Mon-Fri 9-5

Bit by Bit rents computers made by leading brand names as well as IBM compatibles they build themselves. Since this is the main warehouse for the five-store West coast chain, there's always a big supply of used equipment on hand that goes for rock bottom prices.

Checks, Credit cards

Bruno's Computer Warehouse

NEW LISTING
Tukwila: 510 Andover Park West 575-8737
Hours: Mon-Fri 10-7, closed Wed., Sat 10-6, Sun 11-5

This unique 20,000 sq. ft. superstore happens to be the largest Cannon dealer in the state and a major liquidation outlet for computers and related items from leading brand names all over the country, all priced at 30% to 70% below retail. The amazing eclectic inventory varies from the latest CD Rom players to state-of-the-art electronic equipment to 1985 Compaqs, plus a strange assortment of sundry parts no one can identity located in what the staff calls the "Voodoo Section." Hackers buy used or broken computers dirt cheap for their parts. Software titles number over 20,000, with a special section set aside for kids games and educational programs. Computer furniture, office supplies and hundreds of books sell for half their original price. Call the hotline at 575-8748 for an update on weekly specials and liquidation sales, or watch the newspaper ads. One year warranty on new computers, 30 days on used. Variable return policy.

Checks, Credit cards

Compu-Tech

Tacoma: 2107 S. 12th St. 383-6346
Hours: Mon-Fri 8:30-5:30, Sat 10-3

Here's a good place to buy, sell or trade computers and accessories. Used equipment, mainly IBM clones from six months to five years old, comes with a 30-day to 90-day warranty. New computers by leading brand names are also available. Compu-Tech is an authorized service center for Epson and Commodore with a 2-hour turn around on most repairs.

Checks, Credit cards

Computers & Applications

Bellevue: 10623 N.E. 8th St. 451-8077, 1-800-733-8586
Hours: Mon-Fri 8-6, Sat 10-5, Sun 12-5

This retail store, which has been in business since 1981, is backed up by a warehouse stocked with over a million dollars worth of equipment and software. They regularly discount IBM, Hewlett Packard, Compaq, AST and other leading brand names. Watch for a big sale around Christmas. Purchase a computer here and enjoy free software classes for one year plus access to a service department that's open seven days a week. Prices shown are for cash or checks. Add 3% for bank cards. Seven-day return policy.

Checks, Credit cards

Computer Exchange Northwest

Kirkland: 12006 98th Ave. N.E., #103 820-1181
Hours: Mon-Fri 9-5

A brokerage firm for new and used computers with a large clientele and an excellent reputation. Buyers pay 10% to 30% less for new models. Sellers pay a 15% commission when their equipment is sold. If you know what model and price range you're interested in, call and they'll send a list of what's available. Payment is held in escrow during the inspection period.

Cash only

Computer City

NEW LISTING
Kirkland: 12526-A Totem Lake Blvd. 820-1600 *Totem Lake Mall*
Tukwila: 404 Strander Blvd. 439-1600
Hours: Mon-Sat 9-9, Sun 11-6

The superstore concept applied to computers! The 25,000 sq. ft. space houses more computers, hardware, software and related items than you'll ever find under one roof and its all the latest, hottest equipment on the market by every leading brand name you can think of. In the CPU category alone they offer more than 60 models from desktop systems to notebooks with a multitude of hardware options. Thousands of software titles stretch for aisles.

As part of a new, fast-growing, national chain owned by the Tandy Corporation, the stores work on a high volume, low profit margin to keep prices down. 30-day return policy.

Checks, Credit cards

Computers 'n' Things

Tacoma: 3213 S. 38th St. 474-1383
Hours: Mon-Fri 8-6, Sat 10-5

Although their main business is on-site service and custom-built systems, used computers are sold on consignment or purchased outright. There's always a big selection of accessories and parts for do-it-yourselfers.

Checks, Credit cards

CT Compu-Tech

NEW LISTING
Tacoma: 2107 S. 12th 383-6346
Hours: Mon-Fri 9-5:30, Sat 10-3

Another good resource for used computers, printers, and monitors. CT Compu-Tech will buy outright or take your old computers in on trade. They also carry a full line of accessories at low prices.

Checks, Credit cards

Discount Computer Software

Burien: 641 S.W. 152nd 431-0180
Hours: Mon-Fri 10-7, Sat 10-5

All software is discounted 10% off the suggested retail price, with most programs geared to home entertainment. Join the Installment Buying Club and you can preview titles for three days for a $6 fee. The store used to rent software which is now being sold off. Reconditioned and used equipment sold on consignment.

Checks, Credit cards

Egghead Software

Bellevue: 14330 N.E. 20th 644-4545
    1105 Bellevue Way N.E. 451-3701
Lynnwood: 4201 196th S.W. 672-9397
Seattle: 1122 4th Ave. 623-4851 *Downtown*
    2111 Northgate Way 361-5002 *Northgate*
Tacoma: 2505 S. 38th 473-5195
Tukwila: 17326 Southcenter Pkwy. 575-0445 *Parkway Plaza*
Hours: Mon-Sat 10-7; Bellevue Mon-Fri 9-7, Sat 10-7;
Downtown Seattle Mon-Sat 9-6; All stores Sun 12-5

Egghead, the largest software chain in the country, stocks over 2,000 programs for business or entertainment purposes, plus a full range of accessories at competitive prices. Sign up for a free Cue Card and you're guaranteed an "eggstra" 5%

discount on everything you buy, plus you'll receive "eggsclusive" benefits such as notice of sales, new programs and a newsletter tailored to your specific interests. 30-day return policy.

Checks, Credit cards

Electronic Mall

NEW NAME / NEW LOCATION
Lynnwood: 19502 56th Ave. W. 776-0311
Hours: Mon-Fri 9-6, Sat 9-5

If you're into building your own computer or tinkering with old ones, this is the place to buy parts and equipment. Prices are low because they buy close-outs, surplus lots and outdated systems. Used printers, terminals, monitors and parts are always in stock. New components can be purchased at low bulk prices. Tools, chemicals, test equipment, and motor drive kits for educational purposes can be purchased here as well as the latest books on computer electronics, robotics, fiber optics and laser applications. Mailing list for special sales. Returns accepted within 30 days.

Checks, Credit cards

Flo Computing

Seattle: 18332 Aurora Ave. N. 542-9600 *Richmond Highlands*
Hours: Tues-Fri 10:30-6, Sat 10-4

For almost a decade Flo Computing has been selling used computers and hardware on consignment. Bargain hunters and hackers love the low prices. Bring in your old system, and depending on age and condition, you'll receive 20% to 50% of the selling price. Five-day return policy.

Checks, Credit cards

Gemini Computers & Software

Seattle: 10331 Aurora Ave. N. 524-0701 *North Park*
Hours: Mon-Sat 10-7

A small store that stocks a big selection of shareware in every category imaginable. They also buy, sell and trade new and used computers and software.

Checks, Credit cards

GroupWare

NEW LISTING
Tacoma: 4826 Tacoma Mall Blvd. 472-1400
Hours: Mon-Fri 8-6:30, Sat 10-5

GroupWare claims they're the largest distributor of CD ROM titles and equipment in the U.S. Prices start as low as $175 for a Mitsumi CD-ROM player kit, $5 for a Windows game disk. Call or write for a free software catalog. For $25 you can order their super CD II Shareware library.

Checks, Credit cards

Half Price Books and Software

NEW LOCATIONS
Bellevue: 15600 N.E. 8th 747-6616 *Crossroads Shopping Center*
Edmonds: 23632 Hwy. 99 670-6199
Seattle: 4709 Roosevelt Way N.E. 547-7859 *U-District*
Tacoma: 6409 6th Ave. 566-1238
Hours: Bellevue: Mon-Thurs 10-9, Fri, Sat 10-10:30, Sun 10-8; Edmonds, Seattle, Tacoma: Mon-Sat 10-10, Sun 12-8, Seattle: Sun 10-10

You can buy, sell and trade software in the same way used books are sold here. Current versions are often 30% or more off retail prices. The day I called the chain had just purchased a big shipment of software from a Mac mail order house going out of business. Some people like to shop here because they can always find older programs for Atari and Commodore. Small peripherals and modems sometimes show up. The Seattle and Bellevue stores have the biggest selection. Returns within 7 days for credit.

Checks, Credit cards

Hi-Tech Rentals

Redmond: 3908 148th Ave. N.E. 881-1113
Hours: Mon-Fri 8:30-6:30

Here's a good place to start if you want to try different systems before buying. The company rents Apple and IBM-compatible systems, plus printers, scanners and CD ROM's for short or long-term use. Call for current rates. They also sell two to six month old systems with warranties.

Checks, Credit cards

GE Rental/Lease

NEW LISTING
Atlanta, GA: 1-800-437-3687
Hours: Mon-Fri 6:30-5

GE sells off used equipment from their nationwide rental network. To find out what's available, call for a catalog which lists top name PC's, peripherals, notebooks, multimedia, and work stations. Warranties vary. Five-day returns.

Checks, Credit cards

The Music Factory

NEW LISTING
Tukwila: 510 Andover Park West 575-2949
Hours: Mon-Fri 10-7, closed Wednesday, Sat 10-6, Sun 11-5

Located in Bruno's Computer Warehouse, you'll find a privately owned and operated department set aside for computer-assisted music systems, where you can buy MIDI keyboards, music software and sound systems at warehouse prices. The store also sells computerized lights, VG systems, and Karaoke equipment for sing-alongs. Electronic instruments sold on consignment. Returns accepted.

Checks, Credit cards

PC Fixx Clearance Center

NEW LISTING
Seattle: 1565 6th Ave. S. 624-2700 *Sodo*
Hours: Daily 10-7

"We sell the world's best computers again" is the motto at this big clearance warehouse, where used computers, printers, and parts sell for ridiculously low prices. The best stuff goes quickly so call or visit frequently. I found a 5-week-old laptop in stock the last time I checked. New IBM compatibles and parts also available. PC Fixx purchases used computers outright on Tuesdays (1 pm to 6 pm) and Sundays (1 pm to 3 pm). Trade-ins accepted. 90-day warranty on used equipment. Seven-day return policy.

Checks, Credit cards

Seattle Micro

Seattle: 2308 4th Ave. 441-9111 *Downtown*
Hours: Mon-Fri 8-6

Used computer rentals and demos turn up at Seattle Micro, a discount retailer specializing in IBM compatibles and accessories for high level users. Since my last edition they've added Hewlett Packard, software, and brand name parts to their inventory. Staff says the first computer they ever sold in 1984 was used. Trade-ins accepted.

Checks, Credit cards

Software Alternative

NEW LISTING
Tacoma: 5965 6th Ave. 566-8986, 1-800-640-1921
Hours: Mon-Fri 8-7, Sat 10-6, Sun 11-5

Commercial software at discount prices plus thousands of shareware programs makes this a popular spot. For a 10%

non-refundable deposit you can preview programs, which must be returned within three days. If you decide to keep the program the fee is applied to the purchase. Computer supplies, accessories and hardware is also available as well as complete systems custom-built on the premises.

Checks, Credit cards

Tacoma Computer Network

NEW LISTING
Tacoma: 2528 S. 38th St. 471-0501
Hours: Mon-Fri 9-6, Sat 10-5

A computer discount store that offers full service on hardware and peripherals custom-made especially for you.

Checks, Credit cards

Trinty Tech Inc.

NEW LOCATIONS
Bellevue: 12031 Northrup Way 455-1288
Seattle: 10724 5th Ave. N.E. 362-7620 *Northgate*
Hours: Mon-Fri 9-6

A local manufacturer of IBM compatibles and printers for the school district and corporations, Trinity Tech sells their Genesis line at bargain basement prices. During periodic clearance sales, excess inventory — hard drives, monitors, keyboards and complete systems — get marked down to cost or below. Watch for special sales via in-store flyers and ads in Computer User. 2% discount for cash. 10 day return policy. One year warranty on parts, two years on labor, which is a terrific deal.

Checks, Credit cards

U.S. Micro Express Inc.

Bellevue: 10216 N.E. 8th 453-4046
Hours: Generally, Mon-Fri 8-6, Sat 10-5, Sun 10-5

Buy factory direct from the state's largest manufacturer of state-of-the-art PC's for business or personal use. Upgrades and custom configurations make up a big part of their business. Call or stop by for a consumer information packet or a price list, which is updated monthly. Service-oriented, U.S. Micro offers a walk-in service center open 7 days a week, technicians available 24 hours a day for on-site emergencies, and one to two year warranties on parts and labor. Seven-day return policy.

Checks, Credit cards

Vetco Electronics

NEW LISTING
Bellevue: 13029 Northrup Way 869-7025
Hours: Mon-Sat 9-5

If you like to build or repair your own computer, this is the place to buy parts and equipment. Prices are super cheap because Vetco purchases closeouts, surplus and outdated systems from dealers, estate sales, and auctions — mainly IBM's and compatibles. The best stuff goes out the door as soon as it comes in, so visit frequently.

Checks, Credit cards

Mail-Order Computer Companies

Those familiar with the computer market know that mail-order prices will usually beat prices in retail stores, but you have to know what you want and order from a dealer who offers telephone support or service by a local representative. "Computer Shopper," a national classified tabloid-size magazine for direct buyers and sellers, is a great resource for both new and used equipment. Look for it at newsstands and in computer stores. The latest copy of PC Magazine will contain ads for hundreds of mail-order sources. When ordering by mail, it's always a good idea to use a credit card, which gives you extra protection in case of problems with delivery, breakage or returns.

Here's a starter list of well-established mail-order computer companies that will provide catalogs or price lists for comparison shopping:

Compuadd

Austin, TX: 1-800-627-1967
Hours: Mon-Fri 7-7 (Central Standard time)

Dell Computers

Austin, TX: 1-800-426-5150
Hours: Mon-Fri 7am-9pm, Sat 10-6, Sun 12-5 (Central Standard time)

47th Street Photo

New York, NY: 1-800-221-7774
Hours: Mon-Thur 8-7, Fri 8-2, Sun 10-5 (Eastern time)
See full listing under Photographic Supplies & Equipment.

PC Connection

Marlowe, NH: 1-800-243-8088
Hours: Mon-Sat 24 hours a day, closed Sun

Paper Products for Home and Office

The cost of paper products adds up fast, especially if you run to the local drugstore or Hallmark shop every time you need something. Get in the habit of buying in volume, especially when it comes to basic office supplies you use around the home on a regular basis. Good places to start are Office Max, Office Depot, membership warehouses, or the outlets for the big local paper distributors Arvey, the Paper Zone and the Paper Merchant, all of whom will quote prices over the phone or send out catalogs.

Arvey Paper & Office Products

Bellevue: 1910 132nd Ave. N.E. 643-4333
Seattle: 2930 1st Ave. S. 622-9232 *South of Kingdome*
Hours: Mon-Fri 8-5:30, Sat 9-5

Arvey's is part of a 38-store nationwide chain that stocks everything from paper clips to fax machines and furniture, as well as janitorial and graphic art supplies. Needless to say, best selling items are envelopes, labels, file folders and paper for computers and copy machines. Discounts vary but you don't have to buy in volume to save. Get on the mailing list to receive notice of monthly sales during which generic 20 lb. bond copy paper gets marked down to incredibly low prices. No freight charge on purchases over $100 in Western King County. Returns accepted.

Checks, Credit cards

Currents

Colorado Springs, CO: 1-800-525-7170
Hours: Daily, 5 am-midnight (Mountain time)

I couldn't pass up the chance to mention this wonderful mail-order resource for original colorful cards, wrapping paper, calendars, stationary and gift items. Special catalogs come out for Valentine's Day, Easter and Christmas. Buy in volume and prices will be 50% less than what you would pay at Hallmark. Currents also prints personalized checks for a lot less than banks. No shipping charge if you include payment with your orders. Call for a complimentary catalog

Checks, Credit cards

Everett Wholesale Paper Company

Everett: 2914 McDougal Ave. 252-2105, 800/448-9314
Hours: Mon-Fri 8-5

Save on cleaning supplies, stationery items, packaging products and paper sold mainly to offices, restaurants, janitorial services and businesses. Ribbon and gift wrap comes in big rolls. Packing boxes of all sizes are available for moving or storage. Not all items must be purchased in large quantities, but keep in mind that this is a wholesale operation and shop accordingly.

Checks

Paper Factory's Party World

Tacoma: 1565 Center 272-2181
Hours: Mon-Fri 9:30-6:30, Sat 9:30-5, Sun 12-5

Here's a great place to shop if you're planning a wedding or a big party. Spend $25 and you automatically qualify for a 10% discount. Brides will love the everyday low prices on wedding invitations. Look for outstanding buys on gift wrap and ribbon sold by the foot from huge rolls. Plan ahead by attending the popular annual "Christmas in July" sale when all holiday merchandise is cleared out at 50% off. Returns accepted.

Checks, Credit cards

The Paper Merchant

NEW LOCATION
Seattle: 4811 Airport Way S. 447-2595 *Georgetown*
Hours: Mon-Fri 7:30-5:30

This retail outlet for Noland papers sells everything from the finest quality paper products to basic stock for copiers, computers, and laser printers, plus an extensive line of stationery and envelopes made from recycled paper. Although merchandise can be purchased by the case, carton or ream, volume buying will save you more. Look for big discounts on discontinued stock. Call in to find out about weekly specials. 30-day return policy.

Checks, Credit cards

The Paper Zone

Everett: 9423 Evergreen Way 355-7703
Redmond: 3838 148th Ave. N.E. 883-0273
Seattle: 1911 1st Ave. S. 682-8644 *South of Kingdome*
Hours: Mon-Fri 8-5

"If it's made out of paper, we have it!" is the motto here. These three outlets, which are affiliated with West Coast Paper, the largest paper distributor in the Pacific Northwest, sell a tremendous variety of paper products for the home and office, as well as janitorial, packaging and restaurant supplies. Copy paper is a big selling item along with party and wedding goods. Look for big discounts in the closeout section and on ever-changing in-store promotions. Get on the mailing list to keep up with special sales. Returns accepted.

Checks, Credit cards

Party for Less

NEW LISTING
Kirkland: 10015 N.E. 137th 820-4751 *Juanita Firs Shopping Center*
Hours: Mon-Fri 9-9, Sat 10-6, Sun 11-8

A huge store jampacked with colorful paper products, decorative and gift items to celebrate any occasion, including weddings. Greeting cards number 5,000 and they're all 50% off the retail price. Gift wrap and ribbon is discounted 25% every day. With over 200 different Mylar balloon designs in stock, you're sure to find one that suits your needs. And there's lots of coordinated party goods for kids' birthdays or more elegant affairs. Returns accepted.

Checks, Credit cards

The Salvage Broker

Seattle: 13760 Aurora Ave. N. 365-7771 *Haller Lake*
Hours: Mon-Sat 10-5

What a find for bargain hunters! The owner buys close-outs, canceled orders, liquidation goods and merchandise damaged in shipment from printers and office suppliers going out of business. With two floors stacked to the ceiling, inventory includes an outstanding selection of quality specialty papers (parchment, linen, and acid-free) for artists and people who like to make their own cards or invitations. There's also party and packaging materials, greeting cards, gift wrap, and cleaning supplies, plus anything you'd find in the office supply section of a drug store, all at super low prices. Returns accepted.

Checks, Credit cards

Boxes

If you need boxes for moving, shipping, or storage, call one of the companies listed below. They all sell surplus, close-out and used boxes which can save you as much as 50%. If you're planning on moving, U-Haul will send you free-of-charge an excellent booklet that tells you how to compute the size of truck and the number and size of boxes you'll need.

Ace Box Company

Tukwila: 18200 Olympic Ave. S. 243-7181
Hours: Mon-Fri 8-5

Carton Service

Tukwila: 1141 Andover Park W., Bldg. C 575-9111
Hours: Mon-Fri 8-4

David James Packaging

Seattle: 587-2411
Hours: Mon-Fri 7-4

Free delivery, even if it's only one box.

Additional Office Needs Outlets

(See Index for page numbers)

Office Furniture, Machines and Supplies

47th Street Photo
AAA Liquidators
Arvey Paper and Office
Products
B&M Liquidators
Brand Name Furniture
Liquidators
Boeing Surplus
Best
Bruno's Computer
Warehouse
Cort
Direct Buying Service
Grantree
Future Shop
Hardwick's Swap Shop
Lee's-Audio-Video-Fax
Liquidators Outlet
The Repo Store
Silo

Computer Hardware

47th Street Photo
Best
Boeing Surplus
Discount Computer
Software
Office Depot
Office Max
The Repo Store
Silo
Viking

Computer Software

Ballard Computer
Bruno's Computer
Warehouse
Computer's and Applications
Computer City
Office Depot
Office Max
Seattle Micro
Viking

Paper Products for Home and Office

A&B Food Market
Auburn Discount Office
Products
Avanti Sports
Bruno's Computer
Warehouse
Crawford's
Drug Emporium
Foster Office Equipment
H.D. Baker
Office Depot
Office Max
Primo's Sales
Sysco Cash & Carry
Viking

Recreation and Hobbies

Sporting Goods and Recreational Clothing

T The Puget Sound area is "Bargain City" when it comes to sporting goods and clothing. The growth of local manufacturers, many of them nationally known, has given rise to a proliferation of factory outlets, discount stores and annual sales where overstock, irregulars and close-outs are sold at clearance prices year-round. Also, because Seattle is a port of entry for goods made in the Orient, many distributors and retailers import and sell merchandise at factory direct prices, frequently under their own label.

Consumer Tips

✔ Wait for annual sales sponsored by local retailers, many of which take place on Labor Day and Memorial Day weekends.

✔ Visit the Capitol Hill area where discount, consignment and factory outlets are clustered around REI.

✔ Good used equipment offers the best value for your money.

✔ Recreational clothing, now a driving force in high fashion, is less expensive in sporting goods stores than in the department stores.

AA Rentals

Seattle: 12700 Lake City Way N.E. 362-5547 *Lake City*
Hours: Mon-Fri 7:30-7, Sat 8-6, Sun 9-5

Every year after Labor Day, AA Rentals sponsors a big "Year-End Summer Fun Sale," during which camping, backpacking and mountain climbing equipment rented throughout the season goes on sale and stays in the store until early October. Savings can sometimes amount to 50%. Snow ski equipment is marked down in April and sold year round.

Checks, Credit cards

Alpine Hut

NEW LOCATION
Kent: 25228 104th S.E. 854-1151
Redmond: 7875 Leary Way N.E. 883-7669
Hours: Mon-Fri 10-8, Sat 10-6, Sun 12-5

A great place to save money on skis for the whole family. In the fall Alpine Hut sells kids' skis on consignment. Around mid-October they put their rental skis, boots and bindings on sale. Used roller blades and snow boards turn up in the summertime. If you decide to sell your equipment here, the store gives you half of the selling price or 75% toward in-store credit.

Checks, Credit cards

Army Surplus Annex & Uncle John's GI Surplus

NEW LISTING
Tacoma: 15401 Union Ave. S.W. 582-7033
  12910 Pacific Hwy. S. 582-3999
Hours: Mon-Sat 11-7

Fans of army surplus will love these two small stores, both of which are owned by the same person and loaded with military stuff at bargain prices. Inventory includes everything from gas masks, helmets and canteens to clothing and camping gear, both new and used. The ever-popular army fatigues sell for $12.95 used, while jump boots start at $25. Or how about trying one of the army's infamous "MRE's", which stands for "meals ready to eat?" I hear that even service men shop at these outlets. Refunds on new merchandise, exchanges only on used items within 7 days.

Checks, Credit cards

Athletic X-Press

NEW LOCATION
Bellevue: 4027 128th S.E. 643-8976 *Factoria Square*
Everett: 1402 S.E. Everett Mall Way 353-1161 *Everett Mall*
Federal Way: 1804 S. 320th St. 839-2838 *Sea-Tac Mall*
Redmond: 2184 148th 643-4862 *Overlake Fashion Plaza*
Tacoma: 10509 Gravelly Lake Dr. S.W. 584-0904 *Lakewood Mall*
Silverdale: 0315 Silverdale Way 698-3310 *Kitsap Mall*
Hours: Generally, Mon-Fri 10-9, Sat & Sun 10-6

Athletic Express, a large national chain, has something on
sale 305 days out of the year. Watch for special promotions on
recreational and athletic shoes by leading brand names Converse, Asics, Nike, and Reebok, which they buy in huge quantities. The family-oriented stores stress good fit for kids. Sports
apparel and accessories are also stocked. Mailing list for sales.

Checks, Credit cards

Avanti Sports

NEW LISTING
Seattle: 4518 University Way N.E. 547-3558 *Ave Arcade,*
U-District
Hours: Mon-Sat 11-6

Tennis and volley ball enthusiasts shop here for equipment
and sportswear at discount prices. Tennis balls cost $2.35 a
can, top-of-the-line warm-up suits by Sergio Tacchini sell for
$170. The owners' son is assistant tennis coach at the Univer-
sity of Washington. Returns accepted.

Checks, Credit cards

Bargain Bob's

NEW LISTING
Seattle: 2401 Utah Ave. S. 682-5446 *Sodo*
Hours: Mon-Fri 10-7, Sat & Sun 10-6

An amazing ever-changing array of sporting goods, recreational equipment and related apparel flows in and out of this big
warehouse operation, which just happens to be a major outlet
in the Puget Sound area for factory overruns, close-outs and
salesmen's samples. The owner, whose name is indeed Bob,
used to work for Eddie Bauer, so he's got an inside line on
where to get good deals. The emphasis is on camping, hiking
and fishing gear; water sports in the summer, snow sports in

the winter. With prices at wholesale or less, you're sure to find some of the best deals in town. A bi-monthly newsletter announces new arrivals. Liberal return policy.

Checks, Credit cards

Big 5

NEW LOCATIONS

Bellevue: 156th & 8th N.E. 746-9407 *Crossroads Shopping Ctr.*
Factoria: 4055 128th S.E. 747-5230 *Factoria Square*
Burien: 125 S.W. 148th St. 246-2707
Everett: 1201 S.E. Everett Mall Way 353-9100 *Everett Mall Plaza*
Federal Way: 1916 S. 320th 941-9991 *Sea-Tac Village*
Kent: 24216 104th Ave. S.E. 852-2524
Kirkland: 12520 120th N.E. 821-4366 *Totem Lake Mall*
Lynnwood: 18600-A 33rd Ave. W. 771-8066 *Alderwood Plaza*
Renton: 503 S. 3rd St. 271-6900
Seattle: 200th & Aurora 546-4443 *Richmond Highlands, Aurora Village Shopping Center*
    1740 N.W. Market 783-0163 *Ballard*
    4315 University Way N.E. 547-2445 *U-District*
Tacoma: 2505 S. 38th 474-1747 *Lincoln Plaza*
Silverdale: 9989 Silverdale Way N.E. 692-3646
West Seattle: 2500 S.W. Barton 932-2212 *Westwood Town Ctr.*
Hours: Generally, Mon-Fri 10-9, Sat 9-9, Sun 10-6

Recreational and athletic equipment of every kind can be found at local outlets for this 160-store chain. Name-brand merchandise is available at below market prices because they buy close-outs and promotional goods in huge quantities, especially shoes. Ski equipment, clothing, and shoes manufactured exclusively for the stores are often good buys. Comparison shop via weekly direct mail supplements. Returns accepted

Checks, Credit cards

Buffalo Bill's Sporting Goods and Toys

NEW LOCATION

Issaquah: 1005 5th Ave. N.W. 392-0228
Hours: Mon-Thurs 10-7, Fri 10-8, Sat 10-6, Sun 10-5

Fishing, hunting and camping gear sells for less here than it does in the big city. The store carries the complete Coleman line and I found a two-mantle propane lantern by Coleman for

$19.99 that mass merchandisers and warehouse clubs had priced at $29.99. The owner, whose family runs the White Elephant, a well-known surplus outlet in Spokane, also stocks close-outs, samples, and merchandise from stores going out of business. Get on the mailing list for discount coupons. Flexible return policy.

Checks, Credit cards

Capitol Hill Camping & Surplus

NEW LISTING
Seattle: 910 E. Pike 325-3566 *Capitol Hill*
Hours: Mon-Fri 10-6, Sat 10-5

A unique little hole-in-the-wall shop that does a bang-up job competing with REI across the street. The owner operates on a low overhead and sells mainly military surplus and top quality knock-offs of hiking, camping and backpacking apparel and equipment. Sleeping bags range from $19.98 to $39.98. You can buy good quality hiking boots for $50 or less, backpacking tents for under $100 and frame packs made by a former employee of Jan Sport at 40% savings. The generic version of Teva's high tech sandals will set you back a mere $11.98 instead of $30. And the original Converse all stars tennis shoes cost only $20. All sales final.

Checks, Credit cards

Doc's Marine Warehouse

NEW LISTING
Seattle: 106 N. 35th 633-1500 *Fremont*
Hours: Mon-Fri 8:30-5, Sat 8:30-3

A fun place to shop because you never know what you'll find. This surplus operation is owned by Doc Freeman's, a marine equipment store located close by on Aurora. While the main focus is on boating equipment, from port-a-potties to deck chairs, fish nets and fuel tanks, they also buy up tools, clothing, housewares, decorative items and whatever else they can get a good deal on from department stores and small dealers all over the country going out of business. The strange assortment of ever-changing goods is priced at 50% or more off retail. All sales final.

Checks, Credit cards

The Down Factory

Seattle: 1101 E. Pike 322-0800 *Capitol Hill*
Hours: Mon-Fri 9:00-4:30, Sat 9-4

If it's made of down, you'll find it here, from bedding to sleeping bags, pillows, hats, booties, long johns and outerware for the whole family. Prices may not be as low as at some retail outlets but everything is made with only premium grade down. Home-sewers can save $100 by purchasing the popular comforter kit: you do the basic sewing, the factory blows the down in and finishes the quilting. Don Shindler, who started this thriving family business in 1933, still works in the store and waits on customers. Watch for bargain basement prices in the summer, when business slows down. Call for a brochure. Liberal return policy.

Checks, Credit cards

Easy Rider Canoe & Kayak Co.

Tukwila: 15666 W. Valley Hwy. 228-3633
Hours: Mon-Fri 9-6, Sat 10-3

Buy a canoe, kayak, or rowing shell factory-direct from the West Coast's largest manufacturer. Seconds, which have blemishes on the finish, can be purchased for $300 off the list price. Canoes can be outfitted for rowing, sailing, fishing or whitewater outings. Kayaks range from economy-priced, entry-level versions to deluxe expedition styles. Call for a brochure or to view an informative two-hour video.

Checks, Credit cards

Eddie Bauer Outlet Store

NEW LOCATION
Silverdale: 9990 Mickleberry Rd. 698-9558
Hours: Mon-Sat 9-9, Sun 11-6

Since Eddie Bauer opened his first store in Seattle in 1920, his name has become synonymous with quality outdoor merchandise, much of which is manufactured exclusively for the 270-store chain and it's popular catalogs. The outlet store carries mainly discontinued or overstock clothing and shoes, but staff tells me hardware, lamps, and even tents have shown up on the shelves. Prices start at 30% off retail and go even lower on certain items, especially during frequent specials which are advertised via mailings or flyers. Flaws on factory rejects are marked with a piece of tape. If you're in Eastern Washington, drop by the Eddie Bauer Outlet store in Spokane, which is a lot bigger. To familiarize yourself with the inventory, visit a nearby store or call 1-800-426-6253 for a catalog. Liberal return policy.

Checks, Credit cards

Ed's Surplus and Marine

NEW LISTING

Lynnwood: 5911 196th S.W. 778-1441

Hours: Mon-Fri 9-9, Sat 9-6, Sun 11-5

For almost 30 years, Ed's, a local, family-owned business, has been offering one-stop shopping for all your fishing, hunting and camping needs, including boats (aluminum, inflatable and canoes), motors, and trailers. The big, low overhead warehouse stocks thousands of items by leading brand names, plus lots of army/navy surplus clothing and equipment, all at competitive or discounted prices. The selection of tents is outstanding, with two or three styles always on sale. Look for good buys on fishing poles, tackle and marine accessories. Get on the mailing list for Ed's discount coupon book and annual Coleman sale in the Spring. 30-day return policy.

Checks, Credit cards

Federal Army & Navy Surplus

NEW LISTING

Seattle: 2112 1st Ave. 443-1818 *Downtown*

Hours: Mon-Sat 9:30-6

Founded in 1917, not only is this the oldest military surplus store in the Pacific Northwest, which is why many items on display look like they belong in a museum, but it's also the largest, with 14,000 sq. ft. of space devoted to clothing and equipment for camping, hiking, and backpacking. The owner buys samples, overstock and irregulars from leading brand names like Therm-Arest, Eureka, Patagonia and L.L. Bean, which keeps prices 10% to 40% below the competition. Bargain hunters save even more on used army navy surplus. Credit or exchanges only.

Checks, Credit cards

Gerry Sportwear

Seattle: 1051 1st Ave. S. 623-4194 *Sodo*

Annual sale in November

Once a year one of the Puget Sound areas well-known ski apparel manufacturers sells off their samples, closeouts and irregulars at up to 75% off retail. The same merchandise turns up in ski shops nationwide (including REI) under the Tempco, Farwest, Colorado Classics, and Gerry Sportswear labels. Pants, bibs, snowsuits and fleece jackets vary from basic to high fashion styles. Come early for the best selection and bring your own shopping bag. Call to get on the mailing list for exact date. All sales final.

Checks

G.I. Joe's Sporting Goods

NEW LISTING
Federal Way: 35020 Enchanted Parkway S. 927-3719
Hours: Mon-Fri 9-9, Sat 9-7, Sun 10-7

This huge 50,000 sq. ft. store houses the largest selection of brand name sporting goods, recreational and athletic equipment you'll ever find under one roof. The big inventory of camping gear attracts a lot of people. As part of a 12-store chain, based in Oregon, volume buying keeps prices competitive on thousands of items, including automotive parts and accessories. A full-service repair shop takes care of any problems. Every year, after the 4th of July, the store sponsors a spectacular sidewalk sale during which tons of special purchase merchandise is sold at blow-out prices. Lenient return policy.

Checks, Credit cards

Golfland Discount Pro Shop

Tacoma: 4701-1/2 Center St. 564-7155
Hours: Mon-Sun. 10-10

Across the board discount pricing and a big selection make this a popular spot for golfers. Name-brand clubs start at $275. When you purchase a full set of top grade irons, the store throws in five private lessons with one of their golf pros. Beginners on a budget can check out the used department. Senior citizens qualify for a discount on the covered driving range. Returns accepted.

Checks, Credit cards

Golf U.S.A.

NEW LISTING
Federal Way: 31830 Pacific Hwy. S. 839-6488
Hours: Mon-Fri 10-9, Sat 10-6, Sun 11-5

With over 60 stores nationwide, this franchise operation buys in volume and passes the savings on to customers. Prices start at 20% off on a full range of golf equipment, clothing, and accessories, all by leading brand names. The store boasts the latest technology: a computerized swing analyzer. Big sale on Father's Day. Credit or exchanges only.

Checks, Credit cards

Jan Sport

Everett: 10411 Airport Rd. 743-2862, 353-0200
Periodic sales

Twice a year this well-known local manufacturer of backpacks opens its warehouse to the public during their popular "Weekend Warehouse Sale." Excess inventory, seconds, and merchandise returned from stores, as well as sporting goods from other local manufacturers, is sold at close to wholesale prices. Kneissl skis, Therm-Arest mattresses, and Pacific Coast sleeping bags have been known to show up. Jan Sport also makes fanny packs, frame packs, book bags and soft-side luggage. Call to put your name on the mailing list. No returns.

Checks, Credit cards

Jerry's Surplus

NEW LOCATION
Everett: 2031 Broadway 252-1176

Duffle Bag

Tacoma: 8207 S. Tacoma Way 588-4433
Hours: Mon-Fri 9-9, Sat 9-6, Sun 11-5

The same family owns and operates these two stores, which have been around for almost 40 years. Taking a low mark-up keeps prices competitive on fishing, hunting, and camping equipment by leading brand names such as Coleman and Helly Hanson. You'll also find reasonably priced heavy-duty work clothes by Levi and Carhartt.

Contrary to what the names suggest, the Tacoma store carries more military surplus while the Everett location houses the best selection of fishing tackle and rods in the area. The stores put out a discount coupon book in the Spring and hold a big inventory reduction sale the end of December. The Tacoma store maintains a mailing list. Returns accepted.

Checks, Credit cards

The Jolly Soldier

NEW LISTING
Seattle: 5463 Leary N.W. 789-6505 *Ballard*
Hours: Tues-Fri 10-6:30, Sat 10-5

Heavy duty clothing for work as well as outdoor recreation make this place a popular stop for commercial fishermen as well as campers and hikers. Much of the inventory is army/navy surplus, which keeps prices low. Irregulars by brand name manufacturers such as L.L. Bean show up as well. Duffle bags and hats are best selling items, along with cold-weather boots. On Thursdays, senior citizens qualify for a 10% discount. Call for a brochure. Credit or exchange only within 10 days.

Checks, Credit cards

Marmot Mountain Works

Bellevue: 827 Bellevue Way N.E. 453-1515
Hours: Mon, Thurs, Fri 10-8; Tues, Wed, Sat 10-6, Sun 12-6

This is one of three retail outlets in the country for state-of-the-art camping, hiking, skiing and mountain climbing gear manufactured by Marmont for their mail-order business. The outstanding selection of hiking boots is legendary. A small section of the store has been set aside for close-outs, clearance and used merchandise from rentals. If you don't mind cosmetic defects, seconds can yield big savings. Call for a free catalog or to find out about big spring and fall sales.

Checks, Credit cards

Mountain Bike Factory Outlet

NEW LISTING
Kirkland: 11320 N.E. 124th 820-6685
Hours: Mon-Fri 10:30-7, Sat 10-6, Sun 11-5

A small shop with a unique concept. Only three different styles of bikes are stocked and they're all made exclusively under the Sherpa label for this store, which has two other outlets on the West coast. The street bike runs $269, the trail bike $399, and the competition bike $499, which is about 10% below comparable models. The purchase price includes unlimited tune-up service for a year. Parts and accessories made especially for these bikes are also available. Three day return policy.

Checks, Credit cards

Nevada Bob's Discount Golf

Renton: 101 S.W. 41st St. 251-1486
Silverdale: 9445 Silverdale Way N.W. 692-9953
Tacoma: 2917 S. 38th 474-8288 *Best Plaza*
Hours: Mon-Fri 9-7, Sat 9-6, Sun 11-5

With over 240 stores nationwide, Nevada Bob's is the biggest discount golf chain in the country. Their incredible buying power puts goods in their stores at prices they claim can't be beat. Make one of their stores your first stop when comparison shopping. Buy used clubs or trade in your old ones for a new set. Get on the mailing list to find out about frequent store specials. Returns accepted.

Checks, Credit cards

Outdoor Emporium

Seattle: 420 Pontius N. 624-6550, 624-6642 Downtown
Hours: Mon-Sat 8-5, Sun 9-4

Check out this 10,000 sq. ft. warehouse for low prices on camping and fishing gear and outdoor clothing. You'll find an outstanding selection of sleeping bags, back packs, and over a dozen different tents on display. Fishermen will find lots of fishing tackle, rods, marine equipment, and the biggest coolers in town to take their catch home in. Return policy varies.

Checks, Credit cards

Play It Again Sports

NEW LISTING
Bellevue: 14339 N.E. 20th 643-2599
Federal Way: 1320 S. 324th 946-2029 *Ross Plaza*
Lynnwood: 19513 Hwy 99 343-5722
Puyallup: 11610 Meridien Ave. E. 845-1927
Seattle: 10738 5th Ave. N.E. 365-6226 *Northgate*
Tacoma: 2941 S. 38th St. 472-0551 *Best Plaza*
Woodinville: 17301 140th Ave. N.E. 481-8676
Hours: Generally, Mon-Sat 10-7, Sun 12-6, Lynnwood Thurs until 9

One of my favorite new additions to the Super Shopper! This national franchise operation, purchases close-out goods from over 200 manufacturers, plus they buy, trade and consign used merchandise from individuals who get 60% of the selling price. The main focus seems to be on golf and exercise equipment, team sports, especially baseball, snow skiing in the winter and water sports in the summer, plus an assortment of camping and hiking gear. The Lynnwood store boasts enough hockey equipment to outfit a team. I spotted brand new roller blades for half the normal retail price. Products by local manufacturers, such as O'Brien water skis, turn up frequently. Used merchandise sold "as is." 30-day return on new items.

Checks, Credit cards

Pro Golf Discount

Lynnwood: 19125 33rd Ave. W. 525-5518
Redmond: 15015 N.E. 24th 641-6766
Seattle: 10746 5th Ave. N.E. 367-3529 *Northgate*
Tacoma: 5015 Tacoma Mall Blvd. 473-4290
Tukwila: 301 Tukwila Pkwy. 431-0100
Hours: Mon-Fri 10-7, Sat 10-6, Sun 11-5

A 21-year old entrepreneur started this local discount chain in 1977, and today the Superstores in Tukwila and Lynnwood house every major brand of golf equipment on the market. Prices are kept low with volume buying and every year, around the end of July, the chain holds a huge tent sale. Merchandise is brought in by the truckload and sold at a small markup. Practice cages, putting greens, club repair, trade-ins and league discounts are other incentives to shop at Pro Golf. Call to get on the mailing list. Price guarantee. 30-day return policy.

Checks, Credit cards

Puetz Golf Centers

NEW LOCATION
Bellevue: 1645 140th Ave. N.E. 747-0664
Seattle: 11762 Aurora Ave. N. 362-2272 *North Park*
Tacoma: 7231 S. Tacoma Way 475-1989
Hours: Generally, Mon-Fri 9-9, Sat & Sun 9-6, Seattle Sat 9-9

Puetz keeps prices low on a complete selection of name-brand equipment and apparel. Service and a big inventory of custom-fit variables have kept customers coming back for almost 50 years. Used and returned equipment is always available. The Aurora store has an outdoor driving range where you can test your new clubs or learn the game. Get on the mailing list for annual sales held in February and September. Flexible return policy.

Checks, Credit cards

REI (Recreational Equipment, Inc.)

NEW LOCATION
Bellevue: 15400 N.E. 20th 643-3700 *Sherwood Center*
Federal Way: 2565 S. Gateway Ct. Place 941-4994 *Gateway Center*
Lynnwood: 4200 194th S.W. 774-1300
Seattle: 1525 11th Ave. 323-8333 *Capitol Hill*
Hours: Mon-Sat 10-6, Sun 12-5, Seattle open Mon & Tues until 7 only

This landmark co-op, founded in 1938 by a group of Seattle mountaineers, is considered by many to be the most comprehensive, quality-conscious store in the nation for backpacking, mountaineering, kayaking and bicycling equipment. Thirty-six stores nation-wide serve over one million members, who pay a $10 lifetime membership fee to receive a 10% dividend on purchases, discounts on rentals, sales notices and voting rights. Non-members are welcome to shop at REI but receive no dividends. Pick up free catalogs at the store nearest you or call 1-800-426-4840 to have them mailed. Smart shoppers hold out for big sales held in May and October when preseason and end-of-season sporting goods sell at drastically reduced prices. Clearance clothing and footwear are sold in the self-serve basement of the Capitol Hill store. Returns with receipt.

Checks, Credit cards

R&E 2nd Gear

Seattle: 1314 N.E. 56th Ave. 527-0360 *U-District*
Hours: Mon-Fri 9-8, Sat 9-6, Sun 11-5

At last! A discount store where cyclists can buy clothing, tools and bike accessories averaging 30% to 50% below retail. Inventory is mostly name-brand close-outs and seconds, last year's styles, or left-overs from the R&E up the street on University Way, one of the area's leading cycle shops. If you are interested in selling your bike, post a notice on the bulleting board. Get on R&E's mailing list for super sales and classes. Once a year they sell out their entire stock of rental and demo bikes (including Terra Tech mountain bikes) at killer prices. 30-day return policy. Located in Cycleplex.

Checks, Credit cards

Scoring Sports

NEW LISTING
Tacoma: 505 Broadway 272-9764
Hours: Mon-Fri 8-6, Sat by appointment

Scoring Sports wholesales clothing and equipment to teams and individuals, with soccer, volleyball, and basketball the main focus. Warm-up suits that normally retail for $100 cost only $39 here. Prices drop dramatically during their year-end sale when over 5,000 jersies get marked down. Plan on waiting on yourself since this is pretty much a warehouse operation. Exchanges only.

Checks, Credit cards

Seattle Ski Show Sale & Swap

NEW LISTING
Seattle: Seattle Center Exhibition Hall 634-3620
Annual Sale: End of October or first week in November

Northwest ski enthusiasts flock to this huge annual event for terrific buys on new and used clothing and equipment for the whole family. Retail stores dump clearance merchandise at bargain basement prices plus bring in a lot of close-out and special purchase goods from leading manufacturers. Individuals can sell items on consignment so they'll have some money to buy new or old stuff. Consignors set the price and the non-profit volunteer ski patrols who handle the swap meet get 20% if the item sells. All sales final.

Checks, Credit cards

Second Base

Seattle: 1101 E. Pine 325-2273 *Capitol Hill*
Hours: Mon-Fri 10-7, Sat 9:30-6, Sun 11:30-5

What a great place for the whole family to browse for secondhand recreational and athletic equipment! Canoes, dart boards, wet suits, baseball mitts, sleeping bags, bike helmets, golf clubs, exercise equipment and balls for every sport imaginable are just a few of the many items that fill the store. Save big bucks on ski equipment in the Fall. I hear this is a hot spot to shop for hiking boots. Merchandise is taken on consignment or purchased from garage sales, auctions and individual sellers. Consignors get a whopping 60% of the selling price. Prices negotiable, returns accepted.

Checks, Credit cards

Sierra Trading Post

NEW LOCATION
Cheynee, Wyoming: 1-307-775-8000
Hours: Mon-Fri 5am-10pm, Sat 7-4 Mountain Time

Outdoor enthusiasts who haven't discovered this wonderful discount mail-order catalog are in for a treat. You can save 35% to 70% on overstock, close-outs and irregular clothing and equipment by famous brand names like Kelty, Lowe, Columbia, Marmot, New Balance, Sportiff USA, and North Face plus a lot of others. Clothing, footwear and accessories for men and women includes basic sportswear as well as high-tech styles. Call now to receive a wonderful, illustrated catalog, free-of-charge.

Checks, Credit cards

Shorebreak Watersports

NEW LISTING
Kirkland: 25 Central Way, Suite 230 822-2100
Hours: Mon-Sat 9-7

Sometimes you can find fantastic deals on surf boards, water skis, and wetsuits because Shorebreak buys up seconds, close-outs, and samples from O'Brien, a well-known local manufacturer. The day I called they had a top-of-the-line demo board at $100 less than the regular price.

Checks, Credit cards

Sir-Plus

NEW LISTING
Seattle: 85 South Lander 624-4584 *Sodo*
Hours: Mon-Fri 7-7, Sat 9-6, Sun 10:30-5

Sir-Plus has been supplying outdoorsmen and workmen with rugged clothing and camping gear for over 15 years. Some of the inventory is army/navy surplus and factory overruns. Look for outstanding buys on duffle bags, rain ware (they stock Helly Hanson irregulars), and used coveralls, which the owner says he always keeps in the trunk of his car in case he has to change a flat tire. Union members who buy work clothes here qualify for a discount as well as those buying in volume. Credit or exchanges only.

Checks, Credit cards

Ski Bonkers

Seattle: 2601 Elliott, *Seattle International Trade Center*
Annual sale: Labor Day weekend

For over a decade families have gone bonkers over the low prices and huge selection of athletic wear and sporting goods at this supersale sponsored by Olympic Sports! Prices average 20% to 70% off retail on name-brand clothing and ski equipment of all kinds. Most of the merchandise is special promotions, close-outs, or clearance items from the local chains seven stores. Watch the newspapers for big ads.

Checks, Credit cards

Ski Rack Sports

Seattle: 2118 8th Ave. 623-5595 *Downtown*
Hours: Mon-Fri 10-7, Sat 10-5, Sun 12-5

Visit Ski Rack in November and December to check out their big inventory of consignment ski equipment for children and adults, all of which meets current safety standards. Prices start at half off and sales personnel will custom-fit boots. In the summertime sail boards are sold on consignment. No returns on used merchandise.

Checks, Credit cards

Sportco

Fife: 4702 20th St. E. 922-2222
Hours: Mon-Fri 9:30-6, Sat 9-5

As a local distributor of sporting goods, this big warehouse stocks over 15,000 items from hundreds of different well-known manufacturers. The general public is welcome to shop here but for a $15 membership fee customers can save another

5% on wholesale prices. Although the store carries a well-rounded inventory of recreational as well as athletic equipment, the selection of hunting, fishing and camping gear is excellent. Returns accepted.

Checks, Credit cards

Sportmart

NEW LISTING
Tacoma: 1905 "B" S. 72nd 572-9900
Tukwila: 17500 Southcenter Parkway 575-3070
Hours: Mon-Fri 9:30-10, Sat 9-10, Sun 10-7

Sportmart is part of a very successful 34-store chain of sporting goods Superstores that offer everyday low prices on everything from rowing machines to racquet balls. With 45,000-plus sq. ft. of floor space, stores stock more inventory under one roof than local competitors. The emphasis in on mass-marketed leading brand name recreational and team sports equipment.

A big attraction at Sportmart is their demo program, which allows customers to try out golf clubs, tennis racquets, etc. via a small rental fee which can be applied to the purchase price if they decide to keep them. Another plus is their popular Technical Centers, where employees string racquets, hot wax skis, drill holes in bowling balls, make adjustments or repair equipment on the spot. The company, which plans on opening two or three more stores in the area, also offers a low price guarantee, frequent buyer program, plus delivery and set-up of exercise equipment for a minimal fee. Liberal return policy.

Checks, Credit cards

Sports Exchange

Seattle: 2232 15th Ave. W. 285-4777 *West Queen Anne*
Hours: Mon-Fri 10-6, Sat 10-5, Sun 12-5. Open until 7 weeknights in winter

A close-out store that specializes in ski equipment and snowboards in the winter, bikes and water skies in the Summer, purchased factory direct from such well-known manufacturers as Connelly, Bianci, Mongoose, Norco, and Burley Trail. You can save 30% on bikes, including heavy terrain models, which sell for $200 to $1300. Some of the merchandise is rental equipment from the Alpine Hut, and some of it is second-hand items on consignment. Cycling clothing is also available. The store liquidates its rental equipment in March and mid-September. All sales on used goods final, seven-days return on new.

Checks, Credit cards

Sports Replay

Lynnwood: 5421 196th St. S.W., #7 775-4088 *Parkview*
Hours: Tues-Fri 10-7:30, Sat 10-5:30, open Thurs until 9,
Sundays vary

Terrific deals on new as well as used sporting goods, athletic
equipment and clothing are jampacked into this large, well established store, which has been around for over a decade now.
I was impressed with the amazing variety of items, from
pooper scoopers to 3-room tents. There's even a special section
for rock climbing. Half the inventory is close-outs, samples,
and seconds purchased from local manufacturers such as Sun-
buster, Snuggler, and Jan Sport. The other half comes from
the 3,000-plus consignors who get 60% of the selling price.
Look for good buys on tents, sleeping bags, biking apparel, and
skis, which the owner purchases from ski rental schools as far
away as Lake Tahoe. Ski packages for kids and adults start as
low as $400. Returns accepted.

Checks

Takson Down

NEW LISTING
Renton: 1000 S.W. 7th 227-8120
Annual Sale

From November to January, this manufacturer of better ski
apparel opens a small outlet in their distribution center to sell
off close-outs and irregulars. Down jackets, pants, and bibs for
men, women and children under the Powder Horn, Alaskan
Express and Grand Targhee labels sell for wholesale or below.
No returns.

Checks, Credit cards

Tom Wells Golf Club Manufacturer

NEW LISTING
Seattle: 8914 Aurora Ave. N. 526-9080, 1-800-248-7124
Greenwood
Hours: Mon-Fri 9-6, open Mon & Thurs until 8, Sat 9-5

Golfers take note! Buy custom hand-made clubs factory direct
from the largest supplier in the U.S., and you'll pay $200 for a
set of irons that would cost twice as much in a pro shop. The
store also sells components to those who want to put together
or repair their own clubs. The owner has spent 28 years
repairing and building clubs so he knows what he's doing. Call to
order a free catalog and to find out about frequent promotions.

Checks, Credit cards

Warshal's

NEW LISTING
Seattle: 1000 1st Ave. 624-7300 *Downtown*
Hours: Mon-Sat 9-5:30

Since 1932 Warshals has been attracting avid sportsmen looking for service, selection and fair prices on camping, hunting
and fishing equipment. As you roam around this big old-
fashioned store, you'll notice lots of special priced items. Bargain hunters head for the 4,000 square foot close-out section
upstairs or hold out for annual sales around Labor Day, the
4th of July, Father's Day and Christmas. One of the most
popular events is their annual gun sale in August. One-hour
free parking in nearby Republic lot with purchase. 30-day
return policy.

Checks, Credit cards

Wilderness Sports

NEW LISTING
Bellevue: 14340 N.E. 20th St. 746-0500
Hours: Mon-Fri 10-8, Sat 10-6

Wilderness Sports has a well-deserved reputation for friendly
service, top quality equipment and low prices. The focus is on
outdoor recreational equipment geared to the Northwest
climate that has been tested for safety and durability. The
selection may be limited but it represents the best products
available. Rental fees for hiking, back packing, mountain
climbing or ski equipment can be applied to the purchase
price. Every Thursday night the store hosts a slide show,
seminar or workshop. Call to get on the mailing list for a flyer.
Liberal return policy.

Checks, Credit cards

Winter's Surplus

NEW LISTING
Seattle: 6169 4th S. 763-2722 *Georgetown*
Hours: Mon-Sat 9-5:30

Winters focuses on clothing and equipment for hiking, fishing,
and camping, much of which is new or used military surplus.
Wool blankets, sleeping bags, duffel bags, combat boots and
big GI issue tents are always best selling items. Army
fatigues, better known as BDU's for "battle dress uniform"
cost only $20 a set. A full line of raingear is always in stock. In
the Spring the store sends out a discount coupon books and

sponsors a big annual Coleman sale, so be sure to get on the
mailing list. 30-day return policy.

Checks, Credit cards

West Marine Products

Seattle: 6317 Seaview Ave. N.W. 789-4640 *Shilshole*
1000 Mercer 292-8663 South Lake Union
Hours: Mon-Fri 9-7, Sat 9-6, Sun 9-5

This big, classy West coast discount chain sells an incredible
variety of top quality clothing and equipment for sail or power
boating enthusiasts. The line-up of ropes and pulleys alone is
mind-boggling. Products for repairing or building your own
boat are even available. Look for good deals on items manufactured exclusively for the chain, such as life slings, inflatables,
cleaning supplies, and state-of-the-art navigational equipment. Visit the superstore on Mercer for the best selection, or
call 1-800-538-0775 for a colorful catalog. Mailing list for frequent sales. Staff compares their hassle-free return policy to
Nordstrom's.

Checks, Credit cards

Wiley's Waterski Shop

Seattle: 1417 S. Trenton St. 762-1300 *South Park*
Hours: Mon-Fri 10-6, Sat 10-4

With the biggest selection in six states and the lowest prices
in town, water sport devotees flock to this place. Wiley's sells
more skis in one day than most sporting goods stores sell in an
entire season. Inventory includes wet suits, dry suits, ropes
and life preservers, plus used skis from trade-ins. Prices hover
close to wholesale in the close-out room where factory
samples, discontinued models, demos and one-of-a-kind items
are displayed. At one time Wiley's manufactured skis and still
does custom bindings. You might want to call for directions
since this isn't the easiest place to find. Flexible return policy.

Checks, Credit cards

Wright Brothers Cycle Works

NEW LISTING
Seattle: 219 N. 36th St. 633-5132 *Fremont*
Hours: Tues-Thurs 10:30-7, Fri-Sat 10:30-5

A must for cycling enthusiasts. Join this co-op and save money
on bike repairs, parts and accessories. A $30 lifetime fee entit-
les you to a $10 discount on all bike repair classes plus the use

of their tools and space. Staff is always available to give free advise. Members also receive a 10% discount on parts, clothing, and accessories, which are already cheaper than at most other stores.

Checks, Credit cards

Repair Services

When your $400 Gore-Tex jacket gets a big rip in it, the soles on your hiking boots wear out, or the zipper on your tent breaks, repair them instead of rushing out to buy brand new items. Rainy Pass and Dr. Zipper restore damaged or worn outdoor apparel, sleeping bags, tents, backpacks, etc. They can also replace lost buttons, snaps, buckles, straps and hardware, as well as the entire floor of a tent. Both stores have a $10 minimum fee. Rainy Pass also runs a laundry service for outdoor gear. Dave Page, who does business nationwide, specializes in repairing footwear, from new eyelets on hiking boots to resoling running shoes to complete reconstruction of Telemark boots.

Rainy Pass Repair Inc.
NEW LISTING
>**Seattle:** 5307 Roosevelt Way N.E. 523-8135, 1-800-733-4340 *Roosevelt*
>**Hours:** Mon-Fri 9-6, Sat 9-1

Dr. Zipper
NEW LISTING
>**Seattle:** 4254 Fremont Ave. N. 547-1247 *Fremont*
>**Hours:** Mon-Fri 10-6, Sat 10-2

Dave Page, Cobbler
NEW LISTING
>**Seattle:** 3509 Evanston Ave. N. 632-8686 *Fremont*
>**Hours**: Mon-Sat 10-6

Cameras and Audio Video Equipment

When shopping for a VCR, CD player, television, camera, stereo, camcorder or other expensive home electronics, it's a good idea to refer to Consumer Reports Magazine or a buying guide to zero in on exactly what make and model you should purchase in order to get the best value for your money.

Consumer Tips

✔ Comparison shopping is easy because the major dealers all advertise in the newspaper frequently and most will give price quotes over the phone.

✔ The classified ads sometimes turn up some fantastic deals on new and used electronics.

✔ Check the back pages of photographic magazines like Shutterbug for low prices on cameras and related equipment if you like to buy through the mail.

✔ Although many camera shops sell used equipment from trade-ins at 30% or more below retail, I've only listed those that have a good selection year round, but it pays to call other stores as you never know what's going to turn up and the best buys go quickly.

✔ Silo is a major discounter in this category but they are listed under Appliances.

✔ The best time to get film developed is right after Christmas, Easter, Mother's Day and other major holidays when drug stores and supermarkets have 50% off specials.

47th Street Photo

New York: 455 Smith Street, Brooklyn, N.Y. 11231
1-800-221-7774
Hours: Mon-Thurs 8-7, Fri 9-2, Sun 10-5

This giant mail-order firm has two retail stores in New York City where they sell name-brand audio-video equipment, cameras, computers, office machines, fax machines, microwaves, stereos, television sets, vacuum cleaners and watches at very competitive prices. For a $3 fee, which is refundable with your first purchase, they will send you a comprehensive catalog upon request. Or you can buy the Sunday edition of the New York Times and check out their two-page ads for weekly specials. Returns vary.

Alpine Camera Repair

NEW LISTING
Issaquah: 45 Front St. S. 391-1759
Hours: Mon-Fri 9-5:30, some Saturdays 9-12

You'll always find a good variety of quality used cameras on consignment here. The owner quoted me some great prices on a near mint condition Cannon, an auto focus Nikon N22 and an Olympic XA, the perfect camera for hikers. Call first to find out what's available. Consignors take home 75% of the selling price but the owners are very particular about what they'll sell.

Checks, Credit cards

Ballard Camera

NEW LISTING
Seattle: 2038 N.W. Market 783-1121 *Ballard*
Hours: Mon-Fri 9:30-6, Sat 9:30-5

With over 250 used cameras in stock by over a dozen leading brand names, you're sure to find just what you're looking for. Prices start at $100 and go up to $1,295 for a new demo F45 Nikon. Cameras and darkrooms purchased outright. Exchanges only.

Checks, Credit cards

Camera Show

Seattle: 7509 Aurora N. 782-9448 *Green Lake*
Hours: Tues-Sat 12-6

A unique shop that specializes in old-fashioned as well as used cameras and hard-to-find accessories. Professionals can pick up some terrific buys on top quality newer models while collectors will go for the vintage cameras. I'm told the owner will negotiate prices on some items. The store buys outright, trades, or will sell your equipment on consignment for a 10% fee. Mailing list announces new arrivals.

Checks, Credit cards

Cameratechs

NEW LISTING
Seattle: 5254-A University Way N.E. 526-5533 *U-District*
Hours: Mon-Fri 10-6, Sat 10-4

Although their main business is repairing photographic equipment, Cameratechs also sells used cameras they take in on consignment or have put in good working order. Prices start at

$100 with most of the cameras single lens reflex models favored by professional photographers. Consignors get 80% of the selling price.

Checks, Credit cards

Dick's Camera and Video

Burien: 15421 1st Ave. S. 244-1101, 1-800-942-FOTO
Hours: Mon-Fri 9-7, Sat 9-5

This has to be one of the largest camera shops in the Puget Sound area, which is why you'll find a full range of photographic and audio visual equipment, including dark room and industrial supplies for professionals. Sony and Nikon are the main lines, and there is always something on sale. Call for low price quotes or watch for discount coupons in local newspapers. The knowledgeable sales staff will gladly show you how to use your new camera or camcorder. Rentals, developing and duplication services also available. Ten-day return policy or 30 days for exchanges.

Checks, Credit cards

Future Shop Discount Super Center

NEW LISTING
Bellevue: 14515 N.E. 20th 644-1984
Sternco Shopping Center
Tacoma: 3326 S. 23rd St. 575-2240
Hours: Mon-Sat 9-10, Sun 9-7

Service, selection and low prices are three good reasons you'll want to shop here when it comes to purchasing a computer, major appliance or audio video equipment. Only top brand names are carried in the huge low overhead warehouses, which are owned by a big Canadian chain, whose volume buying power gives them an edge. Store displays include over 50 VCR's, as well as 350 TV's to chose from. Future shop guarantees the lowest price or they will give you the difference plus 55% of that amount. 15-day return policy.

Checks, Credit cards

Glazer's

NEW LISTING
Seattle: 430 8th Ave. N. 624-1100 *East of Seattle Center*
Hours: Mon-Sat 8:30-5

Glazer's caters to professional photographers so they always have low prices on film and a good selection of better quality used cameras from trade-ins, starting at $200.

Checks, Credit cards

Lee's Video-Audio-Fax

NEW LOCATION

Bellevue: 15625 N.E. 8th St. 643-5555, 643-0562, 643-7774
Hours: Mon-Fri 10-8, Sat 10-6, Sun 11-6

Not only does this locally owned small warehouse-type outlet have an incredible selection of the latest name brand audio equipment, but they guarantee the lowest prices in the state. Fastest moving items are VCR's, camcorders and TV's, which include a dozen big screen models. The store also stocks radar detectors, answering machines, cellular phones and over 30 different fax machines. Since the last edition they've added 35mm cameras. As a member of the largest buying group in the county, Lee can keep prices 20% to 40% below retail. Watch for super deals during seasonal sales. Add 2% to posted prices if paying by credit card. No returns.

Checks, Credit cards

Meiers Photo Technical Service

NEW LISTING

Seattle: 14614 15th N.E. 361-0363 *Paramount Park*
Hours: Mon-Fri 10-6

Check out this camera repair shop if you're in the market to buy or sell a good used single lens reflex camera or a lens from two to 15 years old. An added plus is the six month warranty. Trades also accepted.

Checks, Credit cards

Optechs Camera Supply

Seattle: 133 Dexter Ave. N. 443-1737 *East of Seattle Center*
Hours: Mon-Fri 8:30-6, Sat 9-5

A family-run business that offers a complete selection of film, equipment and darkroom supplies for professional photographers at prices that average 25% to 30% below the market. Only top-brands such as Hasselblad, Bronica, Nikon and Sinar are carried, with about 20% of the inventory used equipment. The big sale of the year takes place in February. Mailing list for sales. Return policy varies.

Checks, Credit cards

Old Technology Shop

Seattle: 7712 Aurora Ave. N. 527-2829 *Green Lake*
Hours: Wed-Sat 12:30-6, Sun 2-6

Step into this fascinating store and you'll feel like you've entered a museum. An odd assortment of obsolete electronic parts, audio equipment, and scientific instruments attracts amateur inventors, radio operators and hobbyists. It's one of the few places where you can find replacement parts for vintage TV's, radios, and bicycles. Fine carpenters' hand tools are another specialty. Return policy varies.

Checks

Quality Photos, Inc.

Hollywood, CA: 1-800-843-9259
Hours: Mon-Fri 8:30-5:25

For the last 40 years, movie stars and celebrities have had their 8" by 10" black and white glossies made here! You can't beat Quality Photos if you need a photo reproduced in quantity for promotional purposes. Prices go as low as 35¢ a piece if you order 100 duplicate pictures. Call the toll free number and they will send you a price list and information.

Checks

Rainer Photographic Supplies

Seattle: 8730 Rainier Ave. S. 722-8700 *Rainier Beach*
Hours: Mon-Fri 8:30-6, Sat 9-2

Rainier wholesales film, videotape, mailers, photo albums, studio and darkroom supplies to professionals, retail stores and big accounts like the University of Washington. The public pays the same price, which is 30% to 40% below list. Look for some of the best buys in town on film and broadcast-quality videotape. Pick up a price list in the store or call to have one sent by mail. The store offers same-day UPS shipping for orders of $10 or more received by 2 pm. Big sidewalk sale in June. 25% percent restocking charge for returns.

Checks, Credit cards

Video Only

NEW LOCATION
Bellevue: 14339 N.E. 20th 644-9400 *Ross Plaza*
Federal Way: 1706 S. 320th 946-4600 *Sea-Tac Village*
Lynnwood: 3703 196th S.W. 776-5900
Seattle: 707 Westlake Ave. N. 623-3388 *East of Seattle Center*
Tacoma: 2941 S. 38th 472-3838 *Cascade Plaza*
Tukwila: 17620 Southcenter Parkway 575-6665
Hours: Generally, Mon-Fri 10-9, Sat 10-6, Sun 11-5

Here's another big discount chain that stays competitive by focusing on a narrow range of products. TV's, VCR's, and camcorders are all they sell, but inventory includes many different styles and leading brands. Blank cassettes and videotapes go for low prices in case lots of ten. Nintendo games are also stocked. Exchange or credit on returns.

Checks, Credit cards

Warshal's Sporting Goods & Photographic Supply Co.

Seattle: 1000 1st Ave. 624-7300 *Downtown*
Hours: Mon-Sat 9-5:30

Over the years Warshall's has been noted for its low film prices and broad selection of cameras and photographic supplies. A large film inventory attracts commercial and amateur photographers who like to take pictures of the scenery as well as their catch. Fuji, Kodak and Ilford film is heavily discounted when you buy more than ten rolls at a time. One-hour free parking validation at nearby Republic lots with purchase.

Checks, Credit cards

Zobrist Electronics & Music

Seattle: 1214 1st Ave. 624-2424 *Downtown*
Hours: Mon-Fri 9:30-6, Sat 9:30-5

For over 60 years Zobrist has been selling electronic products for the car, home, or boat; check them out if you're in the market for a TV, VCR, stereo, telephone, shortwave radio, computer, CB radio or antenna. They are also one of the few places where you can buy multi-system TV's and VCR's (PAL/SECAN) as well as acoustic equipment for the music industry such as PA systems, DJ turntables and electronic instruments. Some of the merchandise is secondhand from trades or outright buys but it's all good quality. Look for big discounts on radio and TV tubes. Knowledgeable sales staff will give advice on home repairs or do-it-yourself projects.

Checks, Credit cards

Audio and Video Recordings

The big record chains and mass merchandisers such as Kmart, Fred Meyer and Target discount new releases when they first come out because they want to recoup their investment right away just in case the recording is a flop. Look for their ads in the Arts and Entertainment section of the newspapers on Fridays. Always check stores' bargain bins for overstock, promos and discontinued labels. Watch for special discounts on current and old releases when recording artists come to town.

Sometimes you can buy current and mainstream music in good condition for half price at stores that specialize in used cassettes, CD's and LP's. Other good places to shop for second-hand recordings are used bookstores, second-hand stores, and thrift shops. If you're selling old records, tapes and CD's, call for an appointment first and don't expect to make a lot of money. Take advantage of trades and credits for a better return on your investment.

If you want to buy a movie, the longer you're willing to wait, the less you pay. The price goes down 50% once a video drops off the current release list. Mass merchandisers and grocery stores sometimes sell at a loss just to get people in the store, hoping they'll buy something else. Previously viewed videos may not be the best quality but for $4.88 to $19.98, you can't beat the prices. For the best selection, look to volume renters like Tower, the Wherehouse, and Blockbuster. For the lowest prices, check out flea markets and swap meets, where video rental stores dump a lot of tapes.

When renting, comparison shop in your own neighborhood for the lowest prices. Why drive an extra mile when the cost of gas will eat up a $1 savings? Check grocery stores and mini-markets where selection may be limited, but prices will be cheaper. Don't forget your local library, which offers popular, informational and children's videos at no charge.

Some video rental stores sell memberships, which include special incentives for those who rent a lot of movies. Look for discount coupon books, two-for-one rentals, or free rentals after you rent a certain number of videos. During my research I discovered some unique incentives for visiting the following video rental shops:

75¢ Video in Bothell sells lifetime memberships for $150 which entitles you to rent any video in the store for only 75¢ for the rest of your life or as long as the company stays in business.

Visions Video in Ballard will rent you two videos for the price of one Sunday through Thursday, but only one can be a new release.

Video Theater in Lake City rents new releases for $1.75; all other movies cost only a dollar.

Tinseltown Video in Bellevue, Kent, Federal Way, North Seattle and Silverdale will let you keep a video for five nights and provide fresh popcorn free-of-charge with your rental.

Backtrack Videos and Records

Seattle: 5339 25th Ave. N.E. 524-0529 *U-District*
Hours: Tues-Fri 12-6:30, Sat 12-5

Ever wondered where you could rent or buy cult classics like "Amazon Women on the Moon" or "Attack of the Killer Tomatoes." Backtrack specializes in psychotronic and Golden Turkey videos in the horror, fantasy, science fiction and rock 'n' roll genre as well as pop, folk and rock from the 1950's, 60's, and 70's. Thirty LP's can be yours for only $30.

Checks, Credit cards

Bargain CD's, Records & Tapes

NEW LISTING
Everett: 1319 Hewitt 259-4306
Hours: Mon-Sat 9-7, Fri 9-8, Sun 11-5

Staff tells me their extensive collection of used recordings covers everything from bird calls to sound effects, although the main focus is on Top 40, country western, movie sound tracks, and easy listening music.

Credit cards

Blow Out Video

NEW LISTING
Seattle: 1418 1st Ave. 624-0993 *Downtown*
Hours: Daily 7-10

Previously viewed videos sell for only $7.88 a piece or $15 for two. With over 25,000 videos in stock, you're sure to find just what you want. Current releases show up about three months after they've been in rental stores.

Checks, Credit cards

Bop Street Records and Tapes

Seattle: 5512 20th Ave. N.W. 783-3009 *Ballard*
Hours: Mon-Sat 12-6

Bop Street offers one of the best selections in town of 45's and LP's from the 1950's and 60's including vintage rock, country, jazz, folk, soul and blues. Prices are negotiable and you qualify for a discount card just by walking in the door. Half the inventory is in storage, so if you can't find what you want, just ask. The owner loves to track down hard-to-find recordings.

Checks, Credit cards

Bubble Records & Videos

Kent: 10451 S.E. 240th 854-7788
Hours: Mon-Fri 12-8, Sat 12-6, Sun 1-5

Shop here for the most extensive selection of current and used records, CD's and cassettes in the South end. All new recordings are discounted. Collectors and radio DJ's often find what they want in the huge out-of-print section, which covers everything from jazz to classical.

Checks, Credit cards

Bud's Jazz Records

Seattle: 102 S. Jackson 628-0445 *Pioneer Square*
Hours: Mon-Sat 11-7, Sun 12-6

Ardent fans will find jazz in all its forms from ragtime to avant garde, and everything in between. Eighty percent of the merchandise is new, and prices are kept low to turn over the 10,000 plus titles in stock.

Checks, Credit cards

Budget Tapes and Records

NEW LOCATION
Everett: 305 S.E. Everett Mall Way 355-0766 *Greentree Plaza*
Puyallup: 11707 Meridian E. 845-2117
Renton: 534 Rainier Ave. S. 228-8298
Hours: Everett Daily 10-9; Puyallup Mon-Fri 11-9, Sat 10-7, Sun 11-6; Renton Mon-Fri 10-9:30, Sat 9-8, Sun 11-7:30

Prices are low because Budget carries a lot of "cut-outs" and used recordings, some of which are less than a month old or promo tapes. Current Top-40 releases are usually discounted when they first come into the store. The selection varies from store-to-store, since they're individually owned.

Checks, Credit cards

Cellophane Square

Bellevue: N.E. 8th & Bellevue Way 454-5059 *Bellevue Sqr.*
Seattle: 1315 N.E. 42nd 634-2280 *U-District*
Hours: Bellevue: Mon-Sat 9:30-9:30, Sun 11-6; Seattle: Mon-Sat 10-midnight, Sun 12-10

A popular hangout for those interested in contemporary, independent and local rock, Cellophane Square stocks a big inventory of new and used records, CD's and tapes. Used current releases go for almost half. The Bellevue store is more mainstream.

Checks, Credit cards

Co-op Video

NEW LISTING
Tacoma: 3124 S. 12th 572-3961
Hours: Mon-Thurs 12-10, Fri & Sat 12-11, Sun 12-9

Here's a novel idea! Become a member and you can buy videos or video games at wholesale prices from this dealer as long as you leave them in the store for a year, during which time you get 50% of the rental fee. Or bring your old videos in to sell or trade.

Checks

Drastic Plastic Records

Tacoma: 3005 6th Ave. 272-2886
Hours: Mon-Sat 11-6, Sun 12-5

Thousands of used albums, cassettes and CD's are sold here, with rock and jazz the main focus. The owner only buys or trades items in good condition.

Cash only

Exotique Imports

Seattle: 2400 Third Ave. 448-3452 *Downtown*
Hours: Mon-Sat 11-9, Sun 12-6

With a local DJ from The Vogue on staff, it's no wonder Exotique specializes in the latest dance music, from underground, independent, and acid jazz to electronics. About half the store is used CD's and records, including collectibles, and classics from the 1960's and 70's. Mail order available.

Checks, Credit cards

Fallout Records & Skateboards

Seattle: 1506 E. Olive Way 323-2662 *Capitol Hill*
Hours: Tues-Fri 11-8, Sat & Sun 12-6

Fallout specializes in independent, experimental, underground and punk records, tapes and CD's. Prices on major labels are competitive with the big record chains. Occasional sales advertised via flyers in the store.

Checks, Credit cards

Golden Oldies Records & Tapes

NEW LOCATION
Auburn: 1325 Auburn Way N. 351-0028 *Auburn North Shopping Center*
Bellevue: 156th N.E. & N.E. 8th 641-9820 *Crossroads Mall*
Lynnwood: 3925 196th St. S.W. 778-7722
Everett: 1902 Hewitt Ave. 252-0707
Renton: 924 S. 3rd St. 228-0866

Seattle: 201 N.E. 45th St. 547-2260 *Wallingford*
Tacoma: 8024 S. Tacoma Way 581-7947
Hours: Generally, Mon-Fri 10-7, Sat 10-6, Sun 11-5

This local chain sells an incredible selection of out-of-print 45's, albums and tapes from the 1940s, 50's, 60's and 70's. Although vintage rock 'n' roll is a big draw, country, jazz, western and big band sounds are also stocked in depth. Rare recordings, used CD's and re-issues of popular rock music round out the inventory. Merchandise varies from store to store, so if you know what you want, call first. The staff hunts nationwide for hard-to-find requests, and the store has an international mail-order clientele.

Checks, Credit cards

House of Records

NEW LISTING
Tacoma: 2609 6th Ave. 627-8231
Hours: Mon-Fri 11-6, Sat 10-6

House of Records is filled with used 45's, LP's, 78's, tapes and CD's with the emphasis on rock 'n' roll, pop and jazz.

Checks

M & L Associates

Seattle: 6504 Ravenna Ave. N.E. 522-8189 *Ravenna*
Hours: Variable, but generally Mon-Fri 1-5, Sat 10-6

If you like rare or vintage jazz, check out the extensive collection of 45's, 78's and LP's at this low-profile store. Customers also praise their outstanding inventory of second-hand rock, country and movie sound tracks. Used CD's may run as low as $5.00. Send $3 to receive a 40-page computerized listing of collectible jazz recordings. Send $1 for separate listings of other categories. For $8.00 you can purchase a 2-inch-thick catalog that includes everything in stock.

Checks, Credit cards

Movie Masters

Tukwila: 17900 Southcenter Pkwy. 575-0717 *Pavilion Mall*
Hours: Mon-Fri 10-8, Sat 10-6, Sun 11-5

A small shop specializing in classic movies, science fiction, and video games. New videos average $20, used $10 or less. Current releases and re-issues come from distributors who dump surplus merchandise. Used videos are purchased from libraries, individuals and rental stores. Trades welcome.

Checks, Credit cards

Northwest Record & Compact Disc Convention

Seattle: 228-3537
Periodic sales

Think of this as a swap meet for recordings. Thousands of records, tapes, CD's and memorabilia are brought in by collectors, dealers and retail stores from as far away as Oregon and Eastern Washington. The convention usually takes place at the Seattle Center in March, July, and October. Call for specific dates.

Orpheum

Seattle: 618 Broadway E. 322-6370 *Capitol Hill*
Hours: Daily 10-midnight

This small shop reflects the diverse tastes of its neighborhood and competes price-wise by taking a lower markup on new releases. Although they stock a little bit of everything, alternative rock and dance music is the main focus. DJ's shop here because of the big selection of 12" singles. Used CD's and LP's available.

Checks, Credit cards

Park Avenue Records & CD Exchange

Seattle: 532 Queen Anne Ave. N. 284-2390 *West of Seattle Center*
Hours: Mon-Sat 10-10, Sun 12-8

Check out the big selection of secondhand imports, oldies and collectibles. Although inventory covers all categories, rock and jazz sections attract the most customers. Mail and special orders available.

Credit cards

Penny Lane Records & Tapes

Tacoma: 11013 Bridgeport Way S.W. 588-1777
Hours: Mon-Fri 10-9, Sat 10-9, Sun 12-6

Penny Lane carries a wide variety of music. New releases, R&B and rap is often discounted. The store also favors 12" singles. Used cassettes and CD's make up about one-third of the inventory. Check music out beforehand in the listening booths.

Checks, Credit cards

Platters

NEW LISTING
Seattle: 8064 Lake City Way N.E. 523-9900 *Lake City*
Hours: Mon-Fri 10-6, Sat 10-5, Sun 11-4

Since 1946 Platters has been selling vinyl and that's still all they sell, from oldies to current releases, on 45's, 78's, LP's, and 12" singles. A new 45 costs only $2.69 and for every 10 you buy, they give you one for free.

Checks, Credit cards

Rubato's

Bellevue: 136 105th N.E. 455-9417
Hours: Mon-Sat 10-9, Sun 12-5

Looking for a good buy on jazz, classical music or vintage rock? Try Rubato's, where quality used CD's, LP's and cassettes sell for $7.99 to $9.99. Current promo copies turn up here as well as soul, pop and movie sound tracks.

Checks, Credit cards

Second Time Around Records, Stereo & Video

Federal Way: 32015 23rd Ave. S. 839-0649 *Sea-Tac Mall*
Seattle: 4209 University Way N.E. 632-1698 *U-District*
Tacoma: 2505 S. 38th 472-0623 *Lincoln Plaza*
Hours: Generally, Mon-Sat 10-11; Seattle open until midnight
Fri & Sat, Sun 10-8

This classic used record store focuses on collectible rock from the 1960's, although they stock everything from pop to big band sounds. Prices are low on new and used CD's, cassettes and music videos. Recordings by local groups turn up here first. The store also buys and sells secondhand stereo equipment, as well as used guitars, TV's, VCR's, camcorders and rock clothing.

Checks, Credit cards

The Sound

NEW LISTING
Lynnwood: 18411 Alderwood Mall Blvd. #F 771-0914
Hours: Mon-Fri 10-9, Sun 11-7

Where music sounds better because it costs less! Look for deep discounts on new releases the first two weeks they come out and low everyday prices on singles and boxed sets. Inventory is based on what's selling at the moment, be it pop, rap, soul or dance music.

Checks, Credit cards

Soundwaves

Burien: 151 S.W. 152nd 248-3959
Hours: Mon-Sat 11-8, Sun 12-5

Burien record collectors celebrated when this small but comprehensive shop opened. Prices are sometimes less on current releases than at the Fred Meyer store down the street and much of the inventory is imported, progressive rock, or obscure tunes from the 1960's and 70's.

Checks, Credit cards

Sun Coast Video

NEW LOCATIONS
Everett: 1402 S.E. Everett Mall Way 347-3273 *Everett Mall*
Federal Way: 1824 S. 320th St. 941-2842 *Sea-Tac Mall*
Lynnwood: 184th St. S.W. & 36th 771-5550 *Alderwood Mall*
Seattle: 400 Pine St. #22 343-7491 *Westlake Center, Downtown*
Tacoma: 47th at Pine 472-0867 *Tacoma Mall*
Tukwila: 266 Southcenter 248-0048 *Southcenter Shopping Ctr.*
Silverdale: 10300 Silverdale Way N.W. 698-0977 *Kitsap Mall*
Hours: Check mall hours

For those who like to own instead of rent movies and videos, Sun Coast, a big national chain, delivers the best selection you'll ever find in one place. They carry over 6,000 titles and have access to thousands more, be they classic movies, documentaries, how-to, exercise or music videos. Average price is $14.98 to $19.98 and new releases are always discounted. Join the Producers Club for dividend certificates, special offers and a newsletter. Laser Discs are also available. 30 day return policy if unopened.

Checks, Credit cards

Tower Records & Video

Bellevue: 10635 N.E. 8th 451-2557]
Seattle: 500 Mercer 283-4456 *Northeast of Seattle Center*
  4321 University Way N.E. 632-1187 *U-District*
Tacoma: 2941 S. 38th 475-9222
Hours: Daily, 9-midnight

Tower leads the pack when it comes to mass market selection and savings on recordings and videos. Top-25 current releases, CD's and cassettes are always on sale, and in-store promotions change constantly. Read the Entertainment section of major newspapers on Fridays to keep up with the weekly specials or hold out for the big clearance sale in January. All stores except the U-District rent videos for only $1.25 Tuesday through Thursday. Previously viewed videos sell for some of the lowest prices in town. The Mercer store is the largest in the Northwest. Credit or exchanges within 7 days.

Checks, Credit cards

The Wherehouse

Bellevue: 1100 Bellevue Way N.E. 454-2235
 2301 148th Ave. N.E. 746-7022
Everett: 1203 S.E. Everett Mall Way 353-1201
Federal Way: 31861 Gateway Blvd. S. 941-8221
Lynnwood: 3000 184th St. N.W. 776-5099 *Alderwood Mall*
 19800 44th Ave. W. 670-2827
Seattle: 4501 Roosevelt Way N.E. 633-4072 *U-District*
 206 Broadway E. 324-2140 *Capitol Hill*
Tacoma: 6409 6th Ave. 564-2336
 10115 Gravelly Lake Dr. 584-1156
Hours: Generally, Daily 10-10

Every week something different goes on sale at this major West coast chain where you can buy the latest tapes, CD's, videos, and video games. Prices go down 20% to 30% during big quarterly sales advertised via colorful bulk mailings which include accessories and blank tapes. The Wherehouse also buys and sells used CDs.

All video rentals are $1.79, including current releases, which makes this one of the cheapest places in town for a one-night rental. Inquire about their Frequent Renter Video Program and earn points that can be applied towards free products. Monthly catalogs available in the stores list sale prices on previously viewed videos and games. Credit or exchanges only on returns.

Checks, Credit cards

Arts and Crafts

Arts and crafts have gained popularity in the last few years, not only as a creative outlet but also as a fun, easy way to stretch the family budget. Sewing is a skill that it pays to master, whether you plan on making clothes for the whole family or simply want to do your own alterations. And you don't have to be an advanced seamstress to make curtains, tablecloths, slipcovers or decorative pillows.

Consumer Tips

✔ Many fabric stores have sales geared to the holidays, so get on their mailing lists and watch the newspapers for ads.

✔ Never pay full price for patterns as most stores now sell them at 50% off the marked price all of the time.

✔ Visit fabric stores and arts and crafts stores when they offer free demonstrations or inexpensive classes.

✔ Make the remnant section your first stop if you are working on a craft project, making a quilt, or a child's garment.

B & B Hobbies & Crafts

NEW LOCATION
Kent: 317 S. Washington Ave. 859-1585 *K-Mart Center*
Redmond: 15752 Redmond Way 861-4486 *Redmond Center*
Hours: Mon-Fri 10-8, Sat 10-6, Sun 11-5

This nationwide chain may not have the biggest stores, but they carry an outstanding variety of arts and crafts supplies, especially if you like to make candles, dolls, miniatures, jewelry, Christmas ornaments, or flower arrangements for fun or profit. B&B beats competitor's prices on may items because they buy by the truckload and manufacture many of their own products. Acrylic paints, craft books and papier-mache supplies are big sellers. Exchange or credit on returns.

Checks, Credit cards

The Creation Station

NEW LISTING

Edmonds: 7533 Olympic View Drive 775-7959
Hours: Mon- Sat 11-5, Tues & Thurs open until 7

What a fun, nifty way to recycle materials that normally end up in land fills! The owner, a former teacher, began using child-safe materials that most businesses throw away to help teach art, math, music and science classes. Now she's opened a store filled with bins containing spools, tubes, trays, fabric, foam, stickers, markers, string, tape and assorted strange looking objects from which kids can create a multitude of things. For $1 to $8 they can fill small to large-size bags up with anything they want. For $3 per child, the Creation Station will supply space and materials for classes, field trips or birthday parties. Materials and a brochure can be ordered by mail.

Checks

Calico Corners

Bellevue: 104 Bellevue Way S.E. 455-2510
Lynnwood: 3225 Alderwood Mall Blvd. 778-8019 *Alderwood Town Center*
Hours: Generally, Mon-Sat 10-6, Wed 10-8, Sun 12-5

The array of gorgeous decorator fabrics and creative displays will inspire you to re-do your whole house, and at these prices you can afford to! Many of the fabrics come from Waverly, a leading name in home fashions, while others come from showrooms only accessible to interior decorators. First quality goods go for a fraction of the their original cost because they have slight imperfections in color or design. Seconds are carefully examined for flaws to make sure a project is viable. Get on the mailing list for exact dates of big sales in April and September. Call the Bellevue store for a schedule of home decorating classes or to inquire about custom labor.

Checks, credit cards

Daisy Kingdom/DK Sports

Portland, OR: 1-800-234-6688
Hours: Mon-Fri 8-5

Send for free catalogs filled with nursery, craft and outerwear kits designed and manufactured exclusively by Daisy Kingdom and you will save 20% or more off the finished product at their Oregon retail stores. The outerwear catalog features stylish ski and activewear apparel for the whole family. Fabrics and notions for these types of garments can be ordered separately.

Checks, Credit cards

Daniel Smith

Seattle: 4150 1st Ave. S. 223-9599 *Sodo*
Hours: Mon-Sat 9-6, Wed 9-8, Sun 10-6

Daniel Smith stocks the largest selection of fine art supplies on the West Coast, and everything is sold at discounted prices. Once a year the company publishes a beautiful 200-page color catalog showcasing 20,000 products with instructions on how to use them. Smaller catalogs, which include a lot of sale items, are also free upon request.

Checks, Credit cards

Everett Tent & Awning Co.

Everett: 2916 Hewitt Ave. 252-8213
Hours: Mon-Fri 8-4:30

Canvas yardage and bolt ends are available starting at $5.50/yd., but inventory depends upon recent work-orders. If you can use little pieces of canvas for craft projects, a box of free scraps sits inside, near the door.

Checks, Credit cards

Famous Labels Fabric Outlet

NEW NAME
Tukwila: 17820 W. Valley Hwy. 251-0067
Tacoma: 3720 S. "G" St. 472-2394
Hours: Mon-Sat 9:30-5:30, Sun 12-5

Factory overruns from well-known manufacturers such as Jantzen, Vanity Fair, L.L. Bean, Osh Kosh, Health Tex, Catalina, and Liz Clairborne turn up here at bargain basement prices. The selection of knits, (especially lycra and nylon) and fabrics for outerwear can't be beat. To save even more, check out the fabrics sold by the pound. Left-over collars, cuffs, zippers, elastic, buttons, drawstrings, and miscellaneous findings are dirt cheap. Call and the store will send you a calendar listing monthly sale items. Senior citizens who shop the first Tuesday of the month get a 15% discount. Free demonstrations every Thursday from 10am to 2pm. No returns.

Checks, Credit card

Hancock Fabrics

Kirkland: 12030 N.E. 85th St. 827-3020
Lynnwood: 3815 196th S.W. 774-4414 *Alderwood Village*
Renton: 2810 N.E. Sunset Blvd. 226-7071 *Greater Highlands Center*
Seattle: 112 N. 85th 783-2434 *Greenwood*
Tacoma: 10401 Gravelly Lake Dr. S.W. 581-2619 *Lakewood Mall*
  3121 S. 38th 474-8681
  5401 6th Ave. 756-9696 *Sixth Avenue Plaza*
West Seattle: 3922 S.W. Alaska 932-1110
Hours: Mon-Fri 9:30-9, Sat 9:30-6, Sun 12-5

Hancock delivers everyday low prices on everything from bridal satin to calico prints to fake furs and home decorating fabrics. Save even more by purchasing fabric by the bolt, whether it's never been cut or only has a few yards left on it. Patterns are always 50% off and budget-conscious seamstresses make a beeline for tables piled high with mill ends and discontinued bolts prices at 50% or more off retail. Watch for big sales around New Years Day, Labor Day, Memorial Day and the 4th of July or get on the mailing list to find out about special promotions. Senior citizens qualify for a 10% discount the first Wednesday or every month. Arts and crafts demos and monthly quilting classes are free-of-charge. Returns accepted.

Checks, Credit cards

Jo-Ann Fabrics

NEW NAME / NEW LOCATION
Everett: 6701 Evergreen Way 355-7373 *Cascade Plaza*
Federal Way: 2200 S. 314th 946-2480 *Hillside Plaza*
Kirkland: 12546-A Totem Lake Blvd. N.E. 821-7187 *Totem Lake Mall*
Kent: 26108 104th Ave S.E. 859-1143 *Kent Hill Plaza*
Renton: 2819 N.E. Sunset Blvd. 271-1733 *Highland Shopping Center*
Seattle: 15236 Aurora Ave. N. 362-8072 *Shoreline*
Silverdale: 13276 N.W. Plaza Rd. 692-7243 *Kitsap Plaza*
Spanaway: 14916 Pacific Ave. S. 535-3241 *Spanaway Shopping Center*
Tacoma: 5943 6th Ave. 564-3081 *Highland Hills Shopping Ctr.*
Hours: Mon-Fri 9:30-9, Sat 9:30-6, Sun 12-5

Inventory focuses on crafts and inexpensive fabrics in the $3 to $10/yd. price range with calicos and holiday prints a specialty. Close-out fabrics purchased direct from the manufacturer start at 88¢. Jo-Ann uses direct mail advertising to promote frequent sales during which you can save 10% to 50% on fabrics, notions and crafts. The day I visited patterns were 60% off retail. Sign up for free craft classes. Returns accepted.

Checks, Credit cards

MacPherson Leather Co.

Seattle: 519 12th Ave. S. 328-0855 *Capitol Hill*
Hours: Mon-Fri 8-4:30

McPherson's sells top quality leather and suede skins. For $80 you can buy half a cowhide and make a skirt or a pair of pants in the latest style. Remnants are priced "as is," and some are large enough for a vest or purse. Left-over scraps for arts and crafts projects sell for $4.50 to $6/lb. You'll also find tools, special thread, patterns and instruction books. 30 days on returns.

Checks, Credit cards

Michaels

NEW LISTING
Federal Way: 32061 Pacific Hwy. S. 946-1191 *Ross Plaza*
Tukwila: 17686 Southcenter Parkway 575-4352 *Parkwood Plaza*
Hours: Mon-Fri 9-9, Sat 9-7, Sun 10-6

As the number one discount arts and crafts store in the nation, this huge chain delivers low prices on a multitude of products. Many people shop here because of their outstanding floral department, party supplies and seasonal decorations. Something different goes on sale every month and newspaper ads will keep you tuned into special promotions like their big "Christmas in July" sale. Craft enthusiasts can attend free demonstrations or sign up for classes. Returns accepted except on seasonal merchandise brought back after the holidays.

Checks, Credit cards

Pacific Fabrics' Warehouse Outlet

Seattle: 2230 4th Ave. S. 628-6237 *South of Kingdome*
Hours: Mon-Sat 9-6, Sun 11-6

Most of the craft items, home sewing and decorating fabrics at this long-standing, no-frills outlet come from Pacific Fabric's retail stores where they have already been marked down 30% to 50%. Something different goes on sale every week and prices have been known to drop as low as 50¢/yd. Patterns are half-price and notions 10% off retail every day. Half of the floor space is filled with big rolls of vinyl, canvas, and upholstery fabric plus foam and batting. Assorted household goods — towels, bedspreads and pillows — show up as well. Senior citizens qualify for a 10% discount. Located on the 2nd floor of Pacific Iron's big non-descript warehouse. While you are in the area, check out their building supplies store down the street. Returns accepted.

Checks, Credit cards

Plenty of Textiles

Seattle: 2909 N.E. Blakely 524-4383 *U-District*
Hours: Mon-Sat 10-6, Thurs 10-9, Sun 12-5

Seamstresses looking for natural fibers and one-of-a-kind cuts from designer showrooms shop here. The store specializes in wool and silk plus unusual, colorful prints from the likes of Liz Clairborne, Betsey Johnson, Michi Moon, and Anne Klein priced from $2 to $14/yd. Once a year the store gets in fine wool suiting remnants. Discounts to students in textile courses. A quarterly newsletter announces sales and new arrivals. Returns accepted.

Checks, Credit cards

Seattle Fabric

Seattle: 3876 Bridge Way N. 632-6002 *Wallingford*
Hours: Mon-Fri 9-5, Thurs 9-7, Sat 10-4

Seattle Fabric boasts the lowest prices and best selection around on outdoor and recreational fabric, including a huge assortment of Polar Tec fleece. Most of their customers are small manufacturers of wind socks, kites, banners, tote bags and outerwear, as well as those who make their own outdoor gear or work in the marine industry. You'll also find patterns, hardware and the notions necessary to complete your project. Restocking fee for returns.

Checks, Credit cards

Shamek's Button Shop

Seattle: 1201 Pine St. 622-5350 *Downtown*
Hours: Mon-Fri 10-5, Thurs 10-6, closed on Mondays in the summer, Sat 11-4

Buttons start at 5 cents a piece or you can purchase a bargain bag assortment of 250 for $4.50. Buy a gross of white Indian buttons and you'll have a lifetime supply for kids clothes, men's shirts and PJ's. You'll also find belting, buckles, fur hooks, zipper pulls, cotton pins, and hand-crafted buttons. Shamek's will custom-make buttonholes and belts if you bring in the fabric. Belts can be shortened or lengthened for $5. The minimum fee for punching holes in belts is $2.00.

Checks, Credit cards

Soft Coverings

NEW LOCATION
Seattle: 323 West Galer 286-7638 *Queen Anne*
Hours: Mon, Thurs, Fri, Sat 10-5, Tues 10-8, Sun 12-4

By buying direct from the mill, Soft Coverings offers super buys on quality decorator fabrics, most of which are natural fibers. The store recently added beautiful upholstery weight tapestries to the inventory which ranges in price from $4 to $40. Some of the fabrics are mill ends or discontinued patterns so they're one-of-a-kind. If you don't see something you like, fabrics can be special ordered from sample books. Trim and findings are available for do-it-yourselfers; in home consultations and custom labor for those who don't have the expertise. Big anniversary sale in October.

Checks, Credit cards

Super Yarn Mart

Seattle: 15208 Aurora Ave. N. *364*-9276 *Parkwood Plaza, Shoreline*
Hours: Mon-Fri 10-8, Sat 10-6, Sun 11-5

Prices are low because Super Yarn Mart is part of a big chain that sells mainly mill ends and yarn manufactured especially for them out of orlon, acrylic and synthetic blends. The best buy is 3-oz. skeins of 100% Dupont Acrylic 4-ply yarn at $1.09. Pattern books, kits and other knitting products are also discounted. The store sometimes gives out discount coupons with purchases. 90 day return policy.

Checks, Credit cards

Treasure House

NEW NAME
Kirkland: 9755 Juanita Dr. N.E. 821-4444
Lynnwood: 4027 198th S.W. 771-6600
Seattle: 5959 Corson Ave. S. 762-0900 *Georgetown*
Tacoma: 4510 95th St. S.W. 582-0314 *Lakewood Industrial Park*
Hours: Mon-Fri 9-9, Sat 9-6, Sun 11-6

These huge warehouses offer not only a staggering array of floral, craft and party supplies, but lots of creative, visual displays that will give you ideas on how to use their products. Look for good buys on holiday crafts (Christmas items are available year-round) and table settings, which come in 18 different colors. Wedding invitations are always 40% off and every year the store hosts a big bridal fair. Buy anything by the case or box and you'll save 10% off the marked price.

Seniors qualify for a 10% discount on Tuesdays but everyone can save big bucks during the gigantic anniversary sale in June. Floral and craft designers are available for free consultations or you can sign up for weekly classes for a minimum fee. 30-day return policy.

Checks, Credit cards

Tacoma Tent & Awning

Tacoma: 121 N. "G" St. 627-4128
Hours: Mon-Fri 8-5

This company custom-makes various outdoor products from canvas, tarp, and tent fabrics. Selection varies from full rolls to bolt ends, priced at $2.50 to $18/yd.

Checks

Tandy Leather

Burien: 14611 1st Ave. S. 244-0351
Seattle: 20003 Aurora Ave. N. 542-1677 *Richmond Highlands*
Tacoma: 5429 S. Tacoma Way 474-1777
Hours: Mon-Sat 9-6

Scraps of leather or suede for making wallets, pouches, knife sheaths and beading projects sell for $2 to $5/lb. The selection of garment leather is not as good here as at McPherson's, but Tandy's carries more commercial items and related accessories for the hobbyist. If you are interested in leather-making classes, call to find out when they are scheduled. 30-day return policy.

Checks, Credit cards

Weaving Works

Seattle: 4717 Brooklyn N.E. 524-1221 *U-District*
Hours: Mon-Fri 10-6, Thur 10-8, Sat 11-5, Sun 11-3

If you're looking for a good buy on natural fibers or imported yarns, check the bargain table at Weaving Works or put your name on their mailing list to find out about the terrific bin sale in June during Mother's Day weekend. Yarn, fleece, basketry supplies, spinning, knitting, and dying equipment get marked down 50%.

Checks, Credit cards

Wellworth's

Everett: 4818 Evergreen Way 252-3293
Hours: Mon-Fri 8:30-5:30, Sat 10-5

Creative seamstresses may be interested in the 26-inch square drapery and upholstery fabric samples sold at this custom workroom. At $1.25 each, you can buy dozens for pillows, patchwork quilts, or to recover kitchen chairs.

Checks, Credit cards

Fur Scraps

If you're interested in fur scraps for doll clothes or other craft project, I've found two furriers who will sell leftovers. Price depends on the pelt and size. Call first to find out what's available and to make an appointment. Bob Manders (622-3076) in downtown Seattle, located at 1424 4th Ave, works with a wide variety of furs including mink, sable, beaver, otter, leopard and Persian lamb. He sometimes has pieces large enough for trimming a garment. Anderson Furs, (763-9989) at 8305 Dallas South in Seattle's, South Park only sells coyote scraps since they make trim for parkas and coats sold in Alaska.

Paper

Looking for inexpensive paper for art projects, tablecloths, banners, signs, or packing? The following newspapers sell roll ends of newsprint for $1 to $5 per roll, depending on how much is left. Roll widths vary, but common sizes are 18-inch, 34-inch, and 45-inch. It's best to call first to find out what is available.

The Everett Herald

Everett: 1213 California St. 339-3000

The Journal American

Bellevue: 1701 132nd N.E. 455-2222

Little Nickel Want Ads

NEW LISTING

Lynnwood: 3619 148th S.W. 367-2121

Snohomish Publishing

Snohomish: 114 Ave. C. 776-7546

The Tacoma News Tribune

Tacoma: 1950 S. State 597-8788

Used Books

Seattle has long been among the top ten cities in the country when it comes to bookstores per capita, so it's no wonder there's a flourishing business buying, selling and trading used books, which is a good way to continually replenish your reading material. Prices depend on condition and demand, but generally you can count on saving 50% or more at used book stores. Books at thrift shops, secondhand stores, rummage and estate sales are even cheaper.

Since most of the stores listed here concentrate mainly on hard-bound books, those interested in bookstores that carry only paperbacks should check the yellow pages for a nearby location.

Most used bookstores do not take returns but you can sell the book back for half of what you paid or get credit on account for future purchases. If the book is a gift, special arrangements can be made at some stores beforehand.

Consumer Tip

✔ If you're selling a rare book or collectible, have it appraised by a reputable dealer. You will have to pay a fee, but it will be worth the money. Some dealers will take more expensive items on consignment if they can't afford to buy outright.

American Bookseller

NEW LISTING
Seattle: 850 N.W. 85th 783-4899 *Ballard*
Hours: Mon-Sat 11-6

Although the main focus is on general literature, the classics, and children's books, subjects covered in depth include Americana, nautical and military history, with a special emphasis on the South Pacific, pirates, transportation, railroading, the Northwest and Alaska. Exchanges or credit.

Checks, Credit cards

Beatty Book Store

Seattle: 1925 3rd. Ave. 728-2665 *Downtown*
Hours: Mon-Sat 11-5

Spend hours browsing through rooms of moderately priced paperback and hardback books at Seattle's second largest used bookstore, where you'll find everything but romance novels and textbooks. Books on art, cooking, fiction, philosophy, poetry, theology, military and regional history abound. I'm told the store pays well for used books.

Checks

Beauty and the Books

Seattle: 4213 University Way N.E. 632-8510 *U-District*
Hours: Mon-Sun 10-10

After 20 years on "The Ave", Beauty and the Books has acquired an eclectic selection of books and collectibles including science fiction, poetry, history, literature, the occult, vintage pornography and books on the Northwest, all in a funky atmosphere that includes several resident cats. In the basement annex thousands of titles sell for a fraction of their original price.

Checks

Biblelots and Books

Seattle: 112 E. Lynn 329-6676 *East Lake Union*
Hours: Tues-Sat 12-5:30

A great resource for classic and illustrated children's books from "Mother Goose" to "Treasure Island," including out-of-print and rare editions!

Checks, Credit cards

Book Affair

Seattle: 15203 Military Road S. 241-0629 *Sea-Tac*
Hours: Mon-Fri 10-6:30, Sat 10-4, Sun 12-8

Book Affair offers a well-rounded selection of used paperbacks and hardbacks with an emphasis on military history and metaphysical subjects.

Checks, Credit cards

Book World

NEW LISTING
Kent: 23406 Pacific Hwy. S. 824-9422
  23824 104th S.E. 859-5826 859-5826
Hours: Pacific Hwy. S. Mon-Sat 10-9, Sun 10-6; 104th Mon-Sat 9-9, Sun 9-6

A good general-purpose bookstore with one of the biggest selections in the south end. There is more fiction than non-fiction, especially in the mystery, western, romance, and science fiction categories.

Checks, Credit cards

Corner Books

NEW LISTING
Kenmore: 6521 N.E. 181st 486-6485
Hours: Mon-Fri 10:30-6, Sat 10:30-5:30, Sun 12-5

The owner says he carries everything under the sun, with his collection of science fiction and mysteries one of the best around.

Checks

Catchpenny Books

Seattle: 9020 Roosevelt Way N.E. 527-4530 *Northgate*
Hours: Tues 10-9, Wed-Sat 10-6

Located in a two-story bungalow, Catchpenny contains rare classics, literary, historical and children's books, along with a good selection on art, poetry, science fiction, the Civil War, westerns, travel, World War II history, and politics. They are also one of the few bookstores that stocks foreign language novels and study books. Poetry readings occur the third Friday of every month.

Checks

Comstock's Bindery and Bookshop

Auburn: 257 E. Main 939-8770
Hours: Mon-Sat 10-6

Used and out-of-print books cover every subject you can think of, with an emphasis on aviation, railroading and military history. Special interest magazines on these subjects are bought and sold. If you have a rare book, Bible, or family heirloom that needs restoration, Comstock still does hand-bookbinding.

Checks, Credit cards

The Couth Buzzard

NEW LISTING
Seattle: 7221 Greenwood N. 789-8965 *Greenwood*
Hours: Tues-Thurs 12-8, Fri-Sun 10-6

Love the name! A well-stocked store owned by two retired school teachers who carry a lot of biographies, mysteries, science fiction and self-help books. A reading lounge furnished with comfortable well-worn chairs encourages brousers to spend the evening.

Checks

Fillipi Book and Record Shop

Seattle: 1351 E. Olive Way 682-4266 *Capitol Hill*
Hours: Tues-Sat 10-5

For over a half-century this venerable old bookstore has served as a collection site for books, sheet music, postcards, vintage photos, piano rolls, phonograph records and ephemera of all kinds. Serious collectors of recordings from jazz to opera rate Fillipi's as one of the best resources on the West coast. An astounding inventory of first and rare editions attracts those with an interest in art, history and literature. Prices may be slightly higher, but everything is well organized, in above-average condition, and the staff is service-oriented.

Checks

Fox Book Company

Tacoma: 737 St. Helens 627-2223
Hours: Mon-Sat 10-6

For 50 years this family-owned book store has supplied readers with one of the largest selections of used, rare and out-of-print books in the Tacoma area. I'm told that many people shop here for modern first editions and Northwest history. Mailings include an annual Christmas catalog.

Checks, Credit cards

Friends of the Seattle Public Library

Seattle: Lincoln High School, N. 44th & Woodlawn 386-4636
Biannual sales held in the Spring and Fall

These sales attract thousands of booklovers, who often buy a year's supply of reading material in one day because prices are so low. The books are donated by patrons at branch libraries all over the city or discarded by the library. Proceeds from these two events help finance special projects and new purchases. Anyone can join Friends of the Seattle Public Library for $15 and receive a monthly newsletter, notice of the sales, and a chance to shop the sales a day in advance. The membership fee is less for students, senior citizens and the physically disabled.

Checks, Credit cards

Globe Books

Seattle: 5220 University Way N.E. 527-2480 *U-District*
Hours: Mon-Sat 11-6, Sun 1-6

The arts, humanities and world literature are the focus at this small shop, which also stocks blues, folk, jazz and classical recordings. Books are both new and used, with cookbooks, travel, nature and religion the strong-suits. This is also a good place to look for information on Native Americans and early exploration

Checks, Credit cards

Gregor Books

NEW LISTING
West Seattle: 3407 California S.W. 937-6223
Hours: Mon-Sat 11-7, Sun 12-5

Stop by Gregor's if you are in the market for literary first editions, books on history, mountaineering or the Vietnam War. Better prices paid for books in these categories.

Checks, Credit cards

Half Price Books, Records & Magazines
NEW LOCATIONS
Bellevue: 15600 N.E. 8th 747-6616 *Crossroads Shopping Ctr.*
Edmonds: 23632 Hwy. 99 670-6199 *Aurora Marketplace*
Seattle: 4709 Roosevelt Way N.E. 547-7859 *U-District*
Tacoma: 6409 6th Ave. 566-1238
Hours: Bellevue Mon-Thurs 10-9, Fri & Sat 10-10:30, Sun 10-8;
Edmonds and Tacoma Mon-Sat 10-10, Sun 12-8; Seattle daily
10-10

> These well-organized shops are part of a very successful 44
> store chain that buys and sells anything printed or recorded
> because the owner doesn't want books to end up in landfills.
> Prices start at half off on a huge inventory of tapes, CD's,
> LP's, magazines and books on every subject known to
> mankind. Look for the best buys in the bargain books section
> where fiction sells for 98¢ to $1.98. Books can even be pur-
> chased by the yard. About 30% of the books are remainders
> and close-outs. Get on the mailing list to find out about special
> promotions and the big year-end sale during which prices
> plummet even more. Credit or exchanges only.
> ***Checks, Credit cards***

Horizon Books
NEW LOCATION
Seattle: 425 15th E. 329-3586 *Capitol Hill*
6512 Roosevelt Way N.E. 523-4217 *Roosevelt*
Hours: Capitol Hill Mon-Fri 10:30-10, Sat & Sun 10-9,
Roosevelt daily 11-6

> The Capital Hill location, which has been around since 1971,
> is an old converted house with a maze of small rooms stacked
> floor to ceiling with books on every subject imaginable. You
> will find antiquarian and scholarly titles, classic literature,
> lots of mysteries, and a collection of science fiction that holds
> its own on the West coast. Used jazz, folk and classical records
> are also available. The Roosevelt location delves more into art,
> pictorials and photography.
> ***Checks, Credit cards***

Leisure Books
West Seattle: 4461 California S.W. 935-7325
Hours: daily 10-6

> Leisure Books focuses on classics and world literature, along
> with a good selection of travel books, science fiction, and any-
> thing published in the 1940's or 50's.

Checks

Magus Bookstore

Seattle: 1408 N.E. 42nd 633-1800 *U-District*
Hours: Mon-Wed 10-8, Thurs & Fri 10-10, Sat 11-6, Sun 12-8

Magus has been catering to the diverse interests of the U-District crowd for over twenty years now, so inventory leans heavily towards modern fiction, the humanities and sciences. They're also strong on gardening, sports, cooking, science fiction and mysteries. Expensive technical computer books can be picked up here at half-price. This bookstore probably buys and sells more books in a day than any other dealer so it pays to visit frequently.

Checks, Credit cards

O'Leary's Books

Tacoma: 3828 100th S.W. 588-2503
Hours: Mon-Fri 9-9, Sat 10-9, Sun 12-5

O'Leary's boasts they're one of the largest bookstores in the Northwest, with over 10,000 sq. ft. of floor space. Stock is evenly divided between comics, paperbacks and hardback books with an emphasis on the history of North America.

Checks, Credit cards

Quiet Companion Books

Tacoma: 21 Tacoma Ave. N. 272-2929
Hours: Mon-Sat 12-7

Inventory includes 40,000 used hardbound books that cover all subjects, with a strong showing in business, economics, and Northwest history. The store also carries used records, specializing in classical music, rock 'n' roll and movie sound tracks.

Checks

Pioneer Square Books

NEW LISTING
Seattle: 213 1st Ave S. 343-2665 *Pioneer Square*
Hours: Mon-Sat 11-6, Sun 12-6

A general interest bookstore that only carries quality used and rare hardbacks and paperbacks. The owner concentrates on science fiction, art, nature, the environment, and politics.

Credit cards

Shakespeare & Co. Books

NEW LOCATION
Seattle: 1501 Pike Place #326 **624**-7151 *Downtown, Pike Place Market*
Hours: Mon-Sat 11-5

New and used hardbacks focus on general fiction and first editions, with mysteries and classics favored. The selection of illustrated children's books is excellent and, since the store is geared to the tourist trade, there is a heavy concentration on Northwest and Native American titles as well as books on ships and trains.

Checks, Credit cards

Shorey Bookstore

NEW LOCATION
Seattle: 1411 1st Ave. 624-0221 *Downtown*
Hours: Mon-Sat 9-6, Sun 12-5

Seattle's oldest bookstore (1890) is the first place many people look for antiquarian books, old magazines, maps, posters, prints and museum-quality ephemera related to the Puget Sound area. Ten rooms contain 200 separate categories from antiques to Western Americana. Prices tend to be high, but Shorey's has satisfied customers all over the world and uses every means possible to track down hard-to-find- titles, even if it takes years. Thousands of used books go for half-price during their famous annual New Year's sale, which always starts on December 26th and lasts two weeks. Don't miss it!

Checks, Credit cards

Signature Bound Booksellers

NEW LISTING
Seattle: 2222 2nd 441-3306 *Downtown*
Hours: Mon-Thurs 12-6, Fri & Sat 12-8

Seventy-five percent of the books are used, mostly 20th Century fiction and poetry. Bring your old books in to trade or sell on consignment.

Checks

Twice Told Tales

NEW LISTING
Seattle: 2210 N. 45th St. 545-4226 *Wallingford*
905 E. John St. 324-2421 *Capitol Hill*
Hours: Capitol Hill Mon-Sat 10-2, Fri all night, Sun 11-12;
Wallingford Mon-Thurs 12-8, Fri & Sat 12-10, Sun 12-8

Both stores carry a great selection of literature, science fiction, mysteries, academic books and current reading material. The Capitol Hill store, which is much larger, caters to night owls: from midnight to 8am everything is discounted 25%. Watch for the big anniversary sale July 14 on Capitol Hill and January 1st in Wallingford.

Checks, Credit cards

Westside Stories

NEW LISTING

Seattle: 12 Boston St.   285-2665 *Queen Anne*
Hours: Mon-Thurs 9:30-8:30, Fri 9:30-7:30, Sat 9:30-6:30, Sun 10:30-5:30

> Queen Anne boasts a top-notch used bookstore featuring contemporary and classic fiction, along with an excellent selection of poetry and children's books. Check them out if you are looking for books on cooking, gardening or fishing.
>
> ***Checks, Credit cards***

Tacoma Book Center

Tacoma: 324 E. 26th   572-8248
Hours: Mon-Fri 10:30-6, Sat 12-5

> Since this store moved next to the Tacoma Dome parking lot, it has become one of the city's largest used, rare and out-of-print booksellers. Standouts in the good general selection include childrens books, mysteries, science, art and history.
>
> ***Checks, Credit Cards***

Titlewave Books

Seattle: 7 Mercer St. 282-7687 *South of Seattle Center*
Hours: Tues-Sat 10:30-7, Fri 10:30-10, Sun & Mon 12-6

> Shop here if you want to find used books in tip-top condition. A general selection favors children's books and fiction.
>
> ***Checks***

Arts and Entertainment

With a little research and careful planning it's easy to save money on entertainment for the whole family. For starters, check out the chapter on coupon books, where you will find discounts on movies, theatrical productions, sporting events and tourist attractions. The Seattle Times Tempo, which comes out on Fridays, has a special column that appears on page three called "Cheap Dates" which lists inexpensive entertainment events for the coming week.

Museums

Following is a list of free days at museums and galleries.

The Frye Art Museum, The Daybreak Star Indian Arts Center and **The Center for Wooden Boats** do not charge an admission fee except during special exhibits; however, donations are requested.

The Bellevue Art Museum, Tacoma Art Museum and **Museum of History and Industry** offer free admission on Tuesdays.

The Henry Art Gallery is free to the public on Thursdays.

The Seattle Art Museum, Nordic Heritage Museum and **Wing Luke Asian Museum** charge no admission fee the first Tuesday of every month.

Better yet, become a member of your favorite museum and you'll qualify for reduced rates on daily admission as well as special events.

Movies

Seattlites love to go to movies but with prices rising to $6.50 a seat for new releases, the ardor may soon cool. There is hope for those who don't like to wait until their favorite flick comes out on video. Some theaters sell passbooks but they're usually not good on weekends or for current releases. Or you can go to matinees and save $3, a good idea if you're taking the whole family.

Don't forget that many libraries and community centers show children's movies free-of-charge. Pick up a brochure at a nearby location to find out what's on the schedule.

For the lowest price in town every day, anytime, I suggest you check out the following movie houses or refer to the "Reel Bargain" column in the Tempo section of the Seattle Times, which comes out every Friday.

Admiral Twin

West Seattle: 2343 California Ave. 938-3456

Four theaters, all shows except special features $2.00.

Alderwood Village Cinema 12

Lynnwood: 3815 196th S.W. 771-6169

Twelve theaters, $1.50 weekdays, $2 weekends, $2 membership fee.

Crest

Seattle: N.E. 165th St. & 5th Ave. N.E. 363-6338 *North City*

Four theaters, all shows $2.00.

Roxy Cinema

Renton: 504 S. 3rd St. 255-5656

Three theaters, all shows $1.50.

United Artists Discount Cinema 150

Seattle: 2131 6th Ave. 443-9591 *Downtown*

Four theaters, all seats, all shows $1.50.

Theaters, Concerts, Dance Performances

If you enjoy the theater, some companies sell subscriptions for previews, which cost less than matinees or week nights. Single tickets are even cheaper but usually only available in small numbers, so call ahead and make a reservation. Most theaters offer discounts for groups of ten or more, so get a bunch of friends together, or a day-care group for children's productions. Senior citizens and students qualify for discounts as well as half-price tickets 15 minutes before the show starts. Better yet, volunteer to be an usher and you can see the show for free!

Here are a couple of other ideas you might be interested in exploring.

The Intiman Theater designates one matinee per show "pay as you can" with a $1.00 minimum. (626-0782) Seattle Center

The Group Theater sells tickets at half price the day of the show starting at noon when the box office opens. (441-1299) Seattle Center.

Bathhouse Theater has a "pay what you will" matinee for seniors and low income families who can make reservations through the Parks Department. General public admitted if seats are available. (524-9108) Greenlake

Empty Space Theater sponsors "pay as you can" performances. (547-7500) Fremont

Seattle Repertory Theater tickets go on sale at half price two hours before the performance starts. (443-2222) Seattle Center

Don't forget to check the classifieds for people selling tickets to theater productions and expensive big-name concerts.

Ticket Master Discount Ticket Hotline

NEW LISTING
Seattle: 1601 5th 233-1111 *Downtown, Westlake Center*
Hours: Mon-Fri 10-9, Sat 10-7, Sun 11-6

A recorded message lists what's available on a daily basis, a brief description of the event and its location. Most tickets are half price plus a service charge and you never know what's going to turn up. Some events are listed in Ticket Master's "Speeding Tickets" column in the Weekly. Tickets must be purchased at the box office the day of the show — there are no phone reservations. It's best to go early in the day to guarantee seats since the more popular events sell out first. Located on the main level.

Cash only

Ticket Ticket

NEW LOCATION
Seattle: 401 Broadway E. 324-2744 *Capitol Hill, Broadway Market, 2nd level*
1st & Pike 324-2744 *Downtown, Pike Place Market Information Booth*
Hours: Broadway Tues-Sun 10-7, Pike Place Tues-Sun 12-6

This walk-up-only service is a great place to save money on local as well as national theater, music, dance and comedy performances. Tickets average half price plus a service charge for almost any show in town. All events are posted on a big board, and tickets can only be purchased the day of the show, unless it's a matinee, in which case they go on sale the day before. Parking is free in the Broadway Market garage or the Public Market garage on Western. Check out the entertainment section of newspapers and pick out a couple of events in case your first choice is sold out or not on the list. Ticket Ticket sells gift certificates in $20 increments, which would make a great present for friends who like to go out a lot.

Cash only

Dining Out

If you dine out frequently, you can save a bundle by checking the weekly entertainment section of local newspapers for discount coupons. Or, invest in coupon books (see special chapter) which are jampacked with 2-for-1 offers on everything from fast food to gourmet cuisine.

Community College formal dining rooms are among the best kept secrets around. Prices are incredibly low when compared to the going rate at restaurants because they only charge enough to break even, but you must pay in cash. Food is prepared fresh on the premises by students in the Culinary Arts Departments, and the menu changes throughout the quarter depending on what the class is studying. Call to make reservations as seating is limited and many dining rooms are closed during quarter breaks. At some colleges, private banquets can be arranged for groups or organizations. Also, food can be special-ordered for take-out, which could be a life-saver if you're planning a last-minute dinner party.

Edmonds Community College

Lynnwood: 20000 68th Ave. W. 640-1405 *Brier Hall*
Hours: Tues-Fri 11:30-1, Open Mon-Thurs during Summer Quarter

Culinary Connections, the formal dining room at Edmonds Community College, features white table cloths and formal service. Reservations are requested. Organizations are welcome to use the room day or evening. Catering is limited.

Lake Washington Technical College

NEW LISTING
Kirkland: 11605 132nd Ave. N.E. 803-2206
Hours: Fall, Winter & Spring Quarter Dinner only 5-8; Summer
Quarter breakfast only 7- 9:30

> The atmosphere and food served in Our Class Act is similar to
> that found in a fine hotel restaurant. The full-service menu in-
> cludes appetizers, ala carte salads, meat, fish and poultry
> entrees along with French pastries made in the school bakery.
> For breakfast you can order souffles, stuffed french toast, and
> other gourmet delights.

North Seattle Community College

Seattle: 9600 College Way N. 527-3779 *Northgate, College
Center Bldg.*
Hours: Mon-Thurs 11-1, Closed Summer Quarter

> Students hone their culinary skills in the North Star Dining
> Room and the Rose Room, a more elegant atmosphere
> reserved for private parties.

Renton Technical College

NEW LISTING
Renton: 3000 N.E. 4th 235-5845 *Building I, Campus Center,
lower level*
Hours: Mon-Fri 11:30-1

> Renton Technical College, along with South Seattle Com-
> munity College, are the only two culinary programs in the
> state accredited by the American Culinary Federation. I'm
> told the food is fresh and innovative. You can choose from fine
> dining in Culinaire or Express dining which includes a pasta
> bar, deli, burger station, and a soup and sandwich bar. Reser-
> vations requested for large parties. Full service catering avail-
> able on or off the premises.

Seattle Central Community College

Seattle: 1701 Broadway 587-5427 *Capitol Hill*
Hours: Tues-Fri 11:15-1

> With the emphasis on international cuisine, the college con-
> tains two restaurants, a gourmet eatery and a less formal,
> medium-priced facility called Square One. During summer
> quarter a $5.95 buffet is served featuring regional cuisine
> from around the world.

South Seattle Community College

West Seattle: 6000 16th Ave. S.W. 764-5344 *Food Science Bldg.*
Hours: Mon-Fri 11-1

South Seattle has a reputation for turning out chefs who end up in the best restaurants in town, so here's your chance to sample their talents before they graduate to higher-priced institutions.

Students practice continental and classic-oriented cuisine in Cafe Alki and the Rainer Dining Room where entrees might include fresh poached sea bass with capers and brown butter or veal tenderloin with raspberry Madeira wine. Once or twice a quarter the department schedules one of their famous connoisseurs' luncheons or four-star gourmet dinners, which feature the finest in food preparation and presentation. Advance tickets are required and space is limited. Call or write for information on special events. Private luncheons and dinners can be scheduled for up to 80 guests as space and time permits. Special menus are developed for each event.

Checks, Credit cards

Coupon Books

I know people who save hundreds of dollars a year by investing in coupon books! They don't plan a vacation, family outing or night on the town without consulting their coupon book first. Savings add up fast for those who eat out frequently because the majority of coupons are 2-for-1 offers at restaurants. Most books also include goods and services, as well as recreational and cultural activities. Although listings will vary, many of the same businesses appear in all the books. However, you may want to buy more than one book since they make great gifts and prices are so low, you only have to use a few coupons to recoup your cost.

Coupon books are usually sold by non-profit organizations for fund-raising purposes. Some publishers sell direct through the mail for the cost of postage and handling. Most have informational brochures they'll send if you wish to buy or sell their book.

Call the publisher's office to find out where you can purchase a book. Don't forget to ask if coupon books get marked down halfway through the year.

Coupon Connection of America

NEW LISTING
West Seattle: 933-2487

If you like using coupons to save money on your grocery bills, you'll love this unique idea. Coupon Connection of America sells grocery certificate books that allow you to pick the products you want to purchase from a list containing over 1200 national brand names. The $24.95 book holds $200 worth of certificates that can be redeemed for coupons, or for $14.95 you receive $80 worth of coupons. So, instead of waiting around until a coupon comes out in a magazine or newspaper, you can keep as many on hand as you need. Call for a brochure.

Checks, Credit cards

College Coupons, Ltd.

Seattle: 600 1st Ave., #512 621-7528
Hours: Mon-Fri 9-5

This company publishes free coupon books offering discounts from businesses located near college campuses. Although the books are geared to students, anyone can use them. They're distributed through the University Bookstore a few days before Fall, Winter, and Spring quarter. Over 75 coupons guarantee savings on goods and services that range from Domino's Pizza to haircuts, video rentals and professional typing.

Entertainment Publications, Inc.

NEW LOCATION
Redmond: 8660 154th Ave. N.E. 556-8333
Hours: Mon-Fri 8:30-5

The cadillac of coupon books, over half of the 600-plus listings in this 3-inch thick, glossy book are for restaurants ranging from four star eateries to fast food outlets. Fine dining coupons include menus and color shots of sample meals. The line-up of cultural activities and professional sporting events is impressive as well as the many retailers who will provide goods and services at a discount.

Travelers Club can save you hundreds of dollars on hotels, condos, resorts, car rentals, cruises, airfares and tours all over the country. A special section includes popular tourist attractions in California, Oregon and British Columbia.

The North Puget Sound edition costs $40, the South Puget Sound edition $35. Similar books are published by the same company in 80 other cities in the U.S. and if you buy one book, it automatically qualifies you for a discount on the others. Books can be purchased at the Entertainment office or call and they will give you the name of a local non-profit organization selling the book.

Gold "C" Savings Spree

NEW LOCATION
Redmond: 8660 154th Ave. N.E. 556-8333
Hours: Mon-Fri 8-5

This family-oriented coupon book includes 2-for-1 coupons for popular fast food chains and family style restaurants, plus discounts on entertainment, merchandise and services — all for $10. Recreational activities include participatory as well as spectator sports. Kids 8 to 18 will have a ball using coupons in the special Youth section. Gold "C" is a subsidiary of Entertainment Publications, Inc. and similar books can be purchased in 26 cities throughout the U.S. Purchase the book direct or from youth-oriented non-profit groups.

For Families and Friends

NEW LOCATION
Seattle: 2107 Elliott Ave #303 441-0191 *Downtown*
Hours: Mon-Fri 9-5

Published by the same company that puts out Seattle Child and Eastside Child, this fun book contains over 375 coupons that can save you 10% to 50% on goods and services geared to families, all for only $14.95. 2-for-1 coupons target popular fast food chains and kid-oriented restaurants. You'll find discounts on classes, recreational activities, clothing, gifts, toys, and educational products. Services cover everything from hair cuts to dry cleaning, video rentals, picture framing, and family portraits. The next time you take a trip, cut the cost of hotels, car rentals and tourist attractions in Washington, Oregon, and California. The book, which is used as a fundraiser mainly by day-care, preschool and public schools, can be purchased at bookstores, advertiser's retail outlets or through the mail.

Golden American

Seattle: 2142 8th N., Suite 205 284-1139, 1-800-562-2112
Hours: Mon-Fri 9-5

If you're over 55, subscribe to Golden American, a quarterly newspaper, and for only $16 you'll save 20% on over 200 restaurants in the Puget Sound area who advertise in this publication. When you dine out, the membership card can be used for a maximum of three guests as long as they're 55 or older. The yearly subscription includes discounts on travel, eye wear, prescriptions and car repairs. Golden American hosts social functions and free financial workshops throughout the year. Call for a complimentary issue.

Let's Eat Ethnic

Seattle: 305 Harrison St. #326 443-1410 *Seattle Center*
Hours: Mon-Fri 8:30-5

Purchase this 2-for-1 coupon book for $15 and explore over 40 ethnic restaurants that give the Seattle area its international flavor. Proceeds support programs sponsored by the Ethnic Heritage Council of the Pacific Northwest, an organization dedicated to preserving cultural diversity. They sponsor a big kick-off party in the Fall. For the price of the book you're invited to sample food from the various restaurants, and enjoy entertainment supplied by local ethnic groups. Call for specific date. Books can be purchased at their office, through the mail or at retail outlets.

Premier Dining

NEW LISTING
Trumbull, CT: 1-800-DINE-241
Hours: Mon-Fri 9am - 10pm, Sat 11-8, Sun 12-5 Eastern Standard Time

An upscale dining card focusing on 2-for-1 coupons at fine dining establishments across the country. Call and they will send you a sample list of what is available locally or for $1.99 you can purchase a 3 month trial membership. If you decide to join, the fee is $49 a year and you'll get a kit containing your premier dining card, a restaurant guide with menus and pictures, an abbreviated pocket guide with a map, and a bonus coupon book that includes movies, fast food and casual eateries. A local 24-hour hotline updates restaurant info on a weekly basis. The Premier Dining Card is usually marketed through banks and retailers to preferred charge card customers but anyone can call and enroll over the phone.

NEW LISTING
Redmond: 8660 154th Ave. N.E. 556-8333
Hours: Mon-Fri 8:30-5

A new publication from the same people who put out the Entertainment book, Saving Spree features thousands of dollars worth of discounts from your favorite mass merchandisers, department stores and specialty retailers. Coupons for apparel, health and beauty products, home decor, toys, pet food, groceries, gift items, and lots of services, including car care, abound. Best of all, if you use a Saving Spree coupon and find the item you purchased for less anywhere within 60 days, Entertainment will refund the difference. Priced at $24, this book is indeed a must.

Seattle Supper Club

Seattle: P.O. Box 81043, 98102 223-0177, 1-800-244-0222
Hours: Mon-Fri 9-5

The majority of coupons in this book are 2-for-1's at over 200 inexpensive, family-oriented restaurants in the Puget Sound area. You'll also find discounts on cultural and recreational activities for the whole family, including movies as well as savings on hotels, restaurants and tourist attractions in Oregon, California, Hawaii, British Columbia and other parts of Washington. Books can be purchased through the mail, at select retail outlets and from a few charitable organizations. Although the Seattle Supper Club book retails for $25, call the office and staff will send you a $5 discount coupon. Better yet, order 5 books and get one free.

Special Savings for Senior Citizens

NEW LISTING
Seattle: Department of Housing and Human Services 684-0500
Hours: Mon-Fri 9-5

This is not a coupon book, but a directory published by the Mayor's office for senior citizens. The directory lists hundreds of businesses and non-profit agencies that offer discounts to senior citizens on goods and services. Qualifications vary from business to business; some extend discounts to those 65 and older while others start at 55. Some listings only accept the Senior Identification card, which is for low income seniors who meet guidelines set by the City of Seattle. Call for a free copy.

Luggage

Luggage

Bergman Luggage
NEW LOCATION
Bellevue: 881 Bellevue Way 454-8689
Lynnwood: 320 Alderwood Mall 774-9533 *Alderwood Mall*
Redmond: 15116 N.E. 24th 643-2344
Seattle: 1930 3rd Ave. 448-3000 *Downtown*
  I-5 & N.E. Northgate Way 365-5775 *Northgate Mall*
Silverdale: 10315 Silverdale Way N.W. 698-0499 *Kitsap Mall*
Tacoma: 4020 S. Steele 473-4855 *Tacoma Mall*
Tukwila: 17900 Southcenter Parkway 575-4090 *Pavilion Mall*
Hours: Generally, Mon-Sat 10-9, Sun 12-5; Downtown Mon-Sat 9:30-6

Volume buying keeps prices 15% or more below retail on moderately priced as well as top-of-the-line luggage. Bergman's also carries briefcases, foot lockers, wallets and travel accessories, plus backpacks and nylon totes. Luggage by Skyway, a local manufacturer, is their main line. Best time to shop is during Christmas, graduation or back-to-school sales. Visit the Tukwila store where clearance merchandise and overstock is sold. 30-day return policy.

Checks, Credit cards

National Luggage Outlet
NEW LISTING
Lynnwood: 3225 Alderwood Mall Blvd. 775-2317
Hours: Mon-Sat 10-8, Sun 11-6

Planning a trip? Shop here for big savings on luggage and travel accessories by over a dozen well-known brand names including Samsonite, Delsey, Tumi and Jordache. Handbags, attache cases, and casual carry-ons are also available. Some of the inventory is overstock or clearance merchandise from Biagio, the local retail chain that owns the outlet store. 14 day return policy.

Checks, Credit cards

Tacoma Luggage & Office Supply
NEW LOCATION
Tacoma: 6722 19th West 565-1580
Hours: Mon-Fri 9-5, Sat 10-4

The only luggage you'll find here is by Skyway, a local manufacturer of soft side suitcases, garment bags and carry-on cases, but it's marked down 25% to 50% every day. Prices on general office supplies and paper products are competitive. Something different goes on sale every month.

Checks, Credit cards

T.W. Carrol & Co.

Tukwila: 350 Upland Dr. 575-1064
Hours: Mon-Fri 8:30-5:30, Sat 9-12

Visit the showroom of the largest wholesale distributor of luggage in the Pacific Northwest and pay way below retail. Choose from dozens of leading name-brands, including Halliburton, one of the most exclusive lines in the marketplace. Briefcases, garment bags, and related travel goods round out the inventory. Look for super buys on surplus and close-out merchandise. 30-day return policy.

Checks

Children's Toys

Ace Novelty Co.

Bellevue: 13434 N.E. 16th 644-1820
Hours: Mon-Fri 9-5

Everything you'd ever need for a birthday party, school carnival, or company picnic! Ace Novelty imports paper products, glassware, decorations, adult jokes, games, and inexpensive toys in volume and wholesales them to drugstores and specialty shops all over the U.S. and Europe. Prices on many items average 25% off retail. A great place to buy party favors or seasonal stuff around Christmas, Easter or Halloween. No returns.

Checks, Credit cards

Archie McPhee Retail Outlet

NEW LISTING
Seattle: 3510 Stone Way N. 545-8344 *Wallingford*
Hours: Mon-Fri 8-6, Sat & Sun 10-5

Archie McPhee sells an amazing assortment of toys, gifts and novelties geared more to adults than to kids through their famous mail-order catalog, which boasts over 10,000 items. The owner travels the world over looking for this stuff which is truly weird, silly and bizarre. The average price is $2.95 and you will find everything from rubber chickens to telephones that look like a potato. Visit the small outlet store if you want to experience popular culture first hand or call for a free catalog. Credit or exchange within 30 days.

Credit cards

Buffalo Bill's Sporting Goods & Toys

NEW LOCATION
Issaquah: 1005 5th Ave. W. 392-0228
Hours: Mon-Thurs 10-7, Fri 10-8, Sat 10-6, Sun 11-5

Buffalo Bill doesn't sell anything that has to do with work, thus the unusual combination of toys and sporting goods, most of which come from close-outs and bank liquidations. Comparison shopping verifies savings of 15% to 30% on toys by leading manufacturers like Mattel. I'm told this is a good place to shop for models, Tonka trucks, Ninja Turtles, Brier horses and Barbie stuff. Located behind Schucks and Kentucky Fried Chicken. Seven-day return policy.

Checks, Credit cards

Kay-Bee Toys, Inc.

NEW LOCATION
Bellevue: Bellevue Way & N.E. 8th 453-0505 *Bellevue Square*
Federal Way: 2001 S. 320th 839-4454 *Sea-Tac Mall*
Tacoma: Tacoma Mall Blvd & S. 38th 474-3730 *Tacoma Mall*
   10509 Gravelly Lake Dr. S.W. 588-6082 *Lakewood Mall*
Tukwila: I-5 at I-405 S. 248-2215 *Southcenter Mall*
Hours: Generally, Mon-Sat 9:30-9, Sun 11-6

The next time a birthday rolls around, check out the big selection of close-outs and samples by famous-name toy manufacturers sold at this big national chain. You can't beat their prices on goods marked "Special Value" Games frequently end up here at 50% or more off their original cost. 30-day return policy.

Checks, Credit cards

Kids Craft

Seattle: 1711 N. 45th 632-5160 *Wallingford*
Hours: Mon-Fri 9-6, Sat 9-5

A popular spot for pre-school and kindergarten teachers or moms looking for something constructive for kids to do. The main focus is art supplies and educational toys for children age ten and under. All Crayola products are discounted 15%. There's a play space where kids can try out new products and art classes are sometimes free. The store sends out a newsletter which announces their big sales held the first week in July and right after Christmas. One week return policy.

Checks, Credit cards

Play It Again Toys

Redmond: 16003 Redmond Way 881-6920
Hours: Mon-Sat 10-5

What a great name for a second-hand toy shop! Prices start at 50% off retail, and infants through five-years-olds will find lots of books, Fisher Price toys, stuffed animals, musical toys and wooden puzzles. For older kids there are legos, G.I. Joe, Barbie, board games and old Nintendo games that hook up to the TV. The store also carries high chairs, cribs, strollers, and car seats. Riding toys and bikes don't stay around for long. The owner buys outright or consigns. Returns within 7 days.

Checks

The Playground Store

NEW LISTING
Maple Valley: 22415 S.E. 231st 432-8000
Hours: Fri 9-5, Sat & Sun 11-4

This local manufacturer of backyard and commercial playground sets frequently sells factory seconds and close-outs at 25% to 40% off the regular price. Call for a free catalog or take the kids down for a "test drive" at their large outdoor showroom. Watch for specials around the 4th of July, Seafair, Labor Day and the Home Show, or get on their mailing list.

Checks, Credit cards

Toys R Us

NEW LOCATION
Bellevue: 103 110th Ave N.E. 453-1901
Everett: 1325 S.E. Everett Mall Way 353-8697
Federal Way: 31510 20th Ave. S. 946-0433
Lynnwood: 18601 Alderwood Mall Blvd. 771-4748
Silverdale: 3567 Randall Way N.W. 698-1882
Tacoma: 4214 S. Tacoma Mall Blvd. 472-4568
Tukwila: 16700 Southcenter Parkway 575-0780
Hours: Mon-Sat 9:30-9:30, Sun 10-6. Christmas season open Mon-Sat until midnight, Sun until 10

Toys R Us dominates the market because of everyday low prices and aisles stacked to the ceiling with every toy imaginable. The baby department offers one-stop shopping, from diapers to nursery furniture and clothing that goes up to size 6X. You'll also find party favors, giftwrap, crafts, records and seasonal items. Staff will assemble bicycles, Big Wheels, play furniture and gym sets for only $10 on 24-hour notice. With 450 stores nationwide averaging over 40,000 sq. ft. each, the company not only buys in quantity, but also has merchandise made exclusively for them. Discounts vary from item-to-item, but since they do so much advertising it's easy to compare prices. One aisle holds clearance merchandise. Check for discount coupons when you enter the store. Lenient return policy.

Checks, Credit cards

If your rec room isn't quite complete, consider shopping at one of these outlets. The first two sell coin-operated machines to arcades. Brand-new video games cost $3,000, but after only a year in use the price goes down as much as 50%. Reconditioned games sell for $200 to $300, as is. Secondhand pinball machines, air hockey games, foosball games, jukeboxes and pool tables are also sometimes available. Inventory fluctuates, so put your name on a list if you want something special.

General Coin Distributors

Seattle: 3901 1st Ave. S. 625-1474 *Sodo*
Hours: Mon-Fri 8-5

Music Vend Distributing Co.

Seattle: 1550 4th Ave. S. 682-5700 *Sodo*
Hours: Mon-Fri 8-5

AAA World of Leisure

NEW LISTING
Woodinville: 17327 140th Ave. N.E. 483-4531
Hours: Mon-Fri 10:30-6:30, Sat 10:30-5

Recreation and Hobbies Additional Outlets

(See Index for page numbers)

Sporting Goods and Recreational Clothing

AAA Liquidators
Best
Chubby and Tubby
Direct Buying Service
Jen-Cel-Lite Corp.
Liquidators Outlet

Cameras and Audio Video Equipment

Best
Bon Marche Clearance Center
Direct Buying Service
Liquidators Outlet
Second Time Around
Silo

Audio and Video Recordings

Fillipi Book & Record Shop
Globe Books
Half Price Books
Horizon Books
Quiet Companion

Arts and Crafts

American Drapery & Blinds
Arvey's Paper & Office Products
Ben Franklin
BRB Manufacturing
Factory Direct Draperies
The Foam Shop

Jen-Cel-Lite Corp.
L.A. Frames
The Original 99¢ Store
Standard Brands
The Salvage Broker

Children's Toys

AAA Liquidators
Best
Chubby and Tubby
Liquidators Outlet
Six Star Factory Outlet
Univalco

Also see Children's and Maternity Consignments and Dollar stores or 99¢ stores under "Mass Merchandiser Discounters"

Luggage

Best
Direct Buying Service

Automotive

Vehicles

Although cars represent the most expensive item people will buy in their lifetime next to a home, studies show that consumers are often guided more by emotional than economic factors. They spend little time investigating the market place, which happens to be the most complicated, confusing and competitive around. You can save big bucks and be assured of a better quality vehicle if you take the time to educate yourself first.

Check out bookstores, libraries and newsstands for unbiased consumer buying guides. Consumer Reports magazine publishes a yearly edition that includes reports on new models and the repair history of used cars.

The Auto series by Consumer Guide magazine is also good. Articles on new and used vehicles can be found in Car & Driver, Motor Trend and Road & Track magazines.

Auto Pricing Guides

Manufacturers sell cars to dealers for a base price plus the cost of factory-installed options and freight. It's easier to negotiate a price if you know the dealer's cost since their profit margin is usually 10% to 20% of the sticker price you see.

Auto makers also give rebates and year-end bonuses to dealers, which is why they sometimes sell selected models at factory invoice price. You will get a much better deal if you start the negotiating at $250 above the dealer's cost. For a breakdown on the wholesale and retail prices of new domestic and foreign vehicles, buy a copy of Edmonds New Car Prices — a small paperback that comes out yearly.

Kelly's Blue Book, a pricing guide for businesses, is probably the most current resource on market values next to the National Automobile Dealer's Association guide, which is used by dealers to set retail prices. For a free trial copy of Kelly's Blue Book, send a written request on your company stationary or accompanied by a business card to: P.O. Box 19691, Irvine, CA 92713-9981, or call 1-800-444-1743 to subscribe.

For a fee you can contact the following auto pricing services to get updated information on what various models are selling for and their cost to dealers.

Car/Puter International

Hollywood FL: 1-800-221-4001
Hours: Mon-Fri 9:30-6, Sat 9-2 (Eastern time)

For $20 plus $3 shipping and handling, you'll receive a computer printout listing the manufacturer's retail price, factory invoice price, plus the cost of options on any new car you're interested in buying. The printout includes a form you can fill out and return if you want Car/Puter to send you the name of an auto dealer in your area who can sell you the car of your choice at the price you specify. Car buyers who want the information instantly can call 1-900-903-2277 24 hours a day, and for $2/minute the computerized data base will give them the information over the phone.

Checks, Credit card

Consumer Reports Auto Price Service

Denver, CO: 303-745-1700
Hours: Daily 24 hours

If you are in the market for a new car or truck, foreign or domestic, call in with the make, model, and exact style of vehicle you want and for $11 Consumer Reports will send you a computer printout of the dealers invoice, including factory installed options, current information on rebate programs, and recommended safety and comfort options from Consumers' Union Auto Test Division. Plus, you receive a free guide entitled "How to Deal With a Dealer," taken from the pages of Consumer Reports. If you want to see the dealer's invoice for more than one vehicle, the charge goes up to $20 for two vehicles, $27 for three and $5 for each additional printout after that.

Credit cards

Consumer Reports Used Car Price Service

1-900-446-0500

Hours: 7am - 2am Eastern time

Consumer Reports charges $1.75/minute to give out the current market value of used cars (sport or utility) pick-ups and vans made from 1984 to 1992. Most calls average five minutes and prices are geared to specific regions of the country. You can also listen to a Trouble Index compiled from Consumer Reports Frequency of Repair records for hundreds of 1987 through 1992 vehicles. Before you call, make sure you know the make, year, mileage, major options, condition of the vehicle and the number of cylinders you want, since the cost is added to your phone bill.

Consumer Tips

✔ Dealer-added options or special services, which must be listed separately from factory options on the window sticker, are usually overpriced and can be purchased for much less elsewhere.

✔ Watch for ADP or ADM on the sticker list of exotic or hot selling models. The letters stand for "added dealer profit" or "added dealer margin" and unless you need the car immediately, or can afford to pay extra, wait a few months until the price comes down.

✔ If you have a used car you need to get rid of, you'll get more money if you sell it yourself rather than if you trade it in on a new car. Dealers tend to under-value used cars in order to pump up their profit. However, if you have to trade in your old car to defray the cost of a new one, don't tell the dealer until after you have settled on a price for the new car and have it in writing. Then you can haggle over the trade-in.

Auto Buying and Referral Services

Going through a buyer's service can save time and money. Tell them exactly what you want and they'll track it down for a fee and you'll never have to set foot on a car lot. State law requires that buyer's services be bonded and licensed just like car dealers, so make sure you're dealing with a legitimate business before you pay up front. Beware of sales people who try to talk you into buying another make or charge you a low-ball price. They may be getting a commission from the car dealer, which is against the law, or charging you more for the car to make up the difference.

Auto Advisor, Inc.

Seattle: 3123 Fairview E. 323-1976, 1-800-326-1976
Hours: Mon-Fri 9-5

Auto Advisor, the oldest auto buyers service in the country, was founded in 1977 by Ashley Knapp, who is a noted consumer advocate and car buying consultant for new vehicles. For many years he has written a column for Triple A Motorist.

The company's philosophy, "A good deal on a bad car is no deal at all," is reflected in their policy of test driving cars before recommending them, staying on top of the latest technology, and putting safety first. They also guarantee the lowest prices and have access to any make or model you want— foreign or domestic. Clients from all over the country utilize this agency. Vehicles are picked up on local dealer lots. Trade-ins can be arranged. If you just want some advise on purchasing a car, consultations, which can be done over the phone, cost $2/minute.

The buying service costs $300 to $1,000, and there's a 10% discount if you pay cash. Call for a free brochure, which includes a fee schedule.

Checks, Credit cards

Auto Insider

Van Nuys, CA: 1-800-446-7433
Hours: Mon-Fri 8:30-5:30

Auto Insider is a private car buying referral service only available to members of specified credit unions, professional organizations and warehouse buying clubs such as Costco, Triple A and the Boeing Credit Union. Participating dealers will sell cars to members at fleet prices or 10% over the factory invoice. Call to see if you belong to a participating organization.

Car Finders

NEW LISTING
Edmonds: 420 5th Ave. S. 771-4090
Hours: Mon-Fri 9-5, Sat by appointment

This company comes highly recommended because of their attention to detail and penchant for personal service. For a flat fee of $319, Car Finders will track down any new or used vehicle you want to buy, negotiate the price you want to pay and have the car on your doorstep in as little time as possible. Part of the service includes inspecting and test driving used vehicles. Call for a brochure.

Checks

Note: Car/Puter International also acts as a car buying as well as car pricing service.

Used Vehicles

If you're an informed mechanical-type and understand all the legal transactions involved in purchasing a vehicle, the best buys on used cars often come from private individuals, who advertise mainly in the classifieds and Auto Trader publications which can be picked up at mini-marts and automotive stores all over the Puget Sound area. Don't forget to check out The Little Nickel and Buy and Sell newspapers, where individuals and low-price dealers advertise because rates are cheaper. If you prefer to shop at a used car lot, where you can sometimes get warranties, be sure the dealer is reputable, has been around a long time, and has no complaints lodged against him at the Better Business Bureau or the State Attorney General's Consumer Protection office.

Consumer Tip

✔ Don't buy a used vehicle without first having it inspected by a knowledgeable mechanic. If you are a good customer at a local garage, they may agree to do it for free. Diagnostic services, listed under "Automotive" in the yellow pages, charge $40 to $65 for an inspection. Triple A members qualify for limited free diagnostic service.

Rental Agency Lots

If you want to buy a late model used car, a good place to start is car rental agencies. They buy cheap and sell often. Rental vehicles are generally well-maintained and less than one year old. Mileage is usually under 20,000 with warranties still intact. The following three rental car lots offer financing and trade-ins. Note that all of them are located out by Sea-Tac Airport's Rental Row on Pacific Highway South. Smaller auto rental agencies have not been listed, but are worth checking out. Call first, since their sales list may include vehicles in service or out on rental.

Budget Rental Car Sales

Seattle: 2655 S. 188th 248-2088 *Sea-Tac*
Hours: Mon-Fri 8:30-8, Sat 9-6, Sun 11-6

Dollar Rent a Car Sales

Seattle: 17600 Pacific Hwy. S. 433-6776 *Sea-Tac*
Hours: Mon-Fri 9-8, Sat 9-7, Sun 11-5

Thrifty Car Rental

Seattle: 19815 Pacific Hwy. S. 243-2277 *Sea-Tac*
Hours: Daily 9-8

Bank Repo Lots

Buying vehicles from bank repo lots can save you money because they don't have to pay commissioned salespeople. However, all sales are "as is," with no financing or trade-ins, and payment must be made in cash.

Lender's Choice Auto Liquidation

NEW LISTING
Kirkland: 11630 Slater Ave. N.E. 820-3400
Hours: Mon-Sat 9-6, Wed 9-8

Repossessed vehicles from Pacific First Bank, Alaska U.S.A. Bank and credit unions end up on this lot. Cars and trucks vary from six months to five years old. Offers below the National Automotive Dealers Association wholesale price, which is listed on the car, will not be accepted.

Seafirst Bank Vehicles Sales Facility

Seattle: 2409 N. 45th 358-1990 *Wallingford*
Hours: Mon-Fri 9-6, Sat 9-1

Offers are submitted via sealed bid, which the bank has the right to refuse. Most vehicles sell for $500 to $800 over the wholesale price. Some are sold below wholesale because they need repairs, have been on the lot for a long time, or are considered soft on the market. If your bid is accepted, you have three days to check out the car and obtain financing. Pick up general information sheets and bidding rules when you visit.

Seafirst checks

Note:

Another good resource is government auctions, where stolen, repossessed and government surplus vehicles are sold. Look under "Auctions" if you want to explore this option.

Parts and Accessories

No one dealer delivers the best buy on everything, so watch for specials and compare prices via newspaper ads. Many stores will give price quotes over the phone, but be sure you can state exactly what you want before calling. It's hard for smaller independent stores to beat the big chains, but that doesn't mean they won't be competitive if asked to meet prices.

Schucks is the most visible auto parts store, with a whopping 33 locations throughout the Puget Sound area. Also check Al's Auto Supply, with half as many stores spread from Bothell to Auburn. Look in the yellow pages for a location near you.

Consumer Tip

✔ Parts that fall into one of the following categories will always be cheaper: (1) re-manufactured original parts, which are rebuilt by independent firms to the original factory specifications;(2) rebuilt and reconditioned parts, which combine used components to produce a part that works; (3) used parts, which are available at auto wreckers. Prices will be lowest at wrecking yards and even lower if you remove the part from the junked car yourself.

Batteries

Budget Batteries

NEW LOCATIONS

Bremerton: 140 N. Callow 373-1778
Burien: 14805 Ambaum Blvd. 246-7075
Everett: 5111 Evergreen Way 339-2289
Federal Way: 2705 Pacific Hwy. S. 839-5880
Fife: 7900 Pacific Hwy. E. 922-3737
Lynnwood: 6306 196th S.W. 778-8684
Puyallup: 318 N. Meridian 841-3664
Seattle: 1501 Elliott W. 285-4075 *Ballard*
   2006 Rainier Ave. S. 322-2075 *Rainier Valley*
   7110 East Marginal Way S. 767-3075 *Georgetown*
   15001 Bothell Way N.E. 365-8015 *Lake City*
Tacoma: 3518 Center St. 572-8075
Hours: Mon-Fri 9-6, Sat 9-5

This local chain sells new, reconditioned and factory-second batteries for cars, trucks, boats, tractors, golf carts and motorcycles at prices that beat the going rate at Sears and most automotive stores. Alternators, solenoids and starters are also available. No charge for installation of batteries. Drop your old batteries off and Budget recycles the lead in them.

Checks, Credit cards

Standard Batteries

NEW LOCATION

Seattle: 5200 4th Ave. S. 763-1244 *Georgetown*
Tacoma: 4713 Washington St. 474-7992
Hours: Mon-Fri 8-5

As part of a big West Coast chain, Standard can offer customers very competitive prices on new and factory-second batteries for any type of vehicle imaginable. The cost includes free testing and installation plus disposal of scrap batteries.

Checks, Credit cards

Tires

You need never pay full price for tires since they are one of the most competitively prices products in the marketplace. Most discounters will offer at least 30% off the list price. Call for price quotes at any of the stores listed below. When comparison shopping, be sure to ask about the cost of balancing, mounting and valve stems. Some places may quote low prices but charge extra for these services.

Comsumer Tips

✔ If you are having trouble trying to decide what kind of tires to buy, call the Auto Safety Hotline at 1-800-424-9393 for a tire-quality grading report, which includes milage and safety ratings.

✔ If you are a member of Costco or Sam's Club be sure to check out their tire department since they are known for low prices.

Check out the following stores for consistently advertised low prices on tires:

Bill's Tire Exchange

Seattle: 4910 Leary Ave. N.W. 789-4759 *Ballard*
Hours: Mon-Fri 8:30-5:30, Sat 9-4

Discount Tires

NEW LISTING
Bremerton: 5034 State Hwy 303 N.E. 479-6852
Bellevue: 12950 Bel-Red Rd. 455-2755
Burien: 14238 1st Ave. S. 248-3832
Everett: 309 E. Casino 355-2455
Federal Way: 31414 Pacific Hwy S. 946-0877
Lynnwood: 19414 44th W. 672-0807
Kirkland: 12410 124th St. 823-3759
Renton: 3123 N.E. 4th W. 226-6706
Seattle: 14713 Bothell Way N.E. 365-1614 *Lake City*
Tacoma: 1029 N. Pearl St. 759-8899
        2410 84th St. 582-1814
Hours: Mon-Fri 8:30-5, Sat 8:30-6

Factory Direct Tire Sales

Edmonds: 22617 76th Ave. W. 774-5131
Hours: Mon-Fri 8:30-5

Pyramid Discount Tires

NEW LISTING
Burien: 266 S.W. 153rd 246-4464
Federal Way: 34611 16th S. 838-1144
Puyallup: 103 River Road E. 838-2840
Seattle: 2701 4th Ave. S. 628-4812 *Sodo*
Hours: Mon-Fri 8-6, Sat 8-4, Sun 10-4

Rick's Tire & Chevron

Seattle: 8506 5th N.E. 525-9392 *Northgate*
Hours: Mon-Fri 7-9, Sat 8-6

Tires Plus

Kirkland: 12540 N.E. 124th St. 821-9200
Hours: Mon-Fri 8-6, Sat 8-5

Used Tires

A sure way to save up to 50% is to buy used or retread tires. Retreads are actually used tire "shells" that have had brand-new treads attached through a heat-curing process. The National Tire Dealers and Retreaders Association (NTDRA) rates the plants that rebuild tires A through F. Tires rated C through F should be avoided. See the yellow pages under "Tires, Retreads" for a dealer near you.

Used tires are economical purchases for spares or to replace tires that wear out before you're ready to buy an all new set. Although many dealers sell used tires, the following specialize in them, so they offer a bigger selection. Most used tires come from "take-offs," which are tires that have been removed by tire dealers when the owner buys a new set of wheels. Some are in like-new condition because the owner just traded up or bought a new car and didn't like the tires on it. Used tires also come from cars that end up in wrecking yards after being in an accident. Sometimes you can even find tires at these stores with the stickers still on them.

American Used Tire & Wheel
NEW LISTING
Tacoma: 3906 Steilacoom Blvd. S.W. 588-0710
Hours: Mon-Fri 9-6, Sat 10-3

Johns Used Tire & Wheel Center
NEW LISTING
Tacoma: 11030 Pacific Hwy. S.W. 584-9562
Hours: Mon-Sat 9-6

Northwest Used Tire & Wheel Co.
NEW LISTING
Lynnwood: 15304 Hwy. 99 742-TIRE
Hours: Daily 8-7

Quality Used Tires
NEW LISTING
Tacoma: 1115 S. 12th St. 383-2680
Hours: Mon-Fri 9-6, Sat 10-4

Used Tire and Wheel Co.
NEW LOCATION
Lynnwood: 15111 Hwy. 99 742-4810
Seattle: 14038 Lake City Way 364-0565 *Lake City*
    2834 N.W. Market St. 781-2099 *Ballard*
Hours: Mon-Sat 8:30-7, Sun 11-5

Used Tires Wherehouse
Federal Way: 35516 Pacific Hwy. S. 838-TIRE
Hours: Mon-Sat 9-7, Sun 10-5

Used Tire World
NEW LISTING
Des Moines: 23018 Pacific Hwy. S. 878-7889
Hours: Mon-Sat 9-6, Sun 10-5

Road Services

American Automobile Association (Triple A)

Bellevue: 13201 Bellevue-Redmond Rd. 455-3933
Bremerton: 5700 Kitsap Way 377-0081
Everett: 909 S.E. Everett Mall Way 353-7222
Lynnwood: 4100 200th S.W. 775-3571
Renton: 3900 E. Valley Rd. #105 251-6040
Seattle: 330 6th Ave. N. 448-5353 *South of Seattle Center*
Tacoma: 1801 S. Union 756-3050
Hours: Generally, Mon-Fri 8:30-5

Founded in 1902, Triple A was the first auto club in the country. Today it's the largest, with over 30 million members throughout the U.S. and Canada. New members pay $51 for the basic plan and $41 for yearly renewals. A spouse or unmarried independent children (age 23 and under) can become associate members for $20 and receive the same services, which include free towing for the first five miles to the nearest repair facility; emergency road service 24 hours a day anywhere in the nation; a trained staff who will help you make arrangements for any trip from a weekend getaway to a cross country trek to a round-the-world tour; a personal accident insurance policy and access to Triple A's own insurance agency; discounts on rental cars, credit cards, passport photos, and Triple A approved lodgings; plus free travel books, maps and camping guides that include Triple A inspected accommodations.

Call for a membership brochure.

Following is a list of auto clubs similar to Triple A. Call their number and they will be glad to send you a brochure with information on membership fees and benefits.

Allstate Motor Club

1-800-347-8880

Amoco Motor Club

1-800-334-3300

Cross Country Motor Club
1-800-225-1575

Montgomery Ward Auto Club
1-800-621-5151

U.S. Auto Club Services
1-800-348-5058

Amway Motoring Plan
Look under Amway in the business section of the white pages for a representative near you.

Automotive Additional Outlets
(See Index for page numbers)

New and Used Autos
Auctions
Boeing Surplus

Automotive Tools
Greenshield's
Tool Town
Your Tool House

Notes

Something For Everyone

Factory Outlet Malls

To avoid competition with department stores that carry the same brand names, factory outlet malls locate some distance from big retail areas, but next to major interstate highways. These stores, which are owned and operated by manufacturers or liquidators, carry mainly first quality, current-season goods, although some outlets stock more seconds and close-outs than others, which is what hardcore bargain hunters look for. Over half of the stores sell clothing and related items. The remainder sell a similar mix of books, toys, kitchenwares, leather goods, household items, decorative accessories, and cosmetics.

Although tenants vary from mall to mall, Jordache, Harvé Bernard, Izod, Guess, Carters, Aileen, Champion, Corning, Revere Ware, Fieldcrest, Maidenform, and American Tourister have stores in all the malls listed below. Some of the stores may not be familiar since their products are not sold in the Pacific Northwest. Others are owned by local manufacturers. If you want to know specifically what stores are located in the different malls, call and they will send you a brochure.

Factory Outlet Center

Centralia: I-5, 82 miles south of Seattle, Exit 82,
1-800-831-5334
Hours: Mon-Sat 9-8, Sun 10-6

This was the first factory outlet mall to open in the state of Washington, turning the quiet little town of Centralia into a shopper's paradise. It seems to have a greater variety of tenants than the other malls, plus it's the only one that is locally owned. Amongst the 40 plus stores in this huge, sprawling complex you won't find at the other outlet malls, are London Fog, Avia, John Henry, Leslie Fay, Florsheim, Arrow, Oneida, Healthtex, Levi's, Lee, Vanity Fair, and Jantzen. For $29 you can take Amtrack from Seattle or Tacoma and spend the day. Visitors who drive up make a weekend of it, taking in the Centralia Square Antique Mall and Mt. St. Helens, which is about an hour's drive away. Centralia publishes a quarterly newspaper with an update on the stores, sale notices and discount coupons. Call and staff will send you a copy.

Great Northwest Factory Stores

North Bend: I-90, 40 miles east of Seattle, Exit 31,
(206) 888-4505
Hours: Mon-Sat 9-9, Sun 10-6

The newest of the off-price malls, Great Northwest now has 35 stores in operation. You'll find a pleasant mix of shops and a peaceful atmosphere in the foothills of the Cascades near beautiful Snoqualmie Falls. Local manufacturers B.U.M. Equipment and Fast Clothing have outlet stores here, but not in the other malls. Before you visit, call the office and they will send you a packet filled with discount coupons.

Pacific Edge Outlet Center

Burlington: I-5, 60 miles north of Seattle, Exit 229
(206) 757-3549
Hours: Mon-Sat 10-9, Sun 10-6

Less than a year after it opened in 1989, this upscale, fashion-oriented mall was already among the top five in the country in gross sales. At last count, 40 stores were clustered within these California-style structures set in the pastoral Skagit Valley. Tenants include some of the best-known, most popular names in the women's apparel market. This is the only mall where you will find Evan Picone, Jones of New York, Liz Claiborne, Adolfo, Chaus, I.B. Diffusion, J.H. Collectibles and

Geoffry Beene for men, plus a spectacular collection of china by Mikasa and Royal Doulton.

Mass Merchandise Discounters

These are stores that sell an incredible variety of merchandise, so it would be impossible to put them under a specific heading. Target, Kmart, Fred Meyer and Payless fall into this category but they have not been listed because they are so visible in the marketplace. It is easy to compare prices because their bulk rate advertisements come out almost every Sunday with the newspapers. Although these big chains feature everyday low prices, you can save the most by buying loss leaders, private labels, and using the many coupon books they put out.

The good news is that in the last few years discount variety stores have made a comeback via the many "99¢" and "dollar" stores that have sprung up in the Puget Sound area. Reminiscent of the old five and dime, they carry thousands of small items that would cost two or three items as much in a grocery store, drugstore or gift shop, which makes them a great place to shop for household items, health and beauty products, seasonal merchandise, inexpensive gifts and toys for the kids. Dollar stores also stock a limited selection of packaged, or canned food, especially snacks and candy, along with bottled drinks.

Most of the merchandise is close-outs, imports or liquidation goods from businesses or manufacturers. Some of the brand names on shampoos, lotions, cosmetics and cleaning products may not be recognizable because they are private labels.

There are only a few surplus and salvage mass merchandisers left but prices will be rock bottom and half the fun is discovering some strange or wonderful thing you never thought you could afford to buy.

AAA Liquidating
Des Moines: 22325 Marine View Dr. 824-3686
Normandy Park: 19801 1st Ave. S. 824-2625
Hours: Mon-Sat 9-6, Sun 12-5

"Good stuff cheap" is the motto here and merchandise ranges from 50¢ to $500. The owner, who travels the world looking for hot deals, wholesales the majority of stuff he buys to other businesses. Inventory changes constantly and you never know what you will find. There's always a good selection of toys, tools, clothing, small electronics, sporting goods, housewares and gift items. Sign up on the mailing list to receive flyers about every six weeks announcing the latest specials. Exchanges or credit only.

Checks, Credit cards

ABC Sales

Seattle: 8817 Renton Ave. S. 722-6303 *Seward Park*
Hours: Mon-Fri 10-4

This small, bare-bones warehouse operation sells surplus and salvaged goods to retail stores and anyone who walks in the door. Inventory usually consists of groceries, mainly canned goods, plus health and beauty aids, drugs and sundries. Some items must be purchased by the case or carton. Selection may be limited, but the prices are great. No returns.

Checks

Big Mike's Factory Outlet

NEW LISTING
Burien: 15226 First Ave. S. 248-6457
Hours: Mon-Fri 9-7, Sat 10-6

Prices hover close to wholesale on a wide variety of products at this mini-warehouse operation. Food, health and beauty aids make up one-third of the inventory. Toys, small appliances, clothing, tools, kitchen utensils, and lawn and garden supplies are only a few of the many items that come and go. I even spotted a gorgeous chandelier. The best stuff goes fast. Exhanges only.

Checks, Credit cards

Ben Franklin

NEW LISTING
Issaquah: 90 Front St. S. 392-1288
Kent: 324 West Meeker 852-5990
Hours: Issaquah Mon-Fri 9:30-9, Sat 9:30-6, Sun 11-6; Kent Mon-Sat 9:30-5:30, Sun 11-4

Part of a big national discount chain, these individually owned old-fashioned variety stores keep prices low on everything they sell. I'm told that they are a good place to shop for toys, gifts, accessories, and craft items. 30-day return policy.

Checks, Credit cards

The Best 99 Cent Store

NEW LISTING
Burien: 13605 Ambaum S.W. 246-6921
Hours: Tues-Sun 10-7

Much bigger than most variety stores, this place carries a lot of items that cost more than a dollar, most of which are made in the Orient. I noticed a big selection of toys, clothing, and large decorative items like porcelain clocks, huge fans, and ceramic figurines.

Credit cards

Best

Bellevue: 888 116th N.E. 454-5696
Everett: Broadway N. & Tower 258-4251
Federal Way: 2200 S. 320th 941-5000
Lynnwood: 19801 40th Ave. W. 775-9311
Tacoma: 2921 S. 38th 474-0771
Hours: Mon-Fri 10-9, Sat 10-6, Sun 11-6

Very few retailers can beat Best's selection when it comes to name-brand small appliances, kitchenware, sporting goods, athletic equipment, electronics for home and office, baby furniture, fine jewelry and gift items. Don't forget to check the clearance rack located near the merchandise pick-up desks for bargains on returns or defective goods. If you want to shop at home, call any of the stores listed above and staff will give you a toll-free number you can call to order a catalog, which is free. Rumor has it that Best will be opening another store in Tukwila. 30-day return policy.

Checks, Credit cards

The Bon Marche Home World Clearance Center

NEW LISTING
Seattle: N.E. Northgate Way & 5th Ave. N.E. 361-2121
Northgate Mall
Hours: Mon-Sat 9:30-9:30, Sun 11-6

Here's a well-kept secret! Located in the basement, behind the luggage department, is a separate area where clearance merchandise from every department except clothing is sold at 50% or more below the regular price. Most of the time you'll find a good selection of linens, bedding, bathroom and kitchen accessories, along with dishes, pots and pans, decorative and gift items. 30-day return.

Checks, Credit cards

Chubby & Tubby

Seattle: 9456 16th S.W. 762-9791 *White Center*
7906 Aurora Ave. N. 525-1810 *Greenwood*
3333 Rainier Ave. S. 723-8800 *Mt. Baker*
Hours: Mon-Sat 9-9, Sun 9-6

Chubby and Tubby is a combination sporting goods, hardware, and variety store that's been around since 1945. The shelves are filled with merchandise of all kinds, some of which is close-outs or discontinued styles. You will find consistently low prices on Dutch Boy paint, leading-brand athletic shoes, fishing tackle, work clothing (Levi's 501's are always in stock), boots, and Revere Ware. In the summer the garden center has some of the best buys in town on fertilizer, peat moss and bark. Toys brought in for the holidays are super cheap, as are Christmas trees. Don't miss the "Sneaky Sunday Coupon" sale held the last week in February or the coupon books that they put out in the spring. Weekly specials appear every Thursday in the Times and P.I. on the page opposite the comic strip. Returns accepted.

Checks, Credit card

Direct Buying Service

Seattle: 915 4th Ave. 623-8811 *Downtown*
Hours: Mon-Fri 9:15-6, Sat 9:30-4

Although the showroom stocks mainly small kitchen applian-ces, jewelry, cameras, clocks and luggage, literally anything you want to buy can be ordered factory-direct at savings of 15% to 20%. Staff says they can beat Silo's prices on major ap-pliances and home and office electronics. Many people make this their first stop when shopping for furniture, household items and decorative accessories. Direct Buying provides manufacturers' catalogs to peruse or suggests you visit other retail outlets to get the brand name, model number, color, size, and any other identifying features you'll need to place your order. Big sales around Christmas and Father's day. Three-day return policy.

Checks, Credit cards

Dollars

NEW LISTING

Kent: 12928 S.E. Kent Kangley Rd. 630-7594
Lynnwood: 19620 Scriber Lake Rd. 778-8956
Puyallup: 900 E. Meridian 952-5047
Seattle: 1410 3rd. Ave. 682-6545 *Downtown*
    4231 University Way N.E. 545-0724 *U-District*
    15230 Aurora Ave. N. 363-0211 *Parkwood Plaza, Shoreline*
Hours: Mon-Fri Kent 9:30-5:30, Lynnwood 9:30-9, *Downtown*
Seattle 8-7, U-District 10-9, Shoreline 9:30-9, Puyallup 10-8; Sat 10-6 generally, Sun 11-5 generally

At these large, well-stocked stores you will be amazed at what you can get for a buck! There's an especially good selection of toys and party supplies as well as gift items, cosmetics, personal care products, fashionable earrings, and hair ornaments. Savings add up fast on household cleaning agents, paper products, hardware and housewares. Some items come in multiples of two, three, or four for $1. Exchanges within 7 days.

Checks

Dollar Days

NEW LISTING

Des Moines: 23237 Pacific Hwy. S. 870-7772
Federal Way: S. 320th & Pacific Hwy. S. 529-3902 *Sea-Tac Mall*
Kent: 329 S. Washington 854-8919
Hours: Mon-Sat 9-9, Sun 10-6

Although everything is priced at a dollar or less, the owner tries to buy better quality stuff to give customers the best value for their money. I spotted silk flowers, Disney story books and ties by Pierre Cardin that would sell for a lot more at retail stores. Around Christmas and the holidays he brings in a terrific selection of seasonal goodies and gift items. Spend $100 and you get a discount. All sales final.

Checks, Credit cards

Dollar Store

NEW LISTING

Bremerton: 2912 6th St. 373-3312
Puyallup: 11012 Canyon Rd. 535-5818 *Summit Country Center*
Tacoma: 2914 6th Ave. 572-2774
    10121 Gravely Lake Rd. 589-0519 *Lakewood Mall*
    8012 S. Tacoma Way 581-3978 *B&I Store*
Hours: Bremerton Mon-Fri 9-7, Sat 9-6, Sun 10-5; *Puyallup*
Mon-Fri 10-7, Sat 10-6, Sun 12-5; Tacoma (6th Ave.) Mon-Sat
10-8, Sun 10-6 (Lakewood Mall) Daily 10-9, (B&I) Mon-Fri 9-9,
Sat 9-7:30, Sun 10-6

Bargain hunters can buy four Everready or Panasonic batteries for only $1. Prices will always be lower on cleaning supplies, beauty care products, plastic containers, toys and hair accessories than what you pay at the local drugstore. No returns.

Cash

Dollar Wholesale

NEW LISTING
Kent: 20648 84th S. 872-4611
Hours: Mon-Fri 9-5

Mini-Marts, gift shops and variety stores shop here but the public is welcome as long as they spend $200. Nothing costs more than a dollar and you can stock up on canned or packaged food and snacks, novelty items, toys, housewares, cleaning products, etc. at wholesale prices. Get a bunch of friends together to share in the cost and the savings. No returns.

Cash

Everything's A Dollar

NEW LISTING
Silverdale: 10315 Silverdale Way #BI 613-0789 *Silverdale Mall*
Tukwila: 1008 Southcenter Shopping Center 431-9338
Hours: Silverdale Mon-Sat 10-9; Tukwila 9:30-9:30, Sun 11-6

You will probably be seeing more of these upscale dollar stores as they represent the first influx of a big national chain. Stores average 3,000 sq. ft. so there are thousands of items to choose from. Bestsellers are artificial flowers, toys, candy, jewelry, toilet paper, cleaning supplies and plastic containers. They even carry socks, underwear, and crystal. Be sure to visit around Christmas and during other holidays for great buys on gifts and seasonal merchandise.

Checks, Credit cards

J.C. Bargains

NEW LISTING
Tacoma: 210 Garfield S. 536-7986
Hours: Mon-Sat 9-9

A low overhead discount variety store that sells housewares, toys, gift items, clothing, and sundries for between 99¢ and $20. Soft drinks, candy and some packaged or canned foods also available. No returns.

Cash

Liquidators Outlet

NEW LISTING
Kent: 222 South Central 854-4390
Hours: Mon-Wed 10-6, Thurs & Fri 10-8, Sat 10-6, Sun 12-5

Wow, what a great new listing! The huge warehouse, formerly a grocery store, houses close-outs, clearance and damaged goods from Costco, Best, Home Base and Fred Meyer, as well as Montgomery Ward and Wallis Furniture catalogs. A new truckload arrives daily and there are thousands of items to choose from, including food, clothing, housewares, electronics and toys, all at rock bottom prices. A vegimax that retails for $59 is only $19.95 here. Furniture goes for 50% off and the selection of upholstered and oak pieces is outstanding. Three-day return policy.

Checks, Credit cards

The Original 99 Cent Store

NEW LISTING
Auburn: 1805 Howard Rd. 833-8289
Puyallup: 725 River Road 841-4212 *Kmart Plaza*
Hours: Auburn Mon-Sat 10-8, Sun 12-6; Puyallup Mon-Fri 10-7, Sat 10-6, Sun 12-5

The Auburn store has been open since 1987 so it truly deserves it's name. The owner buys mainly close-outs which is why the stores carry recognizable brand names and a slightly different inventory mix that include arts and craft supplies, pet food, and baby stuff. The most popular items are toys, household supplies and beauty aids. No returns

Cash

Two Bucks or Less

NEW LISTING
Bellevue: 1915 140th Ave. N.E. 644-1145
Hours: Mon-Fri 9-8, Sat 9-6, Sun 11-5

How would you like to pay $2 for a pair of stirrup pants or a stuffed toy or a pair of shoes that normally retailed for $25? Although the general mix is similar to what you would find at other 99¢ stores, this shop carries a bigger variety and better quality goods since prices go up to $2. Toys are super cheap since this used to be a discount toy store. 30-day return policy.

Checks, Credit cards

Sessions Discount/Variety

Burien: 15415 Ambaum Blvd. S.W. 248-3399
Renton: 809 S. 4th 271-5555
Hours: Generally, Mon-Fri 9:30-6, Sat 9-5

These stores sell merchandise like you'd find in a drugstore or grocery store, plus a limited selection of furniture from surplus and salvage operations. You can save 25% or more on packaged, frozen, or canned food simply because the case was opened or a can dented. Snack foods and candy are best selling items, along with diapers, pet food, paper products and household cleaning supplies. Credit or exchanges in 14 days.

Checks, Credit cards, Food stamps

Six Star Factory Outlet

NEW LOCATION
Bremerton: 4213 Wheaton Way 373-0153 *Bag and Save*
Burien: 166 S.W. 148th 242-5939 *Burien Plaza*
Everett: 1001 N. Broadway 259-4260 *College Plaza*
Kent: 26016 104th Ave. S.E. 859-8409 *East Hill Plaza*
Lynnwood: 19800 44th Ave. W. 672-3144 *Lynnwood Square*
Renton: 16930 116th Ave. S.E. 277-1833 *Cascade Center*
Snohomish: 1207 Ave. D 568-0355 *Safeway Shopping Center*
Tacoma: 8722 S. Tacoma Way 588-7996
    804 E. 72nd St. 475-8819 *East 72nd St. Plaza*
Hours: Generally, Mon-Fri 10-5, Sat 10-6, Sun 11-5

Nothing sells for over $10 at Six Star, and you'd pay twice as much for the same items at a drugstore or gift shop. Stand-out bargains include hundreds of earrings priced at $1, a big selection of fancy hair ornaments, party goods and gift wrap. Printed T-shirts and sweatshirts are big sellers at $6-10 each. You'll also discover good buys on toys, housewares, makeup, decorative accessories and seasonal merchandise. Customers can participate in a Bonus Bucks program where $1 in play money (given out for every $1 you spend) can be used in $10 increments to purchase items worth $20 to $40. Returns accepted but time limit varies from store to store.

Checks, Credit cards

Univalco Bargain Mart

Seattle: 15211 Military Road S. 244-4182 *Sea-Tac*
Hours: Generally, Mon-Sat 12-7

Univalco has been buying merchandise from stores going out of business and then wholesaling it to dealers or other retailers for 12 years. Overflow ends up here. Inventory leans toward the general gift variety, with paintings, prints and posters from the 1920s and later (some rare and original) a specialty, along with earrings, toys and flags from all over the world. Catalogs, available for wholesale buyers and preferred customers, can be purchased in the store or mailed for a fee. Returns accepted.

Checks

Due to space limitations, it would be impossible to list all the 99¢ stores in the Puget Sound area, so here are a few that have been around for a while or that have fairly large stores. They all carry a product mix similar to that mentioned in the chapter introduction so it would be redundant to write about them individually. Remember, most dollar stores don't take credit cards, some take cash only, and usually they take exchanges but no returns. Keep your eyes open because I predict there will be 99¢ stores all over the place before long. So next time you drive by, stop and take a look.

99 Cent Store

NEW LISTING
> **Seattle:** 109 Broadway E. 328-6310 *Capitol Hill*
> **Hours:** Mon-Fri 9-9:30, Sat & Sun 11-9

99 Cent Store

NEW LISTING
> **Seattle:** 10406 Greenwood Ave. N. 789-7293 *Greenwood*
> **Hours:** Daily 9-9

99 Cent Plus Discount Store

NEW LISTING
> **Seattle:** 9861 Aurora Ave. N. 522-7114 *Greenwood*
> **Hours:** Mon-Sat 10-7, Sun 11-6

99 Cent Super Saver

NEW LISTING
> **Seattle:** 19904 Aurora Ave. N. 542-9330 *Richmond Highlands*
> **Hours:** Daily 10-8

Membership Buying Clubs

The two major buying clubs in the Seattle area are Costco and Sam's Club. To become a member of either, you must have a business license or non-profit status, work for a State or Federal agency, or belong to a credit union. You can pick up application forms at any of the warehouses. If you know someone who is already a member, you can go in as their guest, but you must pay cash for your purchases. For those thinking about joining, one-day passes are available if you show proof you can qualify for membership. Fees range from $25 to $35 per year.

Membership buying clubs combine low prices with the convenience of shopping at one location for goods you'd normally have to visit a dozen different stores to find. Thousands of products are stacked on shelves that reach to the ceiling, and members spend hours wandering through buildings the size of a city block. Selection may be limited to one or two items, especially in the electronics, furniture and appliances category, but you're getting a low-ball price, and everything is from well-known manufacturers.

Many people join to take advantage of terrific savings on food, which accounts for over one third of the inventory. Anything you can buy at a grocery store is available, but because restaurants, delis and caterers shop here, canned, frozen, packaged and prepared foods often come in large, institutional sizes. Small containers are shrink-wrapped together and sold as a unit. Most labels will be familiar, but every once in a while you'll encounter something normally found only in the food service industry.

Janitorial supplies, paper products, film, batteries, health and beauty products are also sold in quantity. The clothing department carries basic, but top quality sportswear for the whole family by well-known manufacturers. Housewares, audio-video equipment, office supplies, sporting goods, tools, hardware and automotive represent major departments.

You will even find expensive jewelry, watches, collectibles and designer labels at deep discounts. Around Christmas the warehouses bring in a lot of gift items, toys and seasonal goods.

Sam's Club and Costco look the same, operate under the same basic concept and carry the same merchandise mix, but brand names will vary, particularly on one-of-a-kind and special-purchase items. Costco warehouses are larger, so they have a better selection in some categories. However, at Sam's Club, some items are packaged in smaller quantities.

Costco Wholesale

Federal Way: 35100 Enchanted Pkwy. 874-1888
Kirkland: 8629 120th Ave. N.E. 828-6767
Lynnwood: 19105 Hwy. 99 775-2577
Seattle: 4401 4th Ave. S. 622-1144 *South of Kingdome*
Silverdale: 1000 Mickelberry Rd. 692-9213
Tacoma: 3639 S. Pine St. 475-1892
Tukwila: 1160 Saxon Drive 575-3311
Hours: Mon-Fri 11-8:30, Sat 9:30-6, Sun 10-5. Business
members only, Mon-Fri 10-12

Costco boasts an in-store bakery, deli, fresh meat counter and
big produce area. Apples, oranges and potatoes sold by the
case are among the lowest priced in town. Carpet and window
coverings can be special-ordered in the home decorating center. Vacuum cleaners, TV's, boomboxes, and stereo equipment
are big selling items. Costco warehouses include their own
pharmacy and optical departments, plus they sponsor "Road
Shows" during which they bring in selected items, such as
bicycles, stereos, pianos, artwork, oriental rugs or lawn furniture that can be purchased only during a limited time period.
Call 1-800-4-COSTCO for membership information or to get
price quotes on specific products. Members receive a monthly
newspaper with updates on new products and special events.
Lenient return policy.

Checks, Discover Card

Sam's Club

Seattle: 13550 Aurora Ave. N. 362-6700 *Haller Lake*
Fife: 3900 20th Street E. 922-1265
Hours: Mon-Fri 11-8:30, Sat 9:00-7, Sun 10-6. Business
members only, Mon-Fri 9-11

One thing I like about Sam's Club are the big signs that clearly designate the different departments. Cereal, tuna fish,
juice, pop, cheese, deli meats, cleaning supplies and paper
products are best selling items. Members can shop for
produce, fresh bakery products, and fresh or frozen meats. I
hear that the pizza kiosks have become very popular. The
automotive and optical departments offer similar products
and services as Costco. Membership information will be given
out over the phone as well as price quotes on specific items as
long as you know the make and model.

Checks, Discover Card

United Consumers Club
NEW LISTING
Kent: 7687 S. 180th 251-6063
Redmond: 3926 148th N.E. 885-5830
Fife: 5113 Pacific Hwy. E. #3-0/W 922-9329
Hours: Tues-Fri, Sat 10-4

Established over two decades ago, this nationwide buying club allows members to purchase factory direct from over 500 manufacturers at prices close to cost. Everything is ordered from catalogs and shipped to the nearest club locale. The selection includes anything you'd need for the home, office or recreation, including vehicles. Savings add up quickly on furniture, major appliances, audio-visual equipment, jewelry, computers and floor coverings. You can even buy housewares, decorative items, outerwear and shoes. The membership fees are much higher than those at Sam's Club or Costco, but there is a greater variety of big ticket brand names to choose from. Call for an appointment if you would like to schedule a presentation.

Checks, Credit cards

Thrift Shops

Most thrift shops operate to benefit a charity while others are privately owned establishments that sell second-hand goods for a profit. Value Village, Thriftko and Shop 'n' Save buy their inventory from charitable organizations who have collected the merchandise from donors. So, in a round-about-way, a charity still benefits from the proceeds.

Shoppers with the time and inclination to forage through cast-offs know that perfectly usable goods and even brand-new items are just waiting to be discovered at thrift stores. It's amazing what people throw away in our consumer-oriented society. Smart shoppers can pick up antiques, collectibles and designer clothing for a fraction of what they would normally pay. Some resale stores even sell surplus, seconds and clearance merchandise purchased from or donated by manufacturers and retailers.

Clothing is the biggest volume item, and prices have gone up as more people have discovered that second-hand clothes are both economical and socially acceptable. Housewares, appliances, and furniture are favorites with newlyweds, students and people furnishing rec rooms, rental properties, or vacation homes. Frequent sales ensure a fast turnover on the huge quantity of goods brought into these stores.

It would be impossible to include all of the thrift shops in the Puget Sound area in the Super Shopper because of space limitations and their ever-changing array of merchandise, so here's a rundown on special attractions and sales at some of the better-known outlets. For a complete listing, check the yellow pages under both "Second-hand Stores" and "Thrift Shops."

The Goodwill store on Dearborn houses over one million items, making it the largest thrift store in the country. Check the bulletin board as you enter for daily specials. Certain areas have been designated for designer clothing, antiques and jewelry. Goodwill periodically sells off merchandise collected throughout the year that represents the cream of the crop in a specific category. Computers and related items go on sale in April and October, ski apparel and equipment in August, famous designer clothes in April and October, funky clothing in June. Special seasonal sales include toys and holiday apparel, costumes for Halloween and Fat Tuesday, formal wear and tuxes for the high school prom season. Sometimes Goodwill sponsors sales of collectible records, books, Disney memorabilia, Barbie dolls, western wear or vintage clothing. For specific dates call the store at 329-1000 or sign up on the mailing list and you will get a cute postcard!

Children's Hospital Thrift Stores in Everett, Redmond and downtown Seattle carry many new items that have been donated by local retailers and manufacturers. About 30% of the inventory is purchased off-price, mainly clothing, linens, accessories, household and decorative items.

Value Village, with 14 stores locally, is updating their image. The three newest stores in Lynnwood, Crown Hill and Tacoma look more like department stores than thrift shops, with their bright, clean interiors and clothing neatly displayed on racks by size, style and color. The "Labels" section features brand new housewares, apparel and electronics purchased direct from local stores or manufacturers. Rumor has it that clothing from Nordstroms even graces the racks at Value Village! Stores take in about 5,000 items a day, so prices are cut in half on anything that doesn't sell in five weeks, another 50% after three weeks. On Sundays, all used merchandise goes for 20% less. Clothing is marked down 50% during major holidays. For rock bottom prices, visit the Value Village Clearance center in Tacoma, on South Tacoma Way. Anyone over 62 gets a 20% discount except on sale and green tag merchandise, which is brand new. Returns are accepted for credit or exchange within seven days.

The Wise Penny in the U-District, run by the Junior League of Seattle, has two fantastic sales a year, when they close the store and completely change the inventory for the coming season. Call to get on the mailing list. I'm told that the University Bookstore donates clearance merchandise to the Wise Penny.

City of Hope, in Ballard, hosts a "Brand X" sale in the fall when men's wool clothing by a famous name manufacturer in Oregon arrives. Call 784-0298 for the specific date or become a member and receive a monthly newsletter announcing special sales. Many clothing reps donate samples to this shop.

Thriftko marks everything down 30% on Sundays except for the racks that contain new and better quality stuff. I once spotted clothing from the Spiegel catalog hanging in the Greenwood store.

The **Union Gospel Mission** sends their best stuff to their shop in downtown Seattle on First and Union, which they have dubbed "Market Collectibles."

Deseret Industries carries new sofas, dining tables, desks and mattresses made in their factory in Utah. Every week they take silent bids on collectibles and better quality items, with all sales finalized on Saturday. You can even phone in a last-minute bid.

The Salvation Army sells antiques at their 4th Avenue store and practically gives "as is" and clearance merchandise downstairs away.

St. Vincent de Paul has a big sale once a month, on a Saturday, and usually around the holidays, during which clothing is marked down 50% to 90%.

Like consignment shops, charity thrift shops reflect the neighborhood they are located in. Some organizations attract better quality stuff and their stores tend to look more like well-kept retail shops than the crowded, messy, jumble normally associated with second-hand stores. The American Cancer Society, with six **Discovery Shops** in the Puget Sound area, maintains a clean, bright boutique-like atmosphere and merchandise that is carefully inspected, mended, pressed and cleaned before it goes out on the racks.

Don't forget that most thrift shops do not allow returns or accept credit cards. Items donated to second-hand stores run by charitable organizations are tax deductible. Just be sure to get a signed receipt for your records. Other benefits include the good feeling you get from knowing that your cast-offs help those in need, and that you are recycling!

Swap Meets, Rummage Sales and Special Events

Hardcore bargain hunters know that flea markets, garage sales and rummage sales are the place to shop for rock-bottom prices. The good stuff gets snatched up early but prices are often negotiable and they drop dramatically by the end of the day. Check the classified ads or community events listings in local as well as major newspapers to find out what's happening. Following is a list of swap meets that operate on a regular basis and a few of my favorite periodic sales.

D & M Northwest Productions

Tacoma: 588-8621
Periodic sales

This organization sponsors the big Bargain Fairs that take place at the Puyallup Fairgrounds and in the Kingdome. Merchandise is mostly new or collectibles and some shows include RV and boat swaps. Sales are usually advertised via display ads in major newspapers. Call if you want to rent a space or find out when and where the next one will be held.

Lakeside School Rummage Sale

Seattle: 14050 First Ave. N.E. 368-3600 *Shoreline*
Hours: Mon-Fri 7:30-4:30
Semiannual sales

This is a biggie! The March sale, usually held in the Seattle Center Exhibition Hall, lures over 50,000 shoppers who come to sift through literally tons of donations, including brand-new merchandise, collectibles and designer clothing. All items are half-price on Sunday. Monday shoppers can fill grocery bags for $4. The October sale, which is held at the school, is smaller.

Checks, Credit cards

Mill Creek Garage Sale

NEW LISTING
First Saturday in October and May 337-1116

A carnival atmosphere prevails at this city-wide sale, as hundreds of homes participate in the biggest garage sale you'll ever attend! The city is inhabited mainly by younger families and professional people who recycle their belongings twice a year at this huge community event. I'm told this is a good place to shop for clothing since a lot of sales reps live in the area. Mill Creek is located about eight miles north of Bothell.

Seattle Repertory Theatre's Elegant Elephant Sale

Seattle: Bagley Wright Theatre Scene Shop 443-2210 *Seattle Center*
Annual sale

Every June for over a decade, this rummage sale has been attracting classy patrons and upscale merchandise. Look for great buys on clothing, china, glassware, books, records, art and kitchenware, plus a special section for antiques and jewelry. To get first pick, buy a ticket for the preview party the night before. Mailing list.

Checks, Credit cards

Wholesale Heaven

Seattle: 2601 Elliott Ave. 885-5827 *Seattle Trade Center*
Periodic sales

Call to get on the mailing list, then shop 'til you drop at this bargain hunter's paradise! Over 100 booths are filled with merchandise brought in by local manufacturers, sales reps, retail stores and wholesale distributors, many of which are listed in our pages. Everything is brand-new overstock, discontinued, or clearance items, with the main emphasis on apparel and accessories. Selection varies from the latest fashions to casual attire for the whole family. Best buys are on jeans, outerwear, sweatshirts and costume jewelry. You'll also find toys, giftware, sporting goods, housewares, luggage and decorative accessories. The admission fee was $4 the last time I attended but, mailings include a $1 off coupon.

Buyers and sellers gather at these locations for old-fashioned swap meets:

Midway Drive-In Swap & Shop

NEW LISTING
   Kent: 24050 Pacific Hwy. S. 878-1990
   Hours: Sat & Sun 8-4, Wed 12-7 June, July & August

Puget Park Swap-O-Rama Drive-In Theatre

   South Everett: I-5 at 128th St. Exit 337-1435
   Hours: Sat & Sun 9-4 April through October

Seattle Indoor Swap Shop

Tukwila: 14802 Pacific Hwy. S. 243-8347
Hours: Daily 10-8

Star-Lite Swap & Shop Drive-In Theatre

Tacoma: S. 84th & S. Tacoma Way 588-8090
Hours: Tues-Fri 10-6, Sat & Sun 9-4

Auctions

To find out when and where auctions are taking place, look under "Auction Notices" in daily newspapers, The Seattle Daily Journal of Commerce, or subscribe to the "Auction Greensheet," the only publication of its kind in the country. Weekly editions list auctions in Washington, Oregon and California sponsored by private, commercial, government and community organizations or businesses. Subscription fee is $98/yr or $57/6-months. Call 486-5444 for a complimentary back issue.

Government auctions usually offer the best bargains because they do not use professional auctioneers or spend a lot of money on advertising. Goods will be surplus or used, the latter sometimes in "like new" condition. Government vehicles are sold off every three years so they are still in good condition. Payment usually must be made in cash or by cashier's check and all sales are final. Here's a list of government auctions you might be interested in attending. Call for information about upcoming dates and locations.

General Services Administration/Personal Property Sales

Auburn: 2805 C Street S.W. Bldg #5 931-3931
Public store: Fri 12-2:30. Periodic sales via auctions, sealed bids, and spot bids.

The state of Washington sells off surplus property at this location. Merchandise can include everything from vehicles and heavy duty machinery, to heating and plumbing equipment, office furniture, computers and paper products. I hear you can frequently get a terrific buy on a car at these sales. Call to get on the mailing list.

Police Auctions

Seattle: 684-8187
Hours: Daily 24 hours
King County: 296-4078
Hours: Mon-Thurs 8-4:30, Fri 8-12:30

Two or three times a year the police department auctions off unclaimed, stolen or lost-and-found property, mainly clothing, TV's, VCRs, tools, cameras, jewelry, and household items. Many people attend the Seattle police auctions just to pick up a super deal on bicycles.

School District Auctions

Seattle: 298-7568
Tacoma: 596-1284
Hours: Mon-Fri 7:30-4:30

Call to get on the mailing list if you want to attend school surplus sales once or twice a year where furniture, office machines, audio visual equipment, musical instruments, sewing machines, major appliances, electrical tools and anything found in a school except for books is sold to the highest bidder.

King County Auctions

Seattle: 296-0629
Hours: Mon-Fri 8:30-4:30

Twice a year the county holds a big sale where any item that comes under its jurisdiction can end up on the auction block. A lot of vehicles go on sale in October during their biggest sale. Call to get on the mailing list.

Businesses Offering Senior Discounts

(See Index for page numbers)

Drugs and Sundries

AARP
Cost Plus
Safeway

Grooming Services

Eejay's
BJ's Beauty College
Evergreen Beauty School
Everett Plaza Beauty School
Greenwood Academy
Kent Beauty College
Kirkland Beauty School
Mr. Robert's Beauty School
New Beginnings
Paul Mitchell
Renton Beauty School
Community Colleges

Dental Services

Shoreline Community
College

Hardware

McLendon Hardware
Sherman Supply

Window Coverings and Floor Coverings

Carpeteria
Carpet Exchange
Color Tile & Carpet
Direct Carpet Sales

Furniture

Continental Furniture

Appliances

Seattle Home Appliance
Center

Bedding

Mattress Plus

Food

Buns Master Bakery
Orowheat Bakery Outlet
Wonder Bread Hostess
Sutliff's Candy Company
Central Co-op
Manna Mills
Puget Consumer's Co-op

Sporting Goods

Golfland Discount Pro Shop
The Jolly Soldier

Arts and Crafts

Famous Labels Fabric
Outlet
Hancock Fabrics
Pacific Fabrics
Treasure House

Books

Friends of the Public Library

Entertainment

Bathhouse Theatre

Coupon Books

Golden American
Special Savings for Seniors

Clothing

Ross Dress for Less
Sebastain's Closet
Twice is Nice

Jewelry, Crystal

Dahnken of Tacoma

Thrift Shops

Value Village

Index